THE WORLD FOOD CRISIS:

Food Security
in Comparative
Perspective

Edited by
J. I. Hans Bakker

Canadian Scholars' Press Inc., Toronto, Ontario, Canada, 1990.

The World Food Crisis:
Food Security in Comparative Perspective

First published in 1990 by
Canadian Scholars' Press Inc.
339 Bloor Street West, Suite 220
Toronto, Canada
M5S 1W7

Canadian Cataloguing in Publication Data

Main entry under title:

The World Food Crisis

Includes bibliographical references

ISBN 0-921627-45-9

1. Food Supply. I. Bakker, Hans

HD9000.5.W67 1990   338.1'9 C90-093760-2

Cover design by Hans Bakker

Cover illustration:
Sundanese Food Vendors at Krakatoa

In 1883 the island of Krakatoa, off the west coast of Java, experienced one of the largest volcanic eruptions that has ever been recorded. This photograph was taken at Krakatoa exactly one hundred years after the devastating volcanic explosion. These young Sundanese women have been chosen for the cover to symbolize the possibility of an optimistic future where there is an abundant and secure food supply for all of the world's people.

Photograph by Hans Bakker, 1983.

Table of Contents

Table of Contents I

Table of Contents (Detailed) VII

Foreword... XIX

A.R. MacKinnon,
Director, Centre for International Programs, University of Guelph

Acknowledgements.. XXI

Preface XXV

Sergio Trindade,
United Nations Center for Science and Technology for Development
(UNCSTD), New York
*The Effect of Science and Technology on the Process of
Development*

Part I:
OVERVIEW: CONCEPTUALIZATION OF THE ISSUES

Introduction 3

J. I. Hans Bakker,
Department of Sociology and Anthropology, University of Guelph
*Food Production, Distribution and Exchange: Conceptualizing
Food Security and Insecurity in Comparative International and
Interdisciplinary Perspective*

Conference Summary 45

John C. Cairns and Gayle Valeriote,
Centre for International Programs, Guelph
Science and Technology in the World Food Crisis: Conference Summary

Chapter One: 61

Truman P. Phillips and Daphne S. Taylor,
Department of Agricultural Economics and Centre for Food Security,
University of Guelph
Food Insecurity: Dynamics and Alleviation

Chapter Two: 97

Jorge Nef and Jokelee Vanderkop,
Department of Political Studies, University of Guelph
Food Systems and Food Security in Latin America:
A Systemic Approach to Politics, Ideology and Technology

Part II:
COMPARATIVE REGIONAL CASE STUDIES

Chapter Three: 139

Michael D. Schulman and Patricia Garrett,
Department of Sociology and Anthropology, University of North Carolina,
and Department of Rural Sociology, Cornell University
Socio-economic and Demographic Differentiation Among Smallholders: Implications for Technology Development and Transfer

Chapter Four: 157

Franz von Benda-Beckmann,
Department of Agrarian Law, Wageningen, Netherlands
Sago, Law and Food Security on Ambon

Chapter Five:.. 201
Sarah Southwold-Llewellyn,
Department of Agrarian Sociology of the Tropics and Sub-tropics,
Wageningen, Netherlands
Household Credit Strategies for Food Security:
A Case Study from Sri Lanka

Chapter Six:.. 229
Lila E. Engberg,
College of Family and Consumer Studies, Guelph
Household Resources, Women and Food Security: An Ecosystem
Perspective with Case Studies from Africa

Chapter Seven: 255
Wayne C. Pfeiffer and C. Song,
Department of Agricultural Economics, Guelph
Policy Changes and New Agricultural Technology:
Mean Structural Change in Northern Chinese Agriculture

Part III:
CANADIAN NATIVE PEOPLE AND FOOD INSECURITY

Chapter Eight:.. 281
Edward J. Hedican,
Department of Sociology and Anthropology, University of Guelph
The Economics of Northern Native Food Production

Chapter Nine: 301
Franz M. Koennecke,
Researcher, Parry Island Band, Ontario
Unwanted Change: Canada's Interference With the Balanced
Food Cycle of the Wasauksiwunini

Part IV:
TECHNICAL ISSUES AND ALTERNATIVES:
SOIL, WATER AND FISHERIES MANAGEMENT

Chapter Ten:... 319

Thomas J. Hoban,
Sociology, Anthropology and Social Work,
North Carolina State University, Raleigh, North Carolina
Soil Conservation Technology and World Food Supply:
Obstacles and Opportunities

Chapter Eleven:... 347

Hamid Jorjani,
Agricultural Economics, Guelph and Wageningen
Soil-Water Management and Food Security: An Approach
for Assessing Economic Viability of Agricultural Drainage
in Developing Countries

Chapter Twelve: 385

Janet Marie Huddle,
Food Security, Guelph
The Blue Revolution: The Modernization of Fisheries

Part V:
FOREIGN DONOR ASSISTANCE, FOOD AID,
AND FOOD SECURITY

Chapter Thirteen:.. 419

Robert D'Arcy Henderson,
Political Science, Western Ontario
Food as Economic Statecraft: Canadian and American
Food Aid/Trade with African Countries

Chapter Fourteen: 441

Olga Martinez and E.A. Cebotarev,
Nutrition and Sociology and Anthropology, Guelph
Food Aid as a Strategy for Food Security
in Poor Households: A Review

Chapter Fifteen: 485
John W. Mellor
International Food Policy Research Institute
*"Ending Hunger: An Implementable Program
for Self-reliant Growth"*

Contributors 519

Table of Contents (Detailed)

Table of Contents I

Table of Contents (Detailed) VII

Foreword.. XIX
A.R. MacKinnon
Director, Centre for International Programs,
University of Guelph

Acknowledgements... XXI

Preface XXV
Sergio Trindade,
United Nations Center for Science and Technology
for Development (UNCSTD), New York

The Effect of Science and Technology
on the Process of Development

Trindade provides an overall context for the book in this
preface by discussing the general impact of Science and
Technology (S&T) on Development and then illustrating
the manner in which the general situation is manifested
by the application of S&T to food production,
distribution and exchange. A portion of the preface
consists of extracts from the *Report of the Ad Hoc Panel of
Specialists on Science, Technology and Food Security* (1986).
Trindade stresses the fact that developing countries have
options and that the use of new technologies such as new
crop varieties represents both opportunities and dangers.

Part I:
OVERVIEW:
CONCEPTUALIZATION OF THE ISSUES

Introduction... 3
J. I. Hans Bakker,
Sociology and Anthropology, Guelph

Food Production, Distribution and Exchange:
Conceptualizing Food Security and Insecurity in
Comparative International and Interdisciplinary
Perspective

This introduction briefly discusses definitional and
theoretical considerations. After summarizing the broad
range of topics discussed at the 1986 Guelph conference
on "Science and Technology in the World Food Crisis,"
Bakker clarifies the focus of the book: food security in
comparative international and interdisciplinary
perspective. He then summarizes some of the main
points made by the contributors in the fourteen separate
chapters of the book, and brings out four basic themes
found in the readings: household and smallholder
production, food distribution and exchange, technical
issues and alternatives, and national and international
food policy. Some of the papers emphasize descriptive
("idiographic"), while others attempt to make broader
generalizations ("nomothetic"). Some deal with food
security in a more general conceptual or empirical
manner while others, particularly some of the regional,
national and sub-regional case studies, emphasize more
specific aspects of food production and distribution.
However, they are linked together by an emphasis on the
importance of studying "patterns" which are central to
food security and insecurity. The world food crisis is
conceptualized here as more than an immediate crisis of
hunger. Instead, the crisis concerns the lack of general
agreement on approaches to the problem. The collection
of papers provides insights into the complexity of the
problems of food production, exchange and distribution
as those problems relate to various aspects of food

security in various settings. Considered as a whole, the book deals comparatively with "food security" in terms of economic, political, cultural and/or social "structures" or "systems." The authors point to complexities of the problem of food security within and among: individuals, households, village communities, sub-regions, nation-states, and international bodies.

Conference Summary 45
John C. Cairns and Gayle Valeriote,
Centre for International Programs, Guelph

Science and Technology in the World Food Crisis: Conference Summary

This is a selection from the summary and overview of the international conference held at Guelph on October 23-26, 1986. It provides a synopsis of the remarks made by keynote speakers Alexander King and Margaret Catley-Carlson, as well as panel and workshop moderators or co-ordinators and discussants. The panels concerned: 1. dimensions of the world food crisis, 2. science and technology in the world food system, 3. the carrying capacity of the planet, 4. the politics of food, and 5. options for the future. There were also fifteen workshops. The present volume can be seen as a more focussed continuation of the discussions held during the panels and workshops. Some of the ramifications of topics discussed at the Guelph conference are further developed in this book. However, since the conference covered a broad range of questions, the present volume can only take up a selection of topics. By reviewing the range of topics discussed at the Guelph Conference the reader can clearly see the manner in which the present book is focussed on food security and insecurity, especially questions of food production, exchange, distribution and consumption.

Chapter One: **61**

Truman P. Phillips and Daphne S. Taylor,
Agricultural Economics and Food Security, Guelph
Food Insecurity: Dynamics and Alleviation

This chapter provides an overview of issues that pertain to issues of food security and insecurity, particularly with respect to household-level food insecurity, including: risk factors, household-level "insurance strategies," and the effectiveness of national governmental strategies for increasing the abilities of households to purchase food and increasing national food supplies. The authors provide typological distinctions and empirical examples which make the conceptualization of the world food crisis more precise. While their orientation is primarily "economic," they move beyond the disciplinary boundaries of neo-classical economics and conceptualize food security in a broader manner than it has previously been conceptualized in much of the agricultural economics literature. For example, they are not merely concerned with capitalist "market" mechanisms, but consider informal and pre-capitalist markets as well.

Chapter Two: **97**

Jorge Nef and Jokelee Vanderkop,
Political Studies, Guelph

*Food Systems and Food Security
in Latin America: A Systemic Approach
to Politics, Ideology and Technology*

This study attempts to explain and understand the political economy of food in Latin America and the Caribbean. The concept of food security is explored as the authors look at the economy, society and polity in the context of development. The conditions affecting Latin America and the Caribbean are very different from those affecting the rest of the Third World, it is argued. For example, the ratio of population to land is very favourable, the land is productive, and food consumption per capita is second only to Atlantic countries and Eastern Europe. Reasons why Latin American populations remain undernourished are explored. Statistical data on 30 variables are applied to all of the countries in Latin America which are investigated.

Part II:
COMPARATIVE REGIONAL
CASE STUDIES

Chapter Three:.. 139
Michael D. Schulman and Patricia Garrett,
Sociology and Anthropology, North Carolina, and
Rural Sociology, Cornell

Socio-economic and Demographic Differentiation Among Smallholders: Implications for Technology Development and Transfer

This paper examines how socio-economic characteristics differentiate smallholders in a regionally specific segment of small farm strata. Data are based on a sample of ninety smallholders from three North Carolina Piedmont counties. Respondents were predominantly male, black, and involved in growing flue-cured tobacco. Factor analysis revealed five major dimensions of internal stratification: scale, off-farm labour and income, on-farm family labour, demographic characteristics of the farm operator, and land tenure. Four major types of smallholders are distinguished from this sample, and their needs for agricultural technologies are identified. One major finding is that both socio-economic and resource endowments determine the research and extension needs of different farmers. These results challenge the assumption of socio-economic homogeneity that underlies much of the farming systems literature and speak to a major debate in the theoretical literature concerning peasant economy. This empirical study makes it clear that food security is not merely a problem faced by less developed nations.

Chapter Four: **157**
Franz von Benda-Beckmann,
Agrarian Law, Wageningen, Netherlands

Sago, Law and Food Security on Ambon
 This detailed anthropological study of sago production
in a village on the island of Ambon, Indonesia, highlights
the multiple factors that contribute to food security,
including: legal considerations, kinship alliances, natural
resource endowments, and traditional production
methods. The conclusion reached is that peasant
cultivators are better off controlling their own destinies
than having to rely on new technologies. Therefore, it is
argued that cultivators should continue to rely on
traditional production methods of sago. If new
technologies are introduced rapidly then few cultivators
will continue to produce sago and the remaining
households and individuals will be drawn into "free
labour" arrangements, if available. It is assumed, on the
basis of the field work research, that the total income —
in cash or kind — of cultivators who become labourers
will drop and also that food will not be as readily
available for purchase. This paper is similar to the
previous paper in that it also stresses socio-economic
differentiation.

Chapter Five: **201**
Sarah Southwold-Llewellyn
Agrarian Sociology of the Tropics and Sub-tropics,
Wageningen, Netherlands

Household Credit Strategies for Food Security:
A Case Study from Sri Lanka

This chapter examines various aspects of smallholder
production and distribution in a village in Sri Lanka. It
stresses the importance of the role of middlemen traders
in the exchange and distribution of food and agricultural
cash crops. Also considered are aspects of national food
production policy.

Chapter Six:.. 229
Lila E. Engberg,
Family and Consumer Studies, Guelph

Household Resources, Women and Food Security:
An Ecosystem Perspective with Case Studies from Africa
This chapter discusses individual food security at the
household level, particularly for women. The author
stresses intra-household food acquisition, distribution
and consumption as opposed to inter-household food
security. The context is research conducted in two
villages in Malawi, Africa. Discussion of the differential
roles of men and women in food production and
consumption clarifies the extent to which food insecurity
is not homogeneous within the household. Additionally,
a distinction is made between food insecurity caused by a
shortage of food and food insecurity caused by a
shortage of cooking fuel. The role of indigenous
knowledge and technologies is emphasized. An
ecological systems perspective is proposed as a guide to
our thinking and research about household food security
and insecurity. The concept of "informal economy" is
clarified. The literature on allocation of time-budgets and
the sexual division of tasks in small communities is
reviewed.

Chapter Seven: 255
Wayne C. Pfeiffer and C. Song,
Agricultural Economics, Guelph

Policy Changes and New Agricultural Technology:
Mean Structural Change in Northern Chinese Agriculture

This chapter provides a history of the evolution of the
role of state farms and family farms in Northern China,
particularly the evolution of private farming that has
occurred since 1949. The findings are based on results
obtained through use of a linear programming model of
farming in Northern China. The basic findings include
the generalization that grain output will remain as the
main economic activity and that the livestock industry

will continue to expand and make greater use of excess grain production. In general, agriculture will become more diversified as a result of more "liberal" state agricultural policies. At the present time, it is pointed out, there is a high degree of underemployment of labour in agricultural production. The research indicates that the general expansion of grain and livestock production can be realized by using resources more efficiently, particularly labour.

Part III:
CANADIAN NATIVE PEOPLE
AND FOOD INSECURITY

Chapter Eight:.. 281
Edward J. Hedican,
Sociology and Anthropology, Guelph

The Economics of Northern Native Food Production

This chapter examines the conflict that exists among northern Native people in Canada, particularly Ontario, between traditional food gathering methods and seasonal employment. The general finding is that seasonal employment has restricted hunting and fishing activities. Hedican concludes that it is possible to schedule hunting and fishing employment activities to maximize the benefits to northern Native people.

Chapter Nine: 301
Franz M. Koennecke,
Researcher, Parry Island Band, Ontario

Unwanted Change: Canada's Interference
With the Balanced Food Cycle of the Wasauksiwunini

This chapter contains a detailed historical and anthropological description of the Anishinabek's traditional methods and sources of food. The chapter highlights the negative effects of changes in land use patterns. Koennecke argues that the federal government of Canada restricted the Anishinabek's access to traditional food sources and forced them to purchase most of their food. Hence federal government policy promoted changes in land use patterns that reduced food security rather than improving it. The conclusion is that legal impediments to traditional food gathering methods are being reduced. It is assumed on the basis of intensive, long-term field work and participant observation that the Anishinabek want to increase the extent to which they obtain food in the traditional manner.

Part IV:
TECHNICAL ISSUES AND ALTERNATIVES:
SOIL, WATER AND FISHERIES MANAGEMENT

Chapter Ten:.. 319

Thomas J. Hoban,
Sociology, Anthropology and Social Work,
North Carolina State University, Raleigh, North Carolina

Soil Conservation Technology and World Food Supply: Obstacles and Opportunities

This chapter is based on the history of experience of soil conservation strategies and policies implemented in the United States. Hoban considers food security to be a problem of inadequate national food supplies owing to poor soil conservation practices. He provides strategies for promoting soil conservation and discusses why soil conservation is not more widely adopted in developed countries.

Chapter Eleven:.. 347

Hamid Jorjani,
Agricultural Economics, Guelph and Wageningen

Soil-Water Management and Food Security: An Approach for Assessing Economic Viability of Agricultural Drainage in Developing Countries

This chapter focusses on the role of soil management in

improving agricultural production and hence the supply of food. Jorjani describes a method and a model which can be used to determine if investment in improved soil management, particularly drainage, is beneficial in terms of increased food production.

Chapter Twelve: 385
Janet Marie Huddle,
Food Security, Guelph

The Blue Revolution: The Modernization of Fisheries

This detailed analysis of the "blue revolution" as a parallel approach to the "green revolution" provides an overview of the policies directed at the modernization of fisheries. It is critical of the assumptions made by those who attempted to increase fish production utilizing the same model of food production that was basic to the "green revolution."

Part V:
FOREIGN DONOR ASSISTANCE, FOOD AID,
AND FOOD SECURITY

Chapter Thirteen: 419
Robert D'Arcy Henderson,
Political Science, Western Ontario

*Food as Economic Statecraft: Canadian and American
Food Aid/Trade with African Countries*

Henderson examines Canadian and American food aid and trade policies with respect to Africa. The severe food shortages experienced by a number of African countries led to food aid policies which changed the dominant set of international food relations. In the 1980s the international system can be characterized as West-West competition for global food trade and North-South food aid. The chapter outlines two recent critiques of the utilization of economic instruments for foreign policy. Henderson also analyses the policy options available to

African countries, either individually or jointly, in order to establish "counter-vailing" systems. The chapter concludes with suggestions concerning the prospects for North-South food relations in the 1990s.

Chapter Fourteen: **441**
Olga Martinez and E.A. Cebotarev,
Nutrition and Sociology and Anthropology, Guelph

*Food Aid as a Strategy for Food Security
in Poor Households: A Review*

This paper examines current trends in the conceptualization of food aid and looks at the impact of food aid as a form of income-transfer. Food aid could have an important role in the development of "human capital" through long-term food security. It could both meet food deficits, especially in Sub-Saharan Africa, and facilitate structural adjustment lending. However, in order to do so its use requires more flexibility and efficiency. Traditionally, "program" food aid has been used as budget support at the national level, but its benefits have not reached poor households directly. Modifications must be made so that income obtained nationally from sales of food aid can be made available to help the poor directly. A more realistic approach to evaluating the impact of project food aid would be to consider it in terms of its income-transfer value. Evaluations of nutritional impact have been disappointing largely because people do not use food supplements as good aid donors would like them to. It cannot be assumed that the purchase of non-food items considered important to households does not contribute to long-term food security. The marginal propensity of households to spend increased resources on nutrition must be examined more carefully rather than simply relying on direct nutritional benefits conferred on targeted recipients (supplementation programs) or untargeted projects (food for work schemes).

Chapter Fifteen **485**
John W. Mellor
International Food Policy Research Institute

Ending Hunger: An Implementable Program
for Self-reliant Growth
In this optimistic analysis of future potential strategies
Mellor describes the problems associated with ending
hunger and food insecurity and sets out a large-scale
incremental action plan. The Chapter is divided into two
parts: I) The Opportunity, and II) A Program to Remove
Hunger. Six propositions concerning self-reliant growth
and the elimination of hunger are discussed. It is further
argued that foreign assistance can focus on four basic
principles in order to eliminate hunger: 1) economic
growth, 2) integrated rural infrastructural development,
3) development of high-potential areas, and 4) resource
transfers from wealthier countries to both middle-income
and low-income developing countries. Mellor argues
that: "Now is the time for a major action program to end
hunger." It should be "large enough to have an impact"
and "focussed enough to have visibility." The cost would
be twenty billion dollars a year, with fifteen billion for
rural public works and five billion for feeding programs.
The International Food Policy Research Institute (IFPRI)
could play a major role in monitoring such a massive
effort. However, there are at least five major problems
associated with massive rural infrastructure
improvement, including problems of co-ordination and
the willingness of donors to increase food aid
substantially. Conceptualizing the proposed program for
self-reliant growth and the elimination of hunger and
food insecurity will require further data and analysis.

Contributors **519**

FOREWORD

This book had its origins at a world conference on "Science and Technology in the World Food Crisis" held at the University of Guelph in October, 1986. Participants agreed that a crisis did indeed exist, but that it was not principally a matter of a world food shortage. Rather, the crisis was located with the over 800 million people whose households did not have access throughout the year to a diet that would make possible a healthy and active working life. Those in most need too often lacked land to grow the appropriate food, or the money to buy it. There seemed to be considerable consensus at the conference that the world food crisis is primarily one of economic, political and distributional inequity, not under-production. For such a crisis, science and technology geared to increased production cannot provide all of the necessary answers.

What is needed is to broaden the agenda to address not only the scientific and technological issues of food production and *immediate* food insecurity, but also long-range economic and political issues of food security for future generations. This book indicates one way in which, partially as a result of the conference, the intellectual agenda was re-ordered and expanded. As the editor of the volume, Dr. Hans Bakker used a sociological and comparative viewpoint. He has selected and ordered well in extending the on-going examination of the food crisis and expanding the original conference agenda.

It can be expected that the various intellectual contributions in the book will have an impact on thousands around the world who are struggling to make some sense of the problems and to build the theoretical foundations which might hopefully inform action. May they succeed beyond our most fervent expectations, for millions of lives of quiet people — now and in the future — are at stake. But even if the theorists do succeed, how might we be assured that the crisis is being addressed?

Improvements in the theory of gravity do not help much in the way we skip stones. Similarly, our *theoretical* understanding of food security may not contribute to the alleviation of malnutrition for nomads in Ethiopia, peasant cultivators in Indonesia, or street people in Toronto. What was seen at the conference in 1986, and is also apparent in this publication, is the need for organizations which can help to translate theory into the formulation of policies and action so that there could indeed be more stable access to adequate food for all members of the world's societies.

The October event of 1986 has become the launching pad for the Centre for Food Security located at the University of Guelph. Dr. W. E. Tossell, the first Director of the Centre, gave imaginative and forceful leadership in setting out appropriate paths. The Centre is mobilizing concerned and informed persons across many disciplines and many institutions, nationally and internationally. The Centre is moving simultaneously to bring the scholar and researcher together with the policy-maker, planner and manager. The thrust is towards policies and strategies and not technological fixes.

The work of the Centre is driven primarily by the silent constituents of developing countries and those development institutions and agencies seeking to empower them. The Centre has uppermost in mind the impact of policies and strategies on limited resource households such as subsistence farmers and low wage earners — particularly women. Continuously, the issues of sustainability and environmental protection are on the Centre's agenda and on those of all participating organizations.

This volume succeeds well in delineating the principles which must guide the new Centre's operations. The ultimate test of the success of this publication will be not in how many persons have read it but in how it helped shaped the concerted action which must now be taken on a global scale. There are promising beginnings, but these are still quite insignificant in the face of growing numbers of persons suffering desperately from food insecurity. There are indeed resources to make a difference in the situation. This book, in addition to making a scholarly contribution, should help in the mobilization of those resources.

A. R. MacKinnon, Director
Centre for International Programs
University of Guelph

ACKNOWLEDGEMENTS

Many individuals and organizations have contributed to the making of this book. I owe a debt to many people and would like to acknowledge that debt here. (The final responsibility for errors and omissions, of course, rests with the editor.)

The contributors (listed below) should be thanked first and foremost. They all worked willingly on the project and contributed some of their best work. I would most of all like to thank them for their confidence in the enterprise, despite several unforeseen delays. Due to space limitations in a book that has already grown longer than originally envisaged, we were not able to accommodate several individuals who submitted materials for inclusion in the book.

The project was launched by the Publications Committee of the World Congress on Science and Technology in the World Food Crisis via a Memo from Professor Archie R. MacKinnon, the Director of the Centre for International Programs, to Professor Jack MacDonald, Vice President, Academic, University of Guelph on August 28, 1987. Hence, I would like to thank Professors MacKinnon and MacDonald for having the confidence in me to agree to making me responsible for editing this volume. Ms Kathryn Beaven and Ms Alice Fraser of the Centre for International Programs administered the funds available for the publication in a friendly and efficient manner. The funds for the conference came from about twenty different donors.

The World Congress was held on October 23-26, 1986, and it was agreed at a Publications Committee meeting that a brief and succinct summary of the conference would be compiled from panel and workshop rapporteurs and would be mailed to all participants. The *Summary of Proceedings* was edited by Professor John C. Cairns and Ms Gail Valeriote, prepared by Print

Publications, University of Guelph, and mailed out to everyone who had registered for the conference. The summary contains a complete list of donors who contributed to the conference. (A condensed version of the summary is reprinted in the text.) Everyone receiving the summary was also informed of the possibility of publishing a comprehensive book and requested to send in suitable papers. The general notion was that high quality academic papers written by participants at the conference would be collected together in a book that would be suitable for use in courses that deal with international and national development issues. It was also felt that research institutions, non-governmental organizations (NGOs) and development agencies would also be interested in the publication.

It was decided that the format of the proposed book would attempt to follow the conference themes. An Editorial Committee consisting of Professors Jim Shute, Rural Extension Studies, Truman Phillips, Agricultural Economics and Business, Alexander ("Sandy") Middleton, Instructional Development, plus the editor, Hans Bakker, was set up. Hence, I would like to thank the members of the Editorial Committee, who helped in various ways, especially during the initial stages.

In addition to the editorial committee a number of individuals volunteered to serve as referees. Hence, I would like to thank Professors Gustav van Beers, Nora Cebotarev, Harry Cummings, Bill Graf, Hugh Lehman, John McMurtry, Ab Moore, William Tossell, and Tony Winson for refereeing one or more papers or assisting with the refereeing process.

The Inter-College Activities Fund supplied a small grant to defray the costs of a Symposium/ Mini-Conference on the World Food Crisis. The meeting occurred on February 11, 1988, with Professor Robert Henderson and Dr. Sergio Trindade as guest speakers. Many faculty, graduate students and interested individuals attended the talks. Hence, my thanks to the Fund Committee and to Dr. Wayne C. Marsh for administering it. (Unfortunately, guests from the Institute for Food and Development Policy, San Francisco, were not able to attend, but Dr. Joseph Collins did visit the University of Guelph at a later date.) I especially would like to thank Professor Henderson and Dr. Trindade for their enthusiastic participation in various meetings during the day. I believe that the Mini-Conference helped to keep the book project alive by stimulating faculty at

Guelph to contribute the results of recent work.

Many of those at Guelph interested in food issues have been working with Dr. William Tossell and the Centre for Food Security, which is currently housed at the Centre for International Programs. I would like to thank Dr. Tossell for his insightful comments and support. Wendelin Lapensee of the Centre helped with administrative matters during my brief absence from Guelph in August, 1989.

In negotiations with various publishers I received encouragement from several individuals. I would like to thank Sandra Woolfrey of Wilfrid Laurier University Press and Peter Martin and Janet Shorten of the University of Ottawa Press for their helpful suggestions to an inexperienced editor. My special thanks go to Jack Wayne, Publisher and Shelagh Ross, Managing Editor, Canadian Scholars' Press (CSP), for their flexibility and sustained interest in the project. Thanks to Shelagh Stevenson for her careful proofreading of the manuscript and for offering invaluable suggestions. I would also like to thank Ray Lum and his associates at the Remington Microcomputer Consulting Group for their prompt and efficient work on typesetting and photographs, and Catherine Lew for the hours spent correcting the manuscript.

Ms. Marnie Neve has helped with copy editing and liason with CSP in Toronto. She has also been a valuable partner and friend.

In the Department of Sociology and Anthropology the secretarial staff, Dina Carter, Brenda Hotchkiss, Aruna Mehta, and Nancy Mykitschak, have been most helpful in administrative matters in countless ways. Ms Brenda Hotchkiss typed and retyped four of the papers.

In addition to the contributors a number of individuals offered intellectual support. I would like to mention Professors Tony Fuller and Wout van den Bor of the Integrated Rural Development Network (IRDN) and Professors Jouke Wigboldus and Niels Roling from Wageningen Agricultural University in this regard.

While the following individuals have not been directly concerned with the editing of this book, I would nevertheless like to acknowledge the support and guidance they gave to me when I was just a young scholar starting out.

Many friends in the Canadian Council for Southeast Asian Studies (CCSEAS) and the Canadian Asian Studies Association (CASA) have helped provide an intellectually stimulating environment over the years, particularly Geoffrey Hainsworth and Joachim Voss. Professor Jose Havet of the University of Ottawa has been a valuable colleague in the field of development studies.

I also owe an important debt to Professors Cees Fasseur of Leiden University, Irving Zeitlin of the University of Toronto and John Smail of the University of Wisconsin, Madison, for their contribution to my dissertation and intellectual development. Several colleagues at Guelph have been influential in shaping my views and concerns, especially Professors Nora Cebotarev, Tom Condon, Ron Hinch, Ken Menzies, Frans Schryer, Tony Winson and Victor Ujimoto.

This work would not have been possible without the continued academic and administrative support of Professor Wayne Thompson, Chair of the Department of Sociology and Anthropology. His encouragement of my research endeavours has greatly facilitated my professional growth.

This book is dedicated to all of those children, women and men in the world who suffer needlessly from malnutrition, food insecurity, and even starvation.

PREFACE

THE EFFECT OF SCIENCE AND TECHNOLOGY ON THE PROCESS OF DEVELOPMENT

Sergio C. Trindade

Science and Technology

Technologies exist in socio-economic contexts. Thus, Science and Technology (S & T) are shaped by the state of development of a given society. In return, S & T change society as well. In this preface I will first discuss S & T in general and then examine applications to food security issues.

Today the implications of technological change are central to development and to overall economic growth. Or, in other words: The more effectively a society manages technological change the more likely it will be to overcome development constraints. The higher the 'technological capacity' of a country, (i.e., the ability to make adequate decisions in the national context and to choose appropriate technologies), the more likely it is that country will achieve an autonomous direction in the development process. In short, this ability is a home-grown capacity to make decisions on the use of Science and Technology for development purposes. That is true of the application of S & T to food production, distribution and exchange no less than it is true for other aspects of development.

New and emerging areas of S & T are likely to revolutionize our life. The ability to guide technological change will increasingly determine to what extent impacts of new technologies are accelerating or obstructing the process of development. While S & T may improve the quality of life in developed and developing countries, they are also no panacea for problems that originate in shortcomings of the decision-making process. For this reason, policy-supporting instruments such as the capacity to anticipate and guide technological change are a key factor in the development process. Hence, a policy that promotes aspects of 'technological capacity' directed toward the improvement of food security can have a significant impact on the quality of life.

Over the past four decades there has been a growing recognition of the central role that S & T play in the development process. The analytical perspectives concerning the relationships between S & T and socio-economic development have also changed over this period.

Within the United Nations, the emphasis given to S & T for Development has been reflected in the establishment of organizational structures specifically focussed on this subject. Those include: the Intergovernmental Committee on Science and Technology for Development, the Advisory Committee on Science and Technology for Development, the ACC Task Force on Science and Technology for Development, and the Centre for Science and Technology for Development (CCTD) within the U.N. Secretariat, and the U.N. Fund for Science and Technology for Development (UNFSTD) within the U.N. Development Program (UNDP). Concurrently, a more explicit focus has also emerged on S & T in the programs and activities of the various organs and specialized agencies of the U.N. system.

At the national level, the increased recognition of the importance of S&T to the development process led many developing countries to the establishment of policy and planning structures aimed at strengthening endogenous capacity building. Today some of the major concerns of policy makers in developing countries are:

- the widening technological gap between developed and developing countries, particularly in light of recent

scientific and technological advances;
- the possibilities of expediting the development of national capabilities through the adoption of new and advanced technologies such as microelectronics or biotechnology;
- recognition of the growing degree of interdependence between nations in the area of S & T and the increasing importance of international co-operation;
- the potential contributions that can be made by multi- and bilateral co-operation to the development of endogenous capacity building or home-grown capacity to make sensible decisions in this area;
- the concern to maintain an active role and autonomous direction as related to the application of S & T in light of global impacts of new technologies on the economy, trade and the environment.

In this context the home-grown capacity to be able to select among available options is crucial. These options may be based on national or outside knowledge, but there is no substitute for national decision making. Experiences from India and Brazil are examples that the existence of a home-grown capacity makes a difference. In India, a critical problem was the provision of sufficient grain for the growing population. The country successfully addressed this problem, because it had the local capacity to translate available knowledge into national solutions. In Brazil transportation needs led to the design and production of aircraft for low-density commuter traffic. No major aircraft producer in the world met the specific transportation needs of a country such as Brazil at that time. Both countries could rely on the availability of an infrastructure for applying knowledge to local conditions.

Policy Options

A recent meeting of OECD Member States discussed the issues that a science policy for the 21st century has to address in light of present fundamental techno-economic changes. While participating S & T ministers and senior officials assessed the implications for OECD members, developing countries would have to ask the similar questions:

- How can national science policy ensure that maximum

economic benefits of new and emerging S & Ts are realized?
- How can the internationalization of S & T help to achieve employment and growth?

Other subjects addressed by the OECD representatives were:
- improving the diffusion of scientific knowledge without violating intellectual property;
- integrating S & T policy into the mainstream of economic and social thinking, planning and execution;
- sharing the costs of high-tech-related research.

Although new technologies have an enormous potential to increase the quality of life and the living standard throughout the world, their impact in developing societies has not always been positive. Mechanisms are needed on the national level to assess the implications of new technologies for the development process and the satisfaction of the basic needs of the majority.

The example of New Materials illustrates a problem many developing countries will face in the light of rapid technological developments: With a quantum leap in the development of metal composites, polymers, glass fibres and ceramics developing countries are confronted with threatened mineral exports by less materials-intensive manufacturing in developed countries and with an insufficient access to these new technological achievements. Developing countries need effective strategies to confront this problem and to develop alternatives tailored to specific national needs.

Almost a decade ago, in August 1979, the U.N. Conference for Science and Technology for Development, brought together all Member States of the U.N. as well as many NGCs to discuss the strengthening of the S & T capacities of developing countries, the restructuring of the existing pattern of international scientific and technological relations and the potential role of the U.N. system. The Vienna Program of Action which was adopted by the conference states: "The necessary resources and technological potentials exist for eliminating the under-development of the developing countries and for improving the well-being of humanity as a whole. The achievement of this goal presupposes that developing countries exercise full control over their own resources. It also presupposes an equitable distribution and creation of scientific and technological capabilities of the world." In a later paragraph the program proclaims: "The ultimate goal of science and technology is to serve national development and to improve the well-being of humanity as a whole."

Science, Technology and Food Security

As an example of the work of UNCSTD as it applies to food security and insecurity it is useful to refer to the *Report of the Ad Hoc Panel of Specialists on Science, Technology and Food Security*. The Panel assembled at Harare, Zimbabwe, on 7-13 January, 1986, in a session organized in co-operation with the Ministry of Lands, Agriculture and Rural Resettlement of the Government of Zimbabwe. The full report of the Panel is available from UNCSTD (in typescript). Nguyen Ngoc Luu (Institute of Social Studies, The Hague, The Netherlands) and Kenneth A. Dahlberg (Western Michigan University, Kalamazoo, Michigan) served as rapporteurs. Twenty-one experts took part. They drew attention to the need for a food security strategy based on a food systems approach and oriented towards small farmers and peasants. The importance of contextual variations between regions and zones and the need for locally specific agriculturally relevant data was stressed. The Panel highlighted the need for new concepts and criteria for food security and the importance of hitherto neglected science and technology dimensions for the achievement of food security. The key role of traditional and "folk" science was discussed, as was the complex relationship between agricultural activities and environmental, resource and population issues. The question of technological choice was emphasized in terms of its centrality to the concept of food systems security. The Panel concluded by making specific recommendations with respect to the science and technology dimension of food policies and their implementation and proposed the establishment of local "seasonal observatories" as a mechanism for collecting locally specific data relevant to food systems and as a means of developing endogenous capacities for food security.

The following sections from the Report will help to clarify the context and key concepts used.

I. Context of the Food Crisis

It is well known that, in theory, the world is currently capable of producing enough food to feed its population; if food were more evenly distributed there would be ample to meet global caloric requirements. Various studies have revealed that by the early 1960s the world was already producing in the aggregate enough calories to provide everyone with a nutritionally adequate diet. By the late 1970s, further progress in agricultural production had brought developing countries as a group to within five percent of meeting their average nutritional requirements. It is against the background of these promising figures that one must place the stagnation of average per capita caloric intake in low-income countries and the famines which occur from time to time, claiming the lives of millions of people. More quietly and less visibly, undernourishment takes its toll among children, the most vulnerable group, shortening life expectancy and jeopardizing the full mental and physical development of those who survive.

While agricultural productivity has been vastly enhanced, the growth rate of food output per capita has tended to decline. Grave concern about this situation led to the World Food Conference in 1974 and the internationalization of food issues. Food production and distribution became one of the great critical issues of our time. Population growth rates, particularly in the developing countries, suggested that the problems of providing enough food for people will seriously increase at least through the year 2010.

The persistence of hunger in many parts of the world and the current food crisis in Africa testify that the policy suggestions made in the 1970s at both global and national levels did not help much in alleviating the threat of famine and hunger in the more vulnerable regions of the world. As a consequence, there is an urgent need to critically re-examine food issues and policies in order to explore alternative courses of action.

II. Key Concepts

The food problem is often viewed in terms of the concepts of "food self-sufficiency" and/or "food security." Increasingly, the concept of "food systems" has been used to refer to the larger processes, institutions and resources which encompass and are related to food production, processing and use.

In its broadest sense, *"food self-sufficiency"* denotes the ability to produce enough food for the area or group being analysed (country, region, village or household). Although sometimes used at the household or village level, this concept is more typically used to reflect production at an aggregate level without taking into account the nutritional status of the people in the country, region or area; nor does it address the problem of access to food of specific households or groups. Therefore, even if a country can produce ample food, some regions or specific groups may still suffer from famine, hunger or under-nourishment. "Food self-sufficiency," as a concept primarily used in national policy analysis, describes a country's condition or ability to produce enough food in the aggregate to meet the average food needs of its population.

National cereal self-sufficiency is certainly important for national independence as it allows the country to be free from immediate economic and political pressures applied by large cereal-exporting countries taking advantage of the time-bound character of food crises. It is, however, necessary to qualify national cereal self-sufficiency in relation to its import component (oil for tractors and irrigation pumps, feedstock for nitrogen-based fertilizers, pesticides and so on) and to its possible negative impact on food crops, particularly those nutritionally and culturally important as part of the traditional diet of the poorer groups, such as pulses in India or beans in Latin America. Moreover, the large grain stocks retained in some countries as apparent security for national self-sufficiency can also be seen as a measure of the deprivation of those who, without sufficient purchasing power, are not in a position to buy the food they need.

"Food self-reliance" commonly refers to the determination of a country to reach food self-sufficiency at the national level by means of mobilizing and utilizing its own resources through a variety of strategies and policies.

"Food security" is generally used to refer to a country's ability to have stable and reliable access to the food it needs through a mixture of production, trade, purchase or barter. The mixture is seen to vary according to the resource endowments of the country and its comparative advantage in different types of food, fibre and industrial production. National food security should not, therefore, be confused with national food self-sufficiency, defined by the absence of net food imports or by net food exports. *"Food security"* can also be used at the household level and implies stability in access to food through sufficient food self-provisioning and/or food purchasing power whatever the season of the year.

For some time, food problems have been analysed in terms of food systems. Somewhat broader and more analytic than the previous concepts, *"food systems"* refers to the whole complex of human/natural interactions relating to food production, processing, exchange and consumption. It stresses the interactions and feedbacks between component elements and thus is not linear. It is concerned with the place of the food system within larger environmental resource and social contexts.

The concept of *food security systems* emerged from the Panel discussion. It is based on the need to disaggregate the previous concepts and to stress the need to design, develop and elaborate systems which guarantee to all individuals and groups in a society tangible, real and continuous access to the food needed for a healthy and active life. It focusses on the availability of food and the capacity of people to obtain it, regardless of their region or group status, rather than on levels of production.

Finally, let me quote the conclusions reached by the Ad Hoc Panel.

III. Conclusions and Suggestions

1. In view of the current food crisis and population and resource trends, there is an urgent need to *review existing strategies and policies* in order to develop a new perspective for strategy design and policy formulation as they relate to food security systems.

2. The Panel suggested *the adoption and creative application of end-user approaches* in order to work towards an effective and

sustainable strategy and food system which takes *peasants and small farmers* as the focus of development and the starting point of the planning process.

3. In developing these new approaches, and dealing with them in terms of the longer-term time horizons and problems discussed, *new and interdisciplinary scientific and research initiatives will be needed.* A necessary part of this will be the development of a widespread network to collect *localized and seasonal data.*

4. While tackling the food problems at their root in the countryside, the Panel was equally concerned with the problem of food security of the *urban population. Policies and strategies are needed which will guarantee all individuals, households and groups reliable access to nutritious food.* Pursuit of this objective embodied in the concept of a *"food security system"* is particularly crucial to highly *depressed regions* where the food crisis is already acute, as well as to potentially vulnerable areas.

5. *Because women are so directly involved in all aspects of the food system, their activities, needs and roles were seen to be of strategic importance,* particularly in terms of food production, food processing and income generation.

6. While the development of an efficient and sustainable food security system is the overall objective for all levels and groups in society, *the peasant/small farmer-based strategy was seen as the key component,* involving, of necessity, the development of *rural infrastructures* and the *provision of social services.*

7. While increases in productivity and production by various technical means is desirable, it was noted that *resource losses* (soil, water and genetic materials) as well as food losses were issues of great importance. *Socio-economic and political factors, as well as technical factors that cause resource and food losses, should be seriously analysed.*

8. In reviewing ways to increase food availability, the Panel discussed a *range of options:* new land settlement, the encouragement of urban gardens and food production systems, intensification of cultivation on existing lands, institutional reforms relating to land and water rights, and various technical and pricing reforms. It was recognized

that these *options have to be considered in the context of the demands, possibilities and constraints of each country.*

9. The Panel stressed the need for *policy adjustments in the areas of financing, pricing and marketing* in order to obtain a set of policies which would effectively support the development of a food security system.

10. Attention was drawn to the desirability of designing policies and measures to *enhance the ability of marketing and processing intermediaries* to transfer technological inputs to small farmers and to perform essential post-harvesting activities.

11. Both to provide access to reliable and nutritious food and to help guard against any widespread harvest losses, the Panel suggested the concept of *a "mixed food basket" strategy* whereby a mix of basic staple foods would be consciously encouraged, taking into account the crop structures, food requirements and habits of different countries and cultures.

12. Strong emphasis was placed on the need to develop countries' *endogenous capabilities* to initiative development, to be able to evaluate the potential of upgrading existing or *traditional technologies*, to assess the impacts of *new technologies*, and to make effective technological *choices.*

13. This will require *comprehensive* and more *integrated policies* on the part of Governments, industry, non-governmental organizations and international organizations.

14. *Research and development capacities will have to be strengthened in terms of longer-term strategic planning.*

15. New mechanisms of co-ordination and co-operation among the *specialized agencies* will have to be found to reflect and apply the interdisciplinary approaches developed at the conceptual and scientific levels.

16. *Co-operation on a fairly equal footing between Governments and donor organizations to develop various networks for increasing food security was considered desirable.*

Conclusion

At the UNCSTD we have been concerned for over a decade with a broad range of applications of S & T for development. One of our "substantive themes" or specific areas of concern is "food security." Food production and distribution is one of the critical issues facing the United Nations, as well as individual nations and communities around the world. Even in the developed nations the problem of undernourishment takes its toll, particularly among members of disadvantaged groups.

Cultivators in developing countries face severe constraints to food security, as do urban wage earners. The problems are real. Hence, I am pleased to see that the scholars who have contributed to this book have focussed on many of the key issues concerning food security that we at the United Nations are also concerned with.

Therefore, it has been my pleasure to address researchers at the University of Guelph who are interested in "Science and Technology in the World Food Crisis." Although I was not able to attend your October 23-26, 1986, international conference on that theme, I am pleased to have had the opportunity to meet with you at this follow-up "mini-conference," along with Professor Henderson (February 11, 1988). The challenges we face in finding appropriate and humane solutions to problems of food insecurity require sustained effort by many groups of people all around the world. This collection of scholarly papers on the world food crisis is a useful contribution to improved understanding of the complex problems involved.

Developing countries have options. The adequate choice of options determines the effect of S & T on the process of development. New technologies imply immense opportunities and immense dangers. The potential and the risk of a technology are often very close to each other. Biotechnology, for instance, can help to develop new resistant crops that adapt easily to harsh soil and weather conditions, but generally altered micro-organisms released into the environment without sufficient analysis and testing can lead to the extinction of whole species and severe environmental damages as well. The appropriate decision and technology choice cannot be done on an ad-hoc basis. Developing countries need an endogenous science and technology policy and they need a basic infrastructure to be relied upon in the decision-making process. Given these two prerequisites S & T are likely to benefit the process of development, leading to peace, stability, and equitable prosperity for all.

Mohandas Karamchand Gandhi — whom some called a Mahatma ("great soul") — said that the best talisman that one can have is to ask yourself: "Will what I am doing, here and now, help the poorest of the poor?" I hope that to some extent this book will help to do just that. I hope it will contribute toward better understanding of the complex issues that we label "food security," issues which surround the establishment of equitable systems of food production, distribution, processing, and exchange in the world. If students, researchers, administrators and others gain some insights from this book then, hopefully, Gandhi's talisman will have been kept in focus.

This photograph shows:
Smt. Radha Bhatt, affectionately known as Radhabehn (centre, her sister (right) and a young student (left) at Laxmi Ashram (the Kasturba Mahila Uthan Mandel) founded on the basis of Gandhian principles by Sarla Devi (Catherine Mary Heilemann) in the foothills of the Himalayas (Uttar Pradesh State, India). It is a living example of the Gandhian approach to food security through self-reliance (Swadeshi).

Photographed by Hans Bakker 1980

Part I

OVERVIEW:
CONCEPTUALIZATION OF THE ISSUES

"SAWAH ON JAVA"
This painting by an Indonesian artist, Gambiranom Suhardi of Yogyakarta, Central Java, shows a traditional padi (sawah) ecology. While somewhat romanticized, the scene does represent one example of a food system in "dynamic equilibrium." However, as Clifford Geertz has pointed out, it depends on "shared poverty" and "involution."

Photograph Courtesy of the Bank Bumi Daya, 1982.

INTRODUCTION

FOOD PRODUCTION, DISTRIBUTION AND EXCHANGE:
CONCEPTUALIZING FOOD SECURITY AND INSECURITY IN COMPARATIVE INTERNATIONAL AND MULTIDISCIPLINARY PERSPECTIVE

J. I. Hans Bakker

Opening Remarks

This book is about food security.

> All of the chapters deal in some way with aspects
> of food production, distribution and exchange.

This collection of academic articles is in part an outgrowth of concern about the fact that many people in the world do not have secure access to food (Brundtland, 1987; FAO, 1985). Through no fault of their own they cannot obtain food in sufficient quantity or quality to lead healthy, productive lives. Some die of famine or starvation. Others live under conditions of malnourishment. Undernourished, they cannot solve their own problems. Poor nutrition saps their energy and makes daily life nothing more than a struggle for existence (Alten, 1975; George, 1976).

Food is one of our most basic needs. In some ways it is even more central to the maintenance of life than the other basic needs: clothing and shelter. There is no reason why anyone should suffer from lack of adequate food in the 1990s. Yet the trends that we see occurring now are indicative of a worsening situation (Warnock, 1987; Dover and Talbot, 1987). Hunger affects the poor first of all. Yet the goal of development should be "sarvodaya" or, "putting the last first" (Chambers, 1983). We need to consider the "people without history" (Wolf, 1982) who have not had secure access to basic, necessary foods. The "condition of the world order" (Hoffman, 1968) is such that food remains an *urgent* problem for the 1990s (Smits, 1986), just as it already was in the 1970s (Scrimshaw, 1968) and even before (Wolf, 1982: 133-135). We can apply the same ingenuity and adaptiveness to the discovery of better forms of social organization for the production, distribution and exchange of food as human beings have applied in the past to many other phenomena (Boorstin, 1983). But, in order to do so we need to understand the complex ramifications of food production, distribution and exchange at many different levels of social organizational structure, from the individual and local community system to the world system.

The 1973-74 World Food Crisis

We have moved into a new decade, the 1990s. But some of the problems that have faced us in the past (Sobel, 1975) continue to haunt our future. The world needs more food, better access to a healthy variety of foods at all times of year, and more equitable mechanisms for the distribution of food (Aten, 1975). The current situation is far from ideal, and that situation has been around for quite some time. As Mitchell put it (1975: 217): "The world food crisis is not a creature of recent discovery its...essential characteristics have been with us throughout the current century." That is to say, the inequities in food distribution which are considered by some authors to be part and parcel of the "capitalist" world food system that has taken shape since the turn of the century (Christensen, 1978).

Of course, hunger has probably been with us since the beginning of human life, and not just since the turn of the

4

century. However, the question of inadequate food has only become recognized as a "social problem" since the turn of the century, much like women's rights and racial equality. The recognition of the right to food is considered by some an inherent part of the basic set of human rights that all human beings share.

Many people have written about the "world food crisis." Others reject that term and play down the severity of the situation. After all, it is difficult to conceive of a "crisis" lasting nine decades!

However, in some respects the situation has gotten worse since the turn of the century, not better. In many ways the current crisis can be considered to have begun in the early 1970s, as part of the energy crisis and the struggles for a new international order after the end of the Vietnam War. A critical approach to the study of international development and international relations (e.g., Alavi and Shanin, 1982) has altered us to the degree to which the world system is characterized by inequities.

The term "the world food crisis" was given wide publicity in the period 1973-74, when shortages meant terrible suffering for tens of thousands of people and significant declines in the quality of life for countless others. International concern about world food shortages was great in the aftermath of the 1973-74 situation. International agencies, national governments, universities, research institutes and prominent individuals became concerned about inadequacies in what can be called the "global food regime" (Hopkins and Puchala, 1978). But the issue was relatively neglected by the mass media and more or less forgotten by the general public ... for awhile.

The Food Crisis in the 1980s

But not for long. In the eighties we experienced television broadcasts of famine in the Sahel in Africa (Shapouri, Dommen, and Rosen, 1986). We read stories of needless starvation of hundreds of children at a time in countries like Ethiopia and Bangladesh. We have also been alerted to natural disasters such as drought and floods that have caused damage to millions of

5

dollars worth of crops and forced large numbers of farmers into bankrupcy.

Nevertheless, for the average citizen of a developed country like the U.S., Canada, England or France, the idea of a real *crisis* in food supply seems less worth worrying about than a host of other concerns. The general public is concerned about many problems, from AIDS to xenophobic terrorism in the Middle East. Nuclear waste and the damaged ozone layer are discussed in major newspapers daily. Food again seems like a distant concern.

Thus, it comes as a bit of a surprise to many people to read a newspaper item like the following one:

"Unchecked pollution, land mismanagement and population growth have pushed the world to the brink of environmental disaster: a global food shortage could starve millions, the Worldwatch Institute says.

The environmental research group, which has surveyed the Earth's condition annually since 1984, has issued perhaps its grimmest report, *The State of the World 1989.*

'We are losing at this point, clearly losing the battle to save the planet,' said the report's chief author, Lester Brown. The impending result, he warned, `will shake the world to its foundation.'.....

Mr. Brown identified two critical concerns: continuing overpopulation, and environmental degradation that has cut farm output. This degradation includes such things as the loss of topsoil, the growing scarcity of water and the apparent global warming caused by air pollution.

Already, he noted, the world is undergoing 'a loss of momentum in the growth of food output.' He cited this evidence:

- World grain production per capita has declined each year since 1984;
- Last year's North American drought cut U.S. harvests by 30 per cent, and other major producers could not make up the loss; China's harvest fell by 3 per cent, the Soviet Union's by 9 per cent.
- Croplands have shrunk by 7 per cent in China since 1978, mostly because of industrial development, and by 13 per cent in the Soviet Union, mostly through land mismanagement.

The Earth is losing 24 billion tonnes of topsoil a year — as much as covers Australia's wheat belt — chiefly from overtilling. 'The world's farmers are now trying to feed 86 million more people each year and trying to do it with 24 billion fewer tonnes of topsoil,' Mr. Brown said.

'Those two trends cannot both continue indefinitely. At some point one is going to have to give,' he said.

Technological advances like hybrid corn, high-yield wheat, chemical fertilizers and irrigation, all of which boosted world crop production 2 1/2 fold from 1950 to 1984, have largely run their course, Mr. Brown said."

-Associated Press, New York
in Globe and Mail (Toronto, March, 1989)

The Food System and Hunger

As stated, we are concerned with the fact that many people do not have secure access to the quantity and quality of food that they need to live healthy lives. They face "food insecurity." But, we are not only interested in the short-term phenomena that tend to capture the headlines and then be forgotten. We attempt to go beyond pat answers and simplistic solutions. We cannot take either complete ignorance of the issues or alarmist reports as the final word. The seriousness of the topic requires a serious approach. Is the world really facing a world food crisis? Has the situation really been getting worse in the last few years?

As Dover and Talbot point out (1987: v):

> In the 1970s concern arose over a possible global food shortage. Experts debated whether the earth could ever produce enough food to feed all its people. Although the headlines have disappeared, the question remains valid, for after a decade of strong agricultural growth there were more hungry people in 1980 — before the Sahelian drought — than there had been in 1970. Despite impressive increases in agricultural productivity, production growth in some areas was matched or outstripped by population growth, and in other cases international debt burdens and falling commodity prices combined to depress food imports to hungry countries.

Academic Contributions

In this book a number of stimulating, original, recent scholarly contributions to the study of food production and food security have been brought together. The authors concentrate on a variety of aspects of food production, distribution and exchange. The overall goal of the book is to deepen our understanding of both:

1) the "loss of momentum in the growth of food output," and

2) the continuation of "food insecurity," even in situations of high or increasing productivity.

That is, both food production and food security are important aspects of one social problem: the world food crisis.

Without increased production it will be impossible to feed increased populations and very difficult to meet increased expectations for greater variety and more protein. Similarly, without better distribution and exchange mechanisms it will be unlikely that food security will improve appreciably for the vast majority of human beings living in so-called "developing" countries.

Is there really a world food crisis?

Many have called the world-wide problems of food production, distribution and exchange not merely a matter of better administration or improved nourishment, but a "world food crisis" (e.g., Sobel, 1975). The basic thesis of this book — taken as a whole — is that: *there is a world food crisis*. Numerous authors have written about aspects of a "crisis-like situation" (Barnet, 1980; Kneen, 1989; Lappe and Collins, 1977; Collins, 1988; Smits, 1986). Not all of the authors represented here would agree on the degree of severity of world food problems, but all are seriously concerned about aspects of food production, distribution and exchange.

Hunger and malnutrition are social problems that require immediate action. The term "crisis" is used in the title of this book because it correctly summarizes the fact that every day there are over one hundred million on earth who suffer needlessly from hunger and malnourishment (Poleman, 1984). There are problems of crisis proportions in the supply of an adequate and secure diet, with proper nutrition for healthy life.

Unless adequate steps are taken soon the situation will continue to get worse. Malnourishment is as dangerous as a life-threatening disease; often it leads to weakness, disease, and death. Protein-calorie malnutrition (PCM) among infants and children leads to kwashiorkor, marasmus, or a combination of both (Poleman, 1984: 25). Starvation, of course, means death, and it is a particularly brutal form of death.

It is clear to everyone that there are major problems in the world, but not everyone would consider the problems of the late 1980s or early 1990s as constituting any more of a "food crisis" than problems in previous decades. Are we really in a situation of crisis? Or are we simply experiencing major difficulties akin to difficulties which have existed before?

The assumption made here is that the world situation has changed to the point where conditions are getting worse. While the crisis may not always be as acute as it was in 1973-74 and the mid-1980s, it remains a social problem of crisis proportions for millions of people, particularly women and children. Yet it is totally unnecessary.

Irony of Glut

It is ironic that all of this is happening in the world at the same time as the people living in industrialized countries are experiencing abundance. In Canada, the U.S. and most of Europe we are more concerned with dieting and "losing weight" than with obtaining food. We have such an abundance of food available to us that it is hard to imagine any place in the world where access to food is a serious problem. Our individual concerns in the industrialized nations often focus on how to reduce the extent to which we indulge in "junk foods." But, while it is difficult for the affluent in the industrialized countries (who, by and large, do *not* suffer from the problem of insecurity of access to healthy food) to fully comprehend what it is like not to have food securely available, nevertheless the problem is a real one. It is a social problem of crisis proportions exacerbated by a host of factors, including the structure of international commodity markets, national foreign trade and aid policies, and continued geometrical expansion of population despite national birth control programs.

Roling has written insightfully about what he calls the "paradigm of glut" (1987). He argues that rural extension activities should be geared to the new situation of increased affluence in the developed countries. The situation we face today presents different problems than the historical situation faced by our ancestors. Thus, for example, the early history of agricultural development in the Province of Ontario (Jones, 1977) makes it clear that the affluence we experience in the rich countries is a relatively new phenomenon. Unfortunately, the development experiences of the rich countries cannot be translated in any simple, straightforward fashion to the problems of the poor countries, yet the international community requires that "our common future" be protected (Brundtland, 1987). In the long run that may require alternative expectations in the developed countries. We may have to pull in our belts.

At the same time the irony of glut is particularly cruel to *disadvantaged groups* in the industrialized world. Emergency feeding programs in the U.S. and Canada are necessary to feed the poor. Social assistance (e.g., unemployment insurance, transfer payments, social services, etc.) is grossly inadequate. Benefits for single parents, for example, provide less than half of the family income established as a poverty line (Riches, 1986). Young mothers spend their welfare allowance on rent and do not have enough left over to provide food for their children. The children suffer from poor nutrition and for many of them the vicious circle of poverty continues. Because social assistance benefits are inadequate to purchase basic needs many people in North America turn to "food banks." But such emergency feeding programs are contrary to the legal entitlement to subsistence. The welfare state "safety net" was never stitched together properly in the U.S. or Canada and recent governments have punctured huge holes in the patchwork net that existed. For example, eligibility requirements have been tightened. Instead of serving the redistributive functions required by law (e.g., Canada Assistance Plan Act, 1966) the net effect of actual arrangements is to "blame the victim" (Djao, 1983). For example, in times of recession and inflation many of the unemployed do not receive an adequate income to remain above the poverty line. That is in part due to the unwarranted assumption that higher social assistance levels will undermine the incentive to work. Hence, even though Canadian law guarantees adequate benefits *de jure*, the *de facto* situation is dependence on food banks

(Riches, 1986). Native people are hard hit, but the problem is not restricted to native people. The ideal of the modern welfare state has not been supported. Despite the law, the reality is significant malnourishment. Despite the legislation guaranteeing basic needs groups of people in Canada are not able to obtain the food they need without resorting to *ad hoc* arrangements. The situation in the U.S. is similar. In North America many aspects of the public welfare system are inadequate.

Sometimes public officials attempt to deflect attention from the issue of malnourishment and food insecurity in North America by pointing out that actual levels of hunger may be far worse in the third world. However, food security is not only an issue of "absolute deprivation." In North America the "relative deprivation" of a significant portion of the population is a reality. People who are malnourished due to the failure of governments to provide social benefits sufficient to ensure adequate nutrition are being denied full citizenship. In North America many expectant mothers, single parents and children are not getting enough nutritious food, despite the abundance of food produced (Riches, 1986).

Hunger as a Social Problem

The increasing recognition that technological and administrative innovations can be used to help ameliorate the plight of the poor in the third world — and even in depressed regions of relatively well developed and industrialized nations — means that hunger has become defined as a "social problem." In previous centuries there were many people who were undernourished, but hunger was not considered a "social problem" because it was believed that there was nothing that could be done about it. Indeed, without adequate transportation and communication there often was nothing that could be done about malnutrition, hunger and even starvation. There are also many historical examples of famine due to complex factors but clearly related to a failure to act forcefully and in the right way. Thus, for example, Sen (1984: 452-484) examines famines in Bengal in 1943, Ethiopia in 1973, and Bangladesh in 1974 as failures in policy. Food was available but the poor could not obtain it. When it was not common to think globally about food it was easier to overlook the continued undernourishment of significant population groups. Now that we are beginning to appreciate more than ever before, however, the fact that we all live on the same planet — a planet which is hurtling through space and which is an ecologically balanced system in dynamic equilibrium — we are also beginning to sense more clearly the inter-dependence of all population groups and segments on earth. We are recognizing the importance of "entitlement" and basic human rights (Sen, 1984).

Real Problems:
Possible Solutions

Luckily, however, something *can* be done about hunger. Not all of the authors represented in this book are optimistic about the potential for Science and Technology to help alleviate the world food crisis and other, related development problems. However, in the concluding chapter (Chapter Fifteen), Dr. John Mellor, of the International Food Policy Research Institute in Washington, D.C., argues convincingly that: not only is the crisis real, but something can be done about it.

Can we hope that problems of "food insecurity" will be alleviated in the near future? What is the "short-term" when we discuss issues as complex as food production, distribution and exchange globally? Indeed, are we talking about problems which could conceivably be solved in a "middle-term" of ten years, or are we dealing with insoluble problems which, like death and taxes, will always be with us?

It is also possible to conceive of doomsday scenarios involving ecological disaster. What will be the impact of the destruction of segments of the ozone layer? What will the Greenhouse Effect do to food production? Can the intensive farming methods used in North America continue to produce as much as they have in the past or will the topsoil quickly deteriorate?

The food crisis is like the proverbial elephant described by the blind sages; it is different things to different scholars. Hence, this book attempts to provide a sense of the diverse range of intellectual strategies used in attempting to analyse the component features of the complex problem we label the world food crisis. It is hoped that the reader will be introduced to the academic analysis of food security through this set of readings and then go on to further reading. The bibliographies provided by the authors provide a wealth of detailed, current references to relevant material.

Of course, a relatively brief book like this cannot cover all of the topics which potentially could be considered relevant. We certainly have not tried to make the analysis completely "comprehensive." Many potentially interesting topics — ranging from aspects of anthropology to zoology — are not covered. We have also refrained from attempting an encyclopedic coverage of geographical and political groupings.

There is no analysis here, for example, of food production, distribution and exchange in some of the republics of the Soviet Union, even though such an analysis would be very significant. There is no attempt to include material on all ecological regions or all types of foods. However, the fifteen chapters do cover a significant set of topics relevant to deepening our understanding of the world food crisis. In a sense, the work published here represents a kind of "sampler" of current academic research on issues pertinent to food production, distribution and exchange.

Food Security

In order to improve the degree of thematic unity most of the authors have concentrated on a subject area that requires attention and that has increasingly become important: food security and insecurity (Smits, 1986; FAO, 1985).

That is why the preface to this book is by the Executive Director of the United Nations Center for Science and Technology for Development (UNCSTD), Dr. Sergio C. Trindade. Like Dr. Mellor, he is relatively optimistic about the potential benefits of the use of improved technology to help promote increased food production and to help facilitate better food distribution and exchange systems. The application of S&T to the resolution of food insecurity problems, drought and desertification is but one of the "substantive themes" under the UNCSTD "Policy, Planning, Implementation and Innovation" cluster. That cluster is, in turn, only one of the four UNCSTD clusters. [The other clusters are: information, harmonization (i.e., co-ordination and liason), and communication (i.e., dissemination of information from UNCSTD)]. Nevertheless, food security is considered an especially important topic. Hence, UNCSTD, although overburdened and underfinanced, has devoted a significant portion of its funds and organizational capacities to the subject of "food security."

The term *food security* may be familiar to many readers, who may simply accept it without raising any questions. But others may have some intellectual doubts about the usefulness of the term "food security" and wonder why we do not simply talk about "food self-sufficiency" or even "alleviation of hunger." After all, is that not what is meant? The answer is that the term "food security" is a broader term than "food self-sufficiency" and encompasses much more than the "alleviation of hunger."

Definition of Food Security

The authors of the separate chapters of this book do not all agree precisely on all of the specific aspects of the definition of the term "food security." For example, Nef and Vanderkop tend to stress the underlying political dimensions of food security in their definition while Phillips and Taylor attempt to provide a fairly rigorous set of distinctions that are particularly central to a macro and micro economics-based analysis of food security. Similarly, von Benda-Beckmann, Hedican and Koennecke tend to consider food security mainly in terms of the secure access to food of individuals and households rather than in terms of national or regional food security. However, there is a good deal of underlying agreement on the general meaning of the term, despite the fact that many of the authors either do not know one another or have not had any structured opportunity to compare their work with one another.

At the very least the term "food security" is useful as a covering label for a number of aspects of food production, distribution and exchange that are related to the problematic aspects of obtaining food on a regular basis. Those problematic aspects of food production, distribution and exchange are considered significant enough to warrant use of the phrase "the world food crisis."

The term also implies an awareness of the importance of specifying the levels of social organizational structure that are especially significant for food issues: macro to micro, or micro to macro. Those levels include everything from the individual consumer (female and male, adult and child) to the global order or "international economic system." As a minimum we would have to recognize the importance of the individual, the household (extended, nuclear, single parent), the community (hamlet, village, town, cluster of villages), the sub-region (county, sub-district, district), the nation (e.g., tribe or tribal confederation, linguistic group, ethnic group), the nation-state (country) and international organizations (UNDP, UNCSTD, FAO, World Bank, ILO, ADB, etc.).

Some of the definitional problems involved in the use of the term "food security" are discussed by Phillips and Taylor in Chapter One and by Nef and Vanderkop in Chapter Two. In the literature reviewed by those authors the term "food security" is widely used. The excellent report put out by the RAWOO (Advisory Council for Scientific Research on Development Problems), for example, is entitled *Food Security in Developing Countries* (Smits, 1986). Whatever term one uses, it is clear that a range of important phenomena dealing with food must be more clearly conceptualized by national governments and international agencies than has been the case in the past.

Thus, it is worthwhile to point out here that — in addition to what has already been said — the term also includes implicit recognition of the systemic and global linkages involved in the contemporary world food situation. Different researchers may disagree on the extent to which those global linkages create food insecurity, but there is increased recognition that some kind of "systemic" inter-relationships have to be taken into account. Thus, for example, the oscillations in world food production are not merely a matter of natural disasters and other calamities peculiar to particular sub-regions, countries or regions. To a large extent, the international system of exchange determines the distribution of food. The wealthy countries have a far larger share of world food — and everything else — than the so-called "middle-income" and poor countries.

Similarly, a study of eleven African countries by the Economic Research Unit of the U.S. Department of Agriculture has emphasized the existence of a "chronic food gap" in nine of those nations. That chronic gap is due to complex factors but will not be compensated by emergency food aid alone. Hence, even the structural arrangements for food aid from "rich" to "poor" have to take the *chronic* problem of food security into account (Shapouri, Dommen; and Rosen 1986).

The term food security is now widely used by the United Nations. At the meeting, sponsored by UNCSTD and the Government of Zimbabwe, for example, the "Ad Hoc Panel of Specialists on Science, Technology and Food Security" made a number of specific recommendations which refer to "food security" rather than "food self-sufficiency."(Dr. Trindade has provided some of the salient conclusions from the Harare Conference in his preface.) The Deputy Minister of Lands, Agriculture and Rural Resettlement of Zimbabwe said at the meeting that the countries of the " Southern African Development Co-ordination Conference" preferred the use of the term "food security" rather than "food self-sufficiency." He emphasized that the food security concept requires measures to increase purchasing power and to ensure, in the short and long terms, that a country's food system provides the total population access to timely, reliable and adequate supplies of food.

Food security, therefore, is a term that attempts to capture some of the complexity of the range of issues involved in one aspect of "development" (Smits, 1986). Of course, not all of the authors represented here are concerned with "food security" in general. Some of the authors — particularly those reporting on empirical field work or survey research work — focus on particular aspects of food production, distribution and exchange.

Cultivators and Food Production

Some of the authors are less concerned with food security *per se* than with the people who grow the food. There is a significant literature in the social sciences on various aspects of the peasantry and food production. One significant contribution to our understanding of the impact of colonialism on underdevelopment, for example, is the excellent book by Clifford Geertz on rice paddy cultivation in Central and Eastern Java during the nineteenth century (Geertz, 1963). Geertz argues that the combined effect of the ecology of Java and the superimposition of Dutch colonialism on Javanese traditional institutions was the phenomenon of "involution." While involution is difficult to define, it basically refers to the idea that no real structural change was taking place. Instead, the "greenhouse" situation in Java encouraged a continued elaboration of traditional forms. Hence, according to Geertz, the opportunity for economic "take off" into sustained growth and modernization was lost. He compares Java and Japan in this respect.

While it is possible to point out significant weaknesses in Geertz's argument (Bakker, 1987b; 1988), the concept of "involution" has nevertheless captured the imagination of many scholars concerned with development and modernization. It is possible to extend Geertz's term — which he borrowed from the anthropological writings of Alexander Goldenweizer — to the current situation in the world. If we consider the whole world as a complex "ecology" then we can consider to what extent the contemporary situation is a form of "involution." That is, are we merely pedalling backwards rather than moving forwards? Will the 1990s allow us to experience significant structural changes in the manner in which food production, distribution and exchange are carried out in the capitalistically-oriented "world system"? Will it be possible to provide more sophisticated analyses of the impact of "entitlement failures" (Sen, 1984) and to develop "linked national models" of the world economy (Fisher, et al., 1988) so that agricultural and food systems can be managed more equitably? Can the principles of the U.N. *International Covenant on Economic, Social and Cultural Rights* (U.N., 1976) be enforced? Such questions cannot be answered globally. There must be a further differentiation of the analytical elements of the question. One aspect, for example, is a better description of the situation faced by individual peasant cultivators and "family farmers" in both developed and developing countries.

Smallholders Highly Differentiated

Thus, for example, Schulman and Garrett are concerned with the socio-economic characteristics of smallholders who grow a cash crop. They distinguish four major types of smallholders and argue that their findings, based on a sample of predominantly black, male, tobacco farmers in North Carolina, have theoretical implications for our empirical study and conceptualization of peasant economies. The impact on food security of differential characteristics and stratification among smallholders — whether they be peasants in a developing country or "family farmers" in

17

poorer sub-regions of a developed country — cannot be underestimated. The Schulman and Garrett chapter has significance not only for understanding smallholders in North Carolina, but also for comprehending the general complexity of relations of production in agriculture around the world. They raise many stimulating questions about the clustering of factors relevant to the analysis of poor family farmers' concerns. While poor blacks in North Carolina may not be as concerned with a lack of food security as smallholders in Indonesia or Mali, they are nevertheless faced with many of the same micro-level problems and macro-level parameters.

Of course, there are important overlaps with the study of "development" in general, as Nef and Vanderkop make clear. Even though their paper is basically about Latin America and the Caribbean, they also formulate some important theoretical statements about the relationship between the study of food security and the study of economic, social welfare and political development. Their contention that the use of the term "food security" is often highly political needs to be understood in terms of the extent to which any definition of a social problem is, in essence, a "politicized" aspect of international relationships.

Paradigmatic Continuum

There are at least two major schools of thought concerning international development. We could label those two polar alternatives: the *Neo-classical "Modernization"* Paradigm (NCMP) (e.g., Brown and Hadwiger, 1986; IRRI, 1975; Rotstein, 1973) and the *Neo-Marxian "Dependency"* Paradigm (NMDP) (e.g., Alavi and Shanin, 1982; Arrighi and Saul, 1973). The arguments put forward by Geertz (1963) are highly critical, but nevertheless tend to be grounded in the NCMP. Hence, Geertz utilized the terminology popularized by Walter Rostow, particularly the term "take off." Geertz does so not only because the term is popular but also because he tends to accept the notion of capitalist development contained in the NCMP.

Basically, however, we are not concerned here with rehearsing that important debate. Instead, the implicit paradigmatic position that has been employed in the editing of this book has been an intermediate position that attempts to employ the insights of both "modernization" NCMP and "dependency" NMDP approaches. To a large extent we are attempting to follow in the academic footsteps of Hopkins and Puchala (1978). Thus, for example, when Hainsworth (1982) entitled his collection of articles "Village-level Modernization" he would seem to have been implying that he followed the NCMP. However, he chose to sub-title his book "The Political Economy of Rice and Water"! That implies that he is *also* quite concerned with the insights of the NMDP.

This book, then, is about both "modernization" and "dependency" and all of the authors clearly try to steer a middle course between the Scylla of excessive sanguinity about the status quo and the Charybdis of total rejection of contemporary efforts at development. Authors as diverse as Long (1984), Wolf (1982), Jacoby and Jacoby (1971) and Molnar and Clonts (1983) tend to steer the same course. Some authors in the literature and in this book tend to be more closely aligned with the NMDP (e.g., Nef and Vanderkop, von Benda Beckmann, Hedican, Henderson) while other authors tend to be more toward the NCMP end of the continuum (e.g., Pfeiffer and Song, Phillips and Taylor, Hoban, Jorjani); but, all of the authors are critical of what they perceive as current inadequacies and deficiencies in development efforts related to food security.

Questions and Answers?

While the papers presented here cover many of the basic aspects of food security and insecurity discussed at the Guelph Conference in 1986, they also go further, and explore some of the important aspects of world, regional, national, sub-regional, community and household food problems that have been understood only in a schematic manner and not yet properly investigated empirically. We are concerned with the manner in which science and technology are used for increasing food production and improving food distribution and exchange. However, we are also concerned with much more.

Professor John Cairns, one of the organizers of the Guelph conference, summarized some themes that, in his opinion, recurred throughout much of the discussion at the conference.

[First], there was widespread agreement that the world

food crisis is not a problem of agricultural production [in and of itself]. There is [or can be] ample food in the world for all. The problem is one of economic, political and distributional equality. Those who most need food too often lack land to grow it or money to buy it. For this, Science and Technology have no answers. The solution lies in the economic and political sphere — a conclusion of importance to policy makers and governments.

Secondly, there was a broad consensus that, if technological innovations are to be productive, they must be adapted to and integrated with the social, cultural and traditional value [systems] of the people they are meant to serve. Otherwise, they will be dysfunctional — if not worse.

Western technology, in short, is a two-edged sword. In the introduction of new technologies, there is need for much closer relationships between natural and social scientists, all of whom, as Margaret Catley-Carlson [President, Canadian International Development Agency, CIDA] stated, should listen to those they are trying to help, "the quiet people whose lives and futures are at stake." (Cairns, 1987: i). [A significant portion of the Conference Summary, compiled on the basis of rapporteur's contributions and edited by Cairns and Valeriote, is reprinted below.]

Of course, the "quiet people" that Mrs Catley-Carlson was talking about are not just located in the regions of Africa and Asia where droughts and floods have created famine and starvation. If there is any truth in the predictions made by Lester Brown and his associates at Worldwatch then all human beings in the world need to be concerned about food, not only for reasons having to do with humanitarian altruism but also for reasons that hit home more immediately.

Multi-disciplinary

All of the authors who contribute to this book approach the questions of world food production, distribution and exchange associated with food security from different angles, with different academic foci and different experiential contexts. This is a truly multi-disciplinary work. However, it cannot be said that all of the papers are "inter-disciplinary" in the sense of a well-worked-out synthesis of disciplinary perspectives. Nevertheless, there is a great deal of overlap.

There has been no attempt to get all of the authors to agree on any of the major topics. Instead, the purpose of this book is to provide a good cross-section of expert opinion on a range of specific topics. While some of the contributions contain somewhat technical language, all of them provide clear introductions to significant problem areas related to the crisis in food production, distribution and exchange in the world. The authors have generally kept technical vocabulary to a minimum, except where it would create a false simplification of complex problems. The articles are written as academic contributions and generalizations are, for the most part, guarded by qualifications and a healthy awareness of the importance of the *ceterus paribus* principle. That is, each contribution has to be read as a separate argument and each conclusion has to be understood in context.

There has been no attempt to provide a unified version of the current world food crisis or even a comprehensive set of general evaluations of the problems of food production, distribution and exchange internationally, regionally or nationally. Instead, some of the major debates that occur among scholars interested in food security are discussed and some of the empirical materials that will help to clarify key points in those debates are discussed in detail.

Diversity of Opinion

The authors of the chapters of this book come not only from diverse disciplinary backgrounds and paradigmatic positions, but also from different countries and intellectual milieux. Hence, the reader will note many differences of opinion. There has been no attempt at reconciling those differences editorially. Instead, intellectual diversity is viewed as an important part of the picture. Different authors single out different aspects of the puzzle for consideration.

In addition to the difference between a NMDP and NCMP discussed above, there is also a difference between those who are attempting to follow in some kind of "Political Economy" tradition and those who are more interested in approaches which are closer to their own specialized disciplines. My own work has been an attempt to examine "social change in rural societies" (Rogers and Burdge, 1972) through the "Canadian Political Economy Tradition" (Bakker, 1987a), but I have not attempted to impose that intellectual framework on the authors. Each of the authors has contributed her or his paper as an outgrowth of work done within separate disciplinary perspectives.

The impetus of the international conference ensured that many of the authors would be from the University of Guelph in Guelph, Ontario, Canada. However, there has also been interest among researchers at other universities, notably Wageningen Agricultural University in Wageningen, the Netherlands, and North Carolina State University in Raleigh, North Carolina, U.S.A.

It is hoped that this selection of academic papers will help to build linkages among researchers actively pursuing answers to the questions raised by the attempt to investigate the impact of the use of S&T to promote food security.

Many of the issues are complex and do not have any straight-forward solutions. It is sometimes even difficult to know exactly where to begin to look for answers.

Technological Solutions

For example there is a fairly major divide between those who definitely favour the use of new scientific findings and new technological innovations (e.g., Jorjani) and those who are in some manner more neutral or even opposed to reliance on science and technology to solve problems of food production, distribution and exchange (Hedican, Koennecke). All of the authors are opposed to "over-reliance" on science and technology to solve the world food crisis; but, there are differences of opinion as to what constitutes over-reliance. Between semi-popular "scientistic" and radically "political" stands there are many intermediate opinions, of course. Most people in the broader community agree that there are useful ways in which science and technology can be used to help provide solutions to current problems of hunger and starvation. But there is a long distance to go yet after that generalization has been widely accepted in the general community or even in the university community. It is necessary to begin to specify the concrete manifestations of the problem of world hunger and undernourishment and the complex inter-relatedness of a host of factors.

Furthermore, a division occurs when people discuss the extent to which adequate utilization of scientific and technological discoveries depends on a proper political and economic environment. For some it is absolutely essential that political and economic solutions *precede* the use of new scientific and technological innovations (Nef and Vanderkop). For others it is not necessary to wait for absolutely the right political or economic climate (Engberg, Hoban). But such issues cannot be resolved a priori. They need to be investigated in terms of specific dynamics in actual historical places during a clearly delimited period of time. All of the authors attempt to move the discussion to a more scholarly framework and get away from simple black and white thinking. Hence, while they have written in order to communicate their knowledge, they have also not oversimplified the complexities of the situation.

Security of Food Imports

It is quite conceivable that the question of food security will become one with which more people in the *developed* world are directly and personally concerned. Will there be global starvation in the twenty-first century? If so, who will it affect most severely? Is it possible that the industrialized nations will be most hard hit precisely because people in the technologized world have the highest level of expectations and cannot easily return to older ways of satisfying basic needs for food? The security of food imports is also an aspect of food security. Food imports in many developing countries have become extremely problematic; the same can easily occur in the developed countries as well. "The developed capitalist countries of North America, Europe and Japan are consuming a disproportionate amount of food per capita relative to world standards. ... In total, 20 per cent of the population living in the most industrialized countries consume as much food as the other 80 per cent of the world's population" (Mitchell, 1975: 198).

Although food security is a world-wide problem it is not a problem which occurs everywhere in the world at the same time and in the same way. In some parts of the world the issues have to do with food production and many of the crisis-like aspects of the problems could potentially be solved by a significant increase in production. In other parts of the world it is not increased production that is called for so much as better distribution. International trade and inter-regional exchange is also an important aspect of the problem. The crisis can take different forms in different countries. (See Shapouri, Dommen and Rosen, 1986, on comparisons within Sub-Saharan Africa, for example.)

The production of staple foods by indigenous populations has been altered greatly by the introduction of expanded trade in commodities which are not used indigenously. Export of food, while it can provide needed capital, can also result in large productivity mixed with low per capita consumption. Countries which export agricultural products such as flowers as a cash crop may at the same time experience famine in some sub-regions due to lack of distribution or problems of exchange.

Agricultural Knowledge Systems

In an important new book (1989), Professor Niels Roling of the Department of Extension Education at the leading Agricultural University of the Netherlands, in Wageningen, provides us with some significant questions concerning the use of "science and technology" in the form of "agricultural knowledge systems." His general thesis is that technical innovations occur in highly inter-connected systems. He has coined the term "agricultural knowledge systems" (AKS) for systems which make deliberate agricultural innovations possible. Such AKSs require a perspective that goes beyond the simple "transfer of technology" model (TOT) that was part of the early "diffusion of innovations" literature. The innovation process is viewed by Roling as an inter-action rather than simply a one-way action and response. As he points out, "In successful systems, utilisers [i.e., cultivators, farmers] often have considerable control over the whole process...." That generalization is exemplified in

24

Roling's work through a case study of rural extension in Kenya. Several of the chapters below continue along similar lines. While the term AKS is not used below, the general idea of systemic inter-connections in agricultural production, distribution and exchange is clearly present in most of the chapters. Those writers who do not emphasize what might be called — in the broad sense of the word — the "ecological" nature of the questions raised nevertheless show an awareness of systemic and structural inter-relatedness.

Theory and Case Studies

This book consists of a set of theoretical statements and seven "comparative regional case studies," two of which concern Native Canadians. We are introduced to smallholders in the American South, Sri Lanka, the island of Ambon in Indonesia, Mali in Africa, and Northern China. From the case studies we begin to see the diversity of ways of obtaining food characteristic of smallholders in different parts of the world.

Whenever possible case studies of particular problems have been used to illustrate broader principles. Thus, rather than simply generalize about the problems in very global terms we will attempt to analyse a world problem in terms of significant factors in selected countries and regions. In essence, the papers in this book represent what Robert K. Merton calls "middle range theory" (1968: 39-72). Such an approach will not allow for treatment of all problems and all regions, of course, but a sufficiently broad cross-section of significant factors and geographic locations will be possible. Hence, there is interesting material presented here on food systems in Latin America (Nef and Vanderkop) and households in Africa as a whole (Engberg). A more specific study of villages on the island of Ambon in the Indonesian archipelago (by von Benda-Beckmann) helps to clarify significant aspects of the transition from a largely "pre-capitalist" set of "relations of production" to an increasingly "capitalist" and market-oriented socio-economic structure. The regional case studies which deal with smallholders in the American South (Schulman and Garrett), Sri Lanka (Southwold-Llewellyn), Africa (Engberg) and Northern China (Pfeiffer and Song) emphasize different aspects of food production, distribution and exchange.

25

There are also chapters which deal with aspects of Native Canadian food production (by Koennecke and by Hedican). They are also "comparative regional case studies," of course, but they are classified separately (as Part III of the book) because we wish to emphasize the fact that food security and insecurity is not just a matter of developing countries. In the developed countries there are disadvantaged groups who suffer from food insecurity. The world food crisis is a crisis for all "nations" in the world, including Native North Americans.

The analyses of specific regions provides useful background for more intensive study of similar issues in other regional settings. Of course, in a book like this there is no opportunity to summarize all of the technical problems that one must face in food production. However, in order to give the reader a sense of the kinds of technical considerations that must be dealt with we have included three chapters that emphasize food production. One of the major issues that is discussed is soil conservation (Hoban). Soil-water management (Jorjani) is a second major technical issue. Thirdly, we are able to read about the "Blue Revolution" and the attempt to modernize fishing.

Complex Problems

The world is complex. In the social sciences we have the insightful work of Max Weber, the great German sociologist (1864-1920) to make it clear to us just how complex human societies are (Weber, 1978). Weber, like other classical theorists in the social sciences, was hampered by a lack of detailed knowledge of cultures outside of Western Europe, even though he attempted to utilize the most current available research in formulating his provocative theories concerning the origins of capitalism, rational-legal bureaucracy and modern complex organizations. Weber, like Marx, Durkheim, Pareto and Simmel, understood that part of the world that was available to his generation. His *Weltanschauung* was cosmopolitan, but still limited. Hence, when we read contemporary social scientists who attempt to build on classical theorists like Weber (e.g., Collins, 1986) it immediately becomes apparent that even the greatest intellectuals cannot capture the full range of complexity of the real world. It is not genius alone that makes for good theory and analysis. Hence, there is a real danger is creating idols of the "masters." What is needed for analysis of social problems is not one "Great Man" — a social science Newton or Einstein — but a concerted effort by large numbers of thinkers and researchers.

When it comes to the world food crisis it is clear that there is no simple solution to the massive intellectual problems posed. Instead, we have to further develop our analytical tools and continue to let theory and research build upon one another.

Thus, there has been no attempt made to simplify the complex problems related to food that confront us at the end of the twentieth century. All of the contributors to this volume regard the issues of food production, distribution and exchange as sufficiently important to devote a considerable portion of their intellectual energy to a thorough examination of details. Such "middle range theory" is extremely useful because it goes beyond the tendency to examine world problems in simplified "grand theoretical" terms.

Although most of the contributors are social scientists who are interested in the relationship between "science" and "society" in the general area of "food security," some of the contributions deal with technical issues that will be of interest to those outside of the social sciences (e.g., natural scientists, rural development practitioners, government officials responsible for food policies, and the educated public).

Potential Readership

The main impetus behind this book is a concern with the global problem of food production, distribution and exchange, viewed both in terms of world trends and in terms of specific regions, nations, sub-regions, communities and households. Hence, it is hoped that this book will be considered useful by the educated public. However, it is also hoped that it will be read by graduate students (i.e., "post-graduates") in courses on the sociology and anthropology of development, agricultural economics, rural extension, rural planning, nutrition, political science, and public administration or management.

This book will also be useful for advanced undergraduate courses in a broad range of different disciplines in the social sciences, history and nutrition: from anthropology to rural development. There are contributions from the disciplines of anthropology, political science, sociology, agricultural economics, home economics, soil and water management, rural extension, and rural planning.

Natural Science, Social Science and Human Ecology

Moreover, those natural scientists who are interested in ecological considerations, broadly conceived, in terms of what is sometimes called the "new human ecology," will find much that is of interest here. (The term "new human ecology" is used by some writers to distinguish the approach one finds in this book from the "human ecology" approach that characterized the Chicago School of sociology in the early decades of this century; see Hawley, 1952.) In general, the authors of the chapters in this book all take a "systemic" approach that concerns a range of inter-dependent phenomena. Hence, they conceptualize social, political and economic issues in terms of an "ecological" framework — broadly defined — that encompasses many aspects of the interface between human beings and the natural environment.

Topics Excluded

1. Population Growth

Specifically excluded in this book, however, is the factor of population growth. Although, obviously, population growth is a key factor in the "ecology" of the world food crisis, it would lead us too far astray to try to explore the variety of complex issues pertaining to population growth in this text.

Naturally, it is recognized that population growth is a key factor in the contemporary world food situation and is an important contributory or background factor that needs to be taken into account in assessing to what extent poor international mechanisms for food distribution and exchange "cause" hunger.

However, population growth is a complex topic in itself and

it would not be possible to do justice to the complex arguments that demographers and economic historians have made about the historical or current impact of population growth (e.g., Drake, 1988). For example, in order to understand development it would be helpful to have a well-accepted theory concerning the Industrial Revolution, which in turn requires a theory concerning demographic change. Was there a "demographic transition" or did death rates not drop quite a bit earlier than birth rates? Is the population growth experienced by some developing countries likely to level off as a certain measure of economic development occurs? While obviously relevant to the issue of international food security, population is not examined in detail by any of the authors represented here.

According to Lappe and Collins (1986) it is a myth to believe that we must slow population growth *before* we can hope to alleviate hunger. They argue that rapid population growth and hunger share a common cause: powerlessness. Hence, only far-reaching political and economic changes will reduce population growth rates *and* food insecurity. For example, *income equity* decreases the birth rate and increases food security, *ceterus paribus*.

2. Migration and Resettlement

Also not considered here is the impact of migration and resettlement on food production, distribution and exchange. The excellent collection of articles edited by Havet (1988) contains several articles which are relevant to that question. Thus, for example, peasant cultivators are often depicted as sedentary people who are limited to their specific village or sub-region. However, several of the contributors to the Havet volume make it clear that peasants tend to make decisions which are "rational" within their own frame of reference. Hence, many peasant cultivators move to urbanized areas in search of work because they know that in the city it is highly probable their lives will be more secure. Even if they are underemployed they are likely to earn as much cash as they would if they stayed in their home village and they are likely to have access to a variety of foods on the market. Hence, food security is important because it also helps to alleviate the problems caused by rural to urban migration. In order to "retain" peasant cultivators in rural areas it is necessary to provide structures of opportunity in rural sub-regions. As Havet points out "Retention of rural populations is in no way synonymous with social stagnation....." (Havet, 1988: 17). In fact, in many ways we could consider the retention of rural populations in the areas where they were born as a positive aspect of good integrated rural development.

That is not to say, however, that resettlement schemes should be rejected across the board. At times the resettlement of populations can actually help to promote food security. In my own work in Indonesia I have seen situations where integrated rural development can be served by resettlement efforts, provided they are truly "integrated" efforts involving multi-sectoral agencies and departments. No development effort will benefit rural peasants in developing countries if it is not conceptualized clearly and in constant consultation with the people themselves (Bakker, 1985; Beange, 1988). Nevertheless, there are many resettlement schemes which are *not* helpful and do not promote an improved quality of life for the people being resettled, even if the stated intent is to provide access to productive agricutural land. Unfortunately that has been the case for many of the so-called "transmigration" (i.e., *transmigrasi*, long-distance resettlement) projects in Indonesia and the resettlement projects in Ethiopia. Often political objectives are more important in dictating the use of resettlement as a tool for development than any cost-benefit analysis of the utility of the move. Food security should never be used as an "excuse" for the promotion of either retention schemes or resettlement projects. Unfortunately, in the present volume we do not have space to pursue this important topic.

3. Specific Inventions

Similarly, we are also not concerned specifically with scientific inventions and technological discoveries *per se*. One of the topics that interested many individuals at the 1986 Guelph international conference was the extent to which new bio-technological discoveries could be used to supplement current agricultural and livestock production methods. This fascinating topic is not taken up here by any of the contributors, but it is worth mentioning.

Thus, in North America there is currently greatly interest in the use of computer technology to provide up-to-date information to "farmers" and "agro-business managers." The topic was discussed at the conference in Guelph in 1986 and there is currently research on computer applications going on at many agricultural universities and research stations. Even though the subject of computer applications is timely it is not included here because it is not considered to be as directly relevant to the major concern of food security in developing countries as the other topics which are discussed. In general, of course, peasant cultivators who cannot afford to purchase sufficient food to supplement what they grow are not likely to be in any position to start utilizing computers to increase their efficiency of output! Nevertheless, it is quite logical to suppose that the use of computer technology at national and sub-regional levels might be extremely useful in many developing countries. For example, it would be helpful to maintain better records of existing food stocks. Nevertheless, we felt that this topic was better left outside of consideration in this relatively brief book.

4. "Gene Erosion"

There were also other topics pertaining to technological innovations which were discussed in Guelph in 1986 which have not been taken up in the present reader. We were warned at the conference, for example, that one danger is the possibility that world genetic strains will be lost. Professor Pat Mooney, an economist from Brandon University in Manitoba, pointed out that there is already a problem of "gene erosion" due to the highly selective use of only a few strains. In order to overcome that problem there are suggestions concerning increasing the number of gene banks. However, then the problem becomes the potential for manipulation of the situation by powerful countries. Some view the Green Revolution, for example, as leading to the unanticipated negative side-effect of disappearance of many indigenous varieties. But the introduction of technology into agriculture has had a significant impact long before the Green Revolution began. "Between 1903 and 1983/84 North America has lost some 95 percent of its plant species," according to Mooney.

A fascinating aspect of the reduction of genetic variety in food species regularly produced and consumed is the continued existence of pockets of traditional agricultural techniques where variety helps to ensure a lower risk from pests and diseases. Wendell Berry, the American "farmer-poet" has written insightfully about traditional agrarian values in both North and South America (Berry, 1981a, 1981b). Also see Weatherwax (1954) on traditional Native corn production.

The articles by Koennecke and Hedican argue strongly in favour of an appreciation of traditional Native food production techniques. Their concern is with the ways in which agrobusiness and logging have disrupted the traditional ways of Canadian Native people. It is certainly important to consider the extent to which we can learn from "first nations" about the importance of maintaining an ecologically well-balanced relationship with the natural environment.

5. Agronomic and Biological Sciences

Of course, there is a risk in becoming too enamoured with the old ways. It is easy to over-romanticize the situation faced by indigenous people in the past. Clearly the world food problems discussed here cannot be reduced significantly simply by returning to agricultural production techniques characteristic of a pre-industrial era. Therefore, we will have to continue to attempt to understand agricultural production scientifically through the application of natural science techniques.

Unfortunately, there are no contributions from bio-chemists, agronomists, or plant biologists. There are no papers by horticulturalists or zoologists. There simply was not space enough to try to encompass such a broad range of disciplines. Hence, our claim that this book is multi-disciplinary should be tempered by the understanding that most of the disciplines represented are social science disciplines. Unfortunately, this book is largely the result of work done by social scientists. There has undoubtedly been significant co-operation between social and natural scientists concerning the world food crisis since 1973-74 and it will be important to become more aware of potential "inter-disciplinary" research utilizing both natural and social science expertise.

Thus, for example, at the IRRI and other international agricultural agencies, there has been increased recognition of the importance of the insights of anthropologists and community development experts (IRRI, 1975). Increasing the productivity of peasant cultivators is not just a matter of isolating the right kinds of ground nuts or soya beans; it also involves a study of the intricacies of their cultural value system and the specific norms governing agricultural cultivation and the distribution of crop yields and other foods.

6. Archaeo-history

Also, we have not been able to include the excellent work of "archaeohistorical agrobotanists" like Professor Jouke S. Wigboldus (1988a, 1988b, 1988c), even though it is extremely important for any long range understanding of the complexities of food production, distribution and exchange. Wigboldus, for example, examines the relevance of Paul E. Lovejoy's "poorly developed technology" thesis as it applies to precolonial Central Sudan (northeastern Africa). Lovejoy argues (1986) on the basis of his examination of salt production technology that Central Sudan had a "poorly developed" technological base and was relatively backward. The work of other ethno-archaeologists has disputed the idea of backwardness, emphasizing ecological continuity. Hopkins (1973), for example, rejects the use of the term "traditional society" and critiques what he calls the "myth of primitive Africa." Wigboldus's seminal work on this topic, however, is too specialized for the current volume.

Second Volume?

Perhaps a parallel volume, emphasizing some of the purely technical aspects of such concerns as the ethno-archaeology of agriculture and critiques of the "transfer of technology" (TOT) approach, would also constitute a welcome outgrowth from the Guelph conference. Agro-archaeologists, agronomists, natural and biological scientists at Guelph, Wageningen, North Carolina State, and other universities and research institutions should consider more multi-disciplinary work on food security and related issues. It may be that many natural scientists have not yet begun to think in terms other than straightforward transfer of technology approaches, but there is no reason that there could not be a greater awareness of what Roling (1987) calls "agricultural knowledge systems."

Therefore, this volume will be useful if it stimulates students and established academics in all fields to consider the possibility that specialized examination of technological solutions — taken by itself — is not sufficient. While natural and biological scientists are, of course, aware that ideas and technological solutions developed in a social vacuum may often contribute unanticipated effects, they nevertheless seem reluctant to publish outside of their specialized disciplinary journals. While such specialized publication can be beneficial because it promotes in depth examination of narrowly focussed topics, it is apparent that, in the long run, it can also do more to exacerbate the problem than to solve it. More work on the interface between the approaches of the social and natural sciences would be very fruitful for a truly "ecological" set of solutions to the pressing problems of world food production, distribution and exchange.

Outgrowth of Guelph Conference

Finally, while the chapters in this book are all an outgrowth of the Guelph conference, none of the papers are "conference papers." While an open letter went out to all conference participants requesting papers, few of the participants responded and none contributed a finished scholarly paper suitable for publication that was based directly on their conference talk. (There were a number of papers which were rejected by the editorial committee as too discursive and requiring too much additional work to be made into academic contributions.) Conference participants were not informed ahead of time of the notion of publication of a book on selected aspects of the question of "Science and Technology in the World Food Crisis." Apparently, few were interested in writing academic papers after the conference had concluded. Hence, the papers printed here are the result of on-going research that is, in some ways, an outgrowth of the conference. But they are not conference papers *per se*.

Hence, this is *not* a "conference proceedings." The work published here is either original work written for other purposes or work written especially for this volume. All of the papers have been read by at least two referees, often by three. In cases of doubt a third (or even a fourth) referee was asked to comment.

Conclusion

No one book can provide all of the information needed to begin to "solve" problems as significant as those discussed here; but, it is hoped that this book will be a contribution to an on-going debate concerning the world food crisis. It is particularly timely to consider the topics discussed by the authors of the chapters of this volume in light of the continued interest in "Ethics and Technology" since approaches to the solution of the world food crisis has many ethical ramifications. Hopefully this volume will make it clear that "food security" (in a broad sense) is a question that must be dealt with both concretely, in terms of very specific empirical questions, and holistically, in terms of "lateral thinking" and innovative solutions to "ecological" problems. Also, hopefully the book will provide an incentive for those interested in agriculture, fisheries, and food, to search for the results of other investigations which provide more of the pieces needed in order to fill out the complex intellectual puzzles related to food production, distribution and exchange.

J. I. Hans Bakker
Sociology and Anthropology
University of Guelph
Guelph, Ontario
August 10, 1989

BIBLIOGRAPHY

Alavi, Hamza, and Teodor Shanin (eds.). 1982. *Introduction to the Sociology of "Developing Societies."* New York: Monthly Review Press.

Arrighi, Giovanni, and John S. Saul. 1973. *Essays on the Political Economy of Africa.* New York: Monthly Review Press.

Aten, A. 1975. *De Wereld Heeft Meer Voedsel Nodig: Enkele Aspecten van het Wereldvoedselprobleem.*[The World Needs More Food: Some Aspects of the World Food Problem]. Amsterdam: Koninklijk Instituut voor de Tropen, Bijlage [Annex] 65th yearly report.

Austin, James E. 1978. "Institutional Dilemmas of the Malnutrition Problem." In Hopkins and Puchala op. cit.: 237-264.

Axinn, George H. 1983. "Host Country Institutions and Diffusion of Technology." In Molnar and Clonts op. cit.: 146-153.

Aziz, S. (ed.) 1975. *Hunger, Politics and Markets: The Real Issues in the Food Crisis.* New York: University Press.

Bakker, J. I. (H.) 1988. "Patrimonialism, Involution and the Agrarian Question in Java: A Weberian Analysis of Class Relations and Servile Labor." In Gledhill, John, Barbara Bender, and Mogens Trolle Larsen (eds.) *State and Society: The Emergence and Development of Social Hierarchy and Political Centralization.* London: Unwin Hyman: 279-301.

Bakker, J. I. (H.) 1987a. "Canadian Political Economy and Rural Sociology: Early History of Rural Studies in Canada." *The Rural Sociologist* vol. 7 (5): 470-484. [The whole issue is devoted to Canadian rural sociology and the sociology of agriculture and primary production generally.]

Bakker, J. I. (H.) 1987b. "The Cultivation System, Ecology and Underdevelopment: An Examination of Geertz's Agricultural Involution Thesis." In Bakker, J. I. and Roy Amore (eds.). *Culture and Development in Southeast Asia: The Political Economy of Social Change in the ASEAN Region.* Guelph, Ontario: Canadian Council for Southeast Asian Studies (CCSEAS) and Canadian Asian Studies Association (CASA).

Bakker, J. I. (H.) 1985. "Data Gathering and Project Design: A

Third World Case Study of Community Development." *Journal of the Community Development Society.* 16 (2): 1-17.

Balaam, David, and Michael Carey (eds.). 1981. *Food Politics: The Regional Perspective.* London: Allenheld, Osman Publishers.

Barnet, Richard J. 1980. *The Lean Years.* New York: Simon & Schuster.

Beange, Judy. 1988. "The Sulawesi Regional Development Project: Support for Decentralization of the Rural Development Planning System." Guelph, Ontario: unpublished paper, for Sulawesi Regional Development Project.

Bennet, John, and Susan George. 1987. *The Hunger Machine.* Toronto, Ontario: Canadian Broadcasting Corporation, CBC.

Bennett, Merrill K. 1954. *The World's Food.* New York: Harper and Brothers.

Berry, Wendell. 1981a. *Recollected Essays, 1965-1980: The Selected Essays of Wendell Berry.* San Francisco: North Point Press.

Berry, Wendell. 1981b. *The Gift of Good Land: Further Essays Cultural and Agricultural.* San Francisco: North Point Press.

Boorstin, Daniel J. 1983. *The Discoverers.* New York: Vintage.

Brady, Nyle C. 1983. "International Technology Transfer." In Molnar and Clonts op. cit.: 16-28.

Brandt, Willy. 1980. *North-South: A Program for Survival.* Cambridge, Massachussetts: M.I.T. Press.

Braudel, Fernand. 1973. *Capitalism and Material Life: 1400-1800.* New York: Harper. Translated by Miriam Kochan.

Brown, Lester R. and Erik Eckholm. 1974. *By Bread Alone.* New York: Praeger and Overseas Development Council.

Brown, William P. and Don F. Hadwiger (eds.). 1986. *World Food Policies: Toward Agricultural Interdependence.* Boulder, Colorado: Lynn Rienner Publishers.

Brown, Lester R. 1986. *State of the World 1986.* New York: W. W. Norton & Co.

Brown, Lester R. 1989. *State of the World 1989.* New York: W. W. Norton & Co.

Brundtland, Gro Harlem, et al. (compilers and eds.). 1987. *Our Common Future: The World Commission on Environment and*

Development. Don Mills, Ontario: Oxford University Press.

Bryant, Coralie. 1988. *Poverty, Policy, and Food Security in Southern Africa*. Boulder, Colorado: Lynn Rienner Publishers.

Burbach, Roger, and Patricia Flynn. 1980. *Agribusiness in the Americas*. New York: Monthly Review Press and North American Conference on Latin America.

Cairns, John and Gayle Valeriot (compilers and eds.). *Science and Technology in the World Food Crisis: Conference Summary*. Guelph, Ontario: Conference Planning Committee, University of Guelph. [A copy of this 14 page summary is available from the Centre for International Programmes, University of Guelph.]

Carty, Robert, and Virginia Smith. 1981. *Perpetuating Poverty: The Political Economy of Canadian Foreign Aid*. Toronto, Ontario: Between the Lines Press and Latin American Working Group (LAWG).

Chambers, Robert. 1983. *Rural Development: Putting the Last First*. London: Longman Group Ltd.

Chisholm, Anthony, and Rodney Tyers (eds.). 1982. *Food Security: Theory, Policy and Perspectives from Asia and the Pacific Rim*. Lexington, Kentucky: D. C. Heath & Co.

Christensen, Cheryl. 1978. "World Hunger: A Structural Approach." In Hopkins and Puchala op. cit.: 171-200.

Collins, Randall. 1986. *Weberian Sociological Theory*. Cambridge, England: Cambridge University Press.

Collins, Joseph. 1988. *What Difference Could a Revolution Make?* San Francisco, CA.: Institute for Food and Development Policy.

Cohen, John. 1975. "Rural Change in Ethiopia: The Chilalo Agricultural Development Unit." *Economic Development and Culture Change*. 22(4): 580-614.

Coward, E. Walter. 1983. "Irrigation Development: Technology Traditions and Transfers." In Molnar and Clonts op. cit.: 154-166.

Dove, Michael R. (ed.). 1988. *The Real and Imagined Role of Culture in Development*. Honolulu, Hawaii: University of Hawaii Press.

Dover, Michael J. and Lee M. Talbot. 1987. *To Feed the Earth: Agro-*

Ecology for Sustainable Development. San Francisco, CA.: World Resources Institute.

Drake, Michael (ed.). 1969. *Population in Industrialization*. London: Metheun [Debates in Economic History Series].

Djao, H. 1983. *Inequality and Social Policy*. Toronto: Wiley.

Etzioni, Amitai. 1966. "Consensus Formation in Heterogeneous Systems." *Studies in Social Change*. New York: Holt, Rinehart and Winston: 136-152.

Fairbairn, Garry Lawrence. 1984. *Will the Bounty End? The Uncertain Supply of Canada's Food Supply*. Saskatoon, Saskatchewan: Western Producer Prairie Books.

FAO. 1985. *World Food Security: Selected Themes and Issues*. Rome: U.N. F.A.O., Economic and Social Paper No. 53.

FAO. 1986. *The State of Food and Agriculture 1985: Mid-Decade Review of Food and Agriculture*. Rome: U.N. F.A.O. Agriculture series, No. 19.

Farnsworth, Helen C. 1961. "Defects, Uses, and Abuses of National Food Supply and Consumption Data." *Food Research Institute Studies* II, 3. Stanford, CA: Food Research Institute: 179 - 201.

Fischer, G., K. Frohberg, M.A. Keyzer and K.S. Parikh. 1988. *Linked National Models: A Tool for International Food Policy Analyses*. Dordrecht, Netherlands: Kluwer Academic Publishers. International Institute for Applied Systems Analysis.

Flinn, William, and Frederick H. Buttel. 1983. "Sociocultural Constraints on the Transfer and Adoption of Agricultural Technologies in Low Income Countries." In Molnar and Clonts op. cit.: 125-145.

Forbes, Malcolm H. and Lois J. Merrill (eds.). 1986. *Global Hunger: A Look at the Problems and Potential Solutions*. Evansville: University of Evansville Press.

Geertz, Clifford. 1963. *Agricultural Involution: The Processes of Ecological Change in Indonesia*. Berkeley, California: University of California Press.

George, Susan. 1976. *How the Other Half Dies: The Real Reasons for World Hunger*. London: Penguin.

Hainsworth, Geoffrey B. (ed.). *Village-Level Modernization in*

Southeast Asia:The Political Economy of Rice and Water. Vancouver, British Columbia: University of British Columbia Press.

Hagerman, Paul. 1989. "Social Effects of the Green Revolution: Concentrating on Indonesia." Guelph, Ontario: unpublished paper, for Department of Sociology and Anthropology, 86-642 "Social Change in Rural Agricultural Systems."

Hartman, Betsy and James Boyce. 1979. *Needless Hunger: Voices from a Bangladesh Village.* San Francisco, CA.: Institute for Food and Development Policy.

Havet, Jose (ed.). 1988. *Staying On: Retention and Migration in Peasant Societies.* Ottawa, Ontario: University of Ottawa Press.

Hawley, Amos. 1952. *Human Ecology: A Theory of Community Structure.* New York: Ronald Press.

Hoffman, Stanley (ed.). 1968. *Conditions of World Order.* Boston: Houghton Mifflin, Daedalus Library Volume 10. [First appeared as *Daedalus* (Spring, 1986).]

Hopkins, A. G. 1973. *An Economic History of West Africa.* London: Longman.

Hopkins, Raymond F. and Donald J. Puchala (eds.). *The Global Political Economy of Food.* Madison, Wisconsin: University of Wisconsin Press.

I.D.R.C. 1987. "After the Harvest: Theme Issue." *The IDRC Reports* vol. 16 (4). Ottawa, Ontario: International Development Research Centre. [IDRC publications can be obtained from the IDRC in English, French and Spanish. Unfortunately, *The IDRC Reports* series has recently been discontinued.]

I.R.R.I. 1975. *Changes in Rice Farming in Selected Areas of Asia.* Los Banos, Laguna, Philippines: International Rice Research Institute (IRRI).

Jacoby, Erich H. and Charlotte F. Jacoby. (eds.). 1971. *Man & Land: The Essential Revolution.* New York: Alfred A. Knopf.

Johnson, D. Gale. 1978. "World Food Institutions: A 'Liberal' View." In Hopkins and Puchala op. cit.: 265-282.

Jones, Robert Leslie. 1977. *History of Agriculture in Ontario, 1613-1880.* Toronto, Ontario: University of Toronto Press [Reprint of the 1946 edition].

King, Alexander. 1987. "The Global Consequences of New Technologies." *ATAS Bulletin* vol. 4 (E.87.II.A.1): 67. [*ATAS Bulletin* can be obtained from the United Nations Centre for Science and Technology for Development, UNCSTD, United Nations, New York 10017.]

Kneen, Brewster. 1989. *From Land to Mouth: Understanding the Food System*. Toronto, Ontario: NC Press, Ltd.

Kramer, Mark. 1987. *Three Farms: Making Milk, Meat, and Money from the American Soil*. Cambridge, Massachusetts: Harvard University Press [updated from 1980 edition].

Lappe, Frances Moore, and Joseph Collins. 1977. *Food First: Beyond the Myth of Scarcity*. Boston: Houghton Mifflin. [Also lists Cary Fowler as a joint author.]

Lappe, Frances Moore and Joseph Collins. 1986. *World Hunger: Twelve Myths*. New York: Grove Press, Inc.

Long, Norman. 1984. *Creating Space for Change: A Perspective on the Sociology of Development*. Wageningen, Netherlands: Inaugural Lecture, printed at Wageningen University.

Long, Norman. 1977. *An Introduction to the Sociology of Rural Development*. London, England: Tavistock Publications.

Lovejoy, P. E. 1980. *Caravans of Kola: The Hausa Kola Trade 1700-1900*. Zaria: Ahmadu Bello University Press.

Lovejoy, P. E. 1986. *Salt of the Desert Sun: A History of Salt Production and Trade in the Central Sudan*. Cambridge, England: Cambridge University Press.

McElroy, Ann, and Patricia K. Townsend. 1989. *Medical Anthropology in Ecological Perspective, Second Edition*. Boulder, Colorado: Westview Press [First published in 1979 by Wadsworth]. 1968.

Merton, Robert K. *Social Theory and Social Structure*. New York: Free Press.

Mitchell, Don. 1975. "Canada and the World Food Crisis." In Mitchell, Don. *The Politics of Food*. Toronto, Ontario: James Lorimer & Co.

Molnar, Joseph J., and Howard A. Clonts. (eds.). 1983. *Transferring Food Production Technology to Developing Nations:*

Economic and Social Dimensions. Boulder, Colorado: Westview Replica Editions.

Nau, Henry R. 1978. "The Diplomacy of World Food: Goals, Capabilities, Issues and Arenas." In Hopkins and Puchala op. cit.: 201-236.

Paarlberg, Robert L. 1978. "Shifting and Sharing Adjustment Burdens: The Role of the Industrial Food Importing Nations." In Hopkins and Puchala op. cit.: 79-102.

Poleman, Thomas T. 1984. "World Hunger: Extent, Causes, and Cures." *Cornell International Agricultural Economics Study.* Ithaca, N.Y.: Cornell University, A.E. Res. 82 - 17.

Potter, Jack M., May N. Diaz, and George M. Foster. (eds.). 1967. *Peasant Society: A Reader.* Boston: Little, Brown and Co. Series in Anthropology.

Puchala, Donald J., and Raymond F. Hopkins. 1978. "Toward Innovation in the Global Food Regime." In Hopkins and Puchala op. cit.: 283-298.

Riches, Graham. 1986. *Food Banks and the Welfare Crisis.* Ottawa: Canadian Council on Social Development.

Roe, Terry. 1983. "Risks and Information: Farm Level Impediments to Transforming Traditional Agriculture." In Molnar and Clonts op. cit.: 85-105.

Rogers, Edward S. (compiler). 1969. Toronto, Ontario: Royal Ontario Museum (ROM).

Rogers, Everett M. and Rabel J. Burdge. 1972. *Social Change in Rural Societies,* Second Edition. Englewood Cliffs, N.J.: Prentice-Hall, Inc.

Roling, Niels. 1987. "Paradigm of Glut: The New Context for Extension." *Journal of Extension Systems.* 3 (2): 25-35.

Roling, Niels. 1989. *Agricultural Knowledge Systems for Technical Innovation.* Wageningen, Netherlands: unpublished book-length manuscript.

Rotstein, Abraham. 1973. *The Precarious Homestead: Essays on Economics, Technology and Nationalism.* Toronto: New Press.

Scrimshaw, Nevin S. 1968. "The Urgency of World Food Problems." In Hoffmann, Stanley (ed.). *Conditions of World Order.* Boston: Houghton Mifflin, Daedalus Library Volume 10.

Sen, Amartya K. 1984. *Resources, Values and Development.* Cambridge, Mass.: Harvard University Press.

Shapouri, Shahla, Arthur J. Dommen, and Stacey Rosen. 1986. *Food Aid and the African Food Crisis.* Washington, D.C.: U.S. Dept. of Agriculture Report No. 221.

Smits, A. P. (ed.). 1986. *Food Security in Developing Countries.* The Hague: RAWOO (Raad van Advies voor het Wetenschappelijk Onderzoek in het kader van Ontwikkelingssamenwerking = (literally) Advisory Board for Scholarly Research in the Framework of Development Cooperation). [This volume, referred to as RAWOO in some of the papers in this collection, contains papers given at a Seminar at Kijkduin, the Netherlands, 28-29 March 1985.]

Sobel, Lester A. (ed.). 1975. *World Food Crisis.* New York: Facts on File.

Spencer, J.E. 1966. *Shifting Cultivation in Southeast Asia.* Berkeley, California: University of California Press, University of California Publications in Geography, Volume 19.

U.S. Congress. 1974. *Food Security Act.* Washington, D.C.: 96th Congress, First Session, U.S. Congress, House Committee on Foreign Affairs.

U.S. Dept. of Agriculture. 1974. *The World Food Situation and Prospects to 1985.* Washington, D.C.: U.S. Dept. of Agriculture, Economic Research Service Foreign Agricultural Economic Report No. 98.

U.N. 1976. *Human Rights: A Compilation of International Instruments.* New York: U.N.

Vago, Steven. 1989. *Social Change,* Second Edition. Englewood Cliffs, N.J.: Prentice Hall. [First edition published in 1980.]

Warnock, John W. 1987. *The Politics of Hunger: The Global Food System.* Toronto: Methuen.

Warnock, John. W. 1978. *Profit Hungry: The Food Industry in Canada.* Vancouver, British Columbia: New Star Books.

Weatherwax, Paul. 1954. *Indian Corn in Old America.* New York: Macmillan.

Weber, Max. 1978. *Economy and Society.* Berkeley, California: University of California Press [Edited and translated by Guenther Roth and Claus Wittich; first published in English in 1968 by Bedminster Press; based on fourth German edition of 1956].

Weiss, Thomas G. and Robert S. Jordan (eds.). 1976. *The World Food Conference and Global Problem Solving*. New York: Praeger Publishers.

Wigboldus, Jouke S. 1986. "Trade and Agriculture in Coastal Benin c. 1470-1660; An Examination of Manning's Early-growth Thesis." *A. A. G. Bijdragen*. 28: 299-380.

Wigboldus, Jouke S. 1988. "Salt and Crop Production in the Precolonial Central Sudan: An Examination of Lovejoy's Poorly-developed Technology Thesis." Paper presented to Philippe Bernardet's group *"Instruments aratoires en Afrique Tropique."* Wageningen, Netherlands: Department of Rural History, unpublished paper, [forthcoming].

Wolf, Eric. 1982. *Europe and the People Without History*. Berkeley, California: University of California Press.

World Bank. 1975. *Rural Development: Sector Policy Paper*. Washington, D.C.: International Development Association (IDA); World Bank Policy Papers.

Wortman, Sterling and Ralph H. Cummings, Jr. 1978. *To Feed This World: The Challenge and The Strategy*. Baltimore: The Johns Hopkins University Press.

Zagorin, Ruth K. 1977. *The Sociology of Food*. Ottawa, Ontario: IDRC.

SCIENCE AND TECHNOLOGY IN THE WORLD FOOD CRISIS: CONFERENCE SUMMARY

John C. Cairns and Gayle Valeriote

I. Introduction

This chapter presents, in summary form, some of the issues which were debated at the University of Guelph Conference on Science and Technology in the World Food Crisis, October 23-26, 1986.

Several themes, not entirely anticipated, recurred throughout much of the discussion.

There was widespread agreement that the world food crisis is not only a problem of agricultural production. There is potentially ample food in the world for all. The problem is also one of economic, political and distributional inequity. Those who most need food too often lack land to grow it or money to buy it. For this, Science and Technology have no ready answers. A significant part of the solution lies in the economic and political sphere — a conclusion of importance to policy makers and governments.

Secondly, there was broad consensus that, if technological innovations are to be productive, they must be adapted to and integrated with the social, cultural and traditional values of the people they are meant to serve. Otherwise, they will be "dysfunctional" — if not worse.

Western technology is a two-edged sword. In the introduction of new technologies, there is need for much closer relationships between natural and social scientists, all of whom, as Margaret Catley-Carlson so eloquently stated, should listen to those they are trying to help, "the quiet people whose lives and futures are at stake."

II. Keynote Address

The World Food Crisis: Problems and Prospects

Alexander King, President, Club of Rome and Past President, International Federation of Institutes for Advanced Studies

Opening the conference with a comprehensive analysis of the world food crisis, Dr. King raised many of the issues which were to recur repeatedly in later panels and workshops. Referring to the recent emergency in the Sahel and Ethiopia, he emphasized the need for a sustainable drive towards food self-sufficiency in the South and reduction of its growing dependence on imports from the North. This would require significant changes in planning and programming.

In an overview of inter-related aspects of the world food situation, he noted ten factors which contributed to the crisis in developing countries: the diminishing availability of fuel wood for cooking; the menace of desertification; the insufficiency of infrastructure and lack of transportation; the vicissitudes of climate; too rapid population growth; insufficient understanding of nutritional needs and their relation to health; the high cost of energy with consequent impact on the use of fertilizers; deforestation; erosion; and the depletion of natural resources.

The core problem — the dilemma of the co-existence of over-production and hunger — he considered essentially a question of economics, politics and logistics, to which technology is only marginally relevant. Although there has long been sufficient food in the world to feed everyone, millions still lack the means to provide a reasonable existence for themselves, and hunger and malnutrition persist. The real problem in the abolition of world poverty is the distribution of wealth.

Outlining the background of the Green Revolution, King noted how technology has changed the scale of agriculture world-wide. The introduction of chemical fertilizers has dramatically increased food production. This has, however, led to agricultural dependency on the availability and price of oil. The 1973 oil price increases, in combination with other factors, had serious effects upon Third World agriculture in particular, and led to growing dependence of many developing countries on food imports. As a result, the crisis of over-production in such countries as Canada and the United States has had serious effects on the food situation in Third World Societies.

In assessing regional problems, King considered sub-Saharan Africa most in danger of an ongoing food crisis. Among other causes, the physical condition of the African environment is much less propitious for agricultural improvement than was the case in Asia. Much, however, can be done.

A particular need exists for more research in labour productivity and technological innovation, oriented not only towards more appropriate high yielding crop production, but also the understanding of African ecological factors in relation to social and economic realities. In this context, the living standards of African women, as the primary producers and suppliers of local food, must be raised. This might be achieved by better education, together with the opening up of credit facilities especially designed for women. Such measures would go a long way to reduce African dependence on imported foods. The import of low priced grain from the West, in King's view, is in itself a strong disincentive to improve the situation of small rural farmers. African agriculture could best be improved by working with small farmers, expanding on their traditional farming methods and indigenous crop varieties, and encouraging their participation in technological innovations.

Pointing out the critical need for studies of the carrying capacity of developing countries at whatever standard of living they hope to achieve, he indicated that the relationship between population, resources and environment is crucial to the survival of existing populations. It is thus essential that soil erosion, climatic change and energy resource depletion be considered, along with population growth, by development planners in terms of impact on food supply and sustainability.

In conclusion, he provided wide ranging proposals for action, including suggestions for Third World debt reduction, greater levels of research on areas related to the food crisis in developing countries, and a stronger role for, and more co-operation among, non-governmental organizations.

"The challenge is great," he said, "the promise is good, but the problems are enormous. Their solution demands a concerted attack by all nations, rich and poor. An immediate requirement is a general public awareness of the importance and complexity of the issues. Public response to the tragedy of the Sahel was heartening, but it must be sustained in the knowledge that the future of all the inhabitants of the world is at stake."

III. Panel Discussions

Panel Number 1: Dimensions of the World Food Crisis

Moderator: Ralph Campbell, Director, International Development Office, Association of Universities and Colleges of Canada

The panel, in analysing world food issues, was in general agreement that the major problem arose from poverty, and from economic and distributive inequities, rather than lack of agricultural production per se. The solutions required were seen as largely social, political and structural, as distinct from technological or scientific.

The opening speaker, Thorold Warley of the University of Guelph, noted that although per capita food production for most regions has improved, chronic under-nutrition exists for hundreds of millions of the world's poor. Their condition is exacerbated by slow rates of economic growth, caused in part by poor export earnings, unfavourable exchange rates and heavy debt service obligations.

Warley pointed out, however, that since the World Food Conference of 1970, the rising world population is now better fed than at any time in history, and with a declining share of personal income. Agricultural and rural development have taken on renewed importance, and Third World farmers have shown great capability in production, when given incentives and access to technology. Co-operation between Third World and Western authorities with regard to food and agriculture has improved steadily. Western humanitarian concern for the hungry is now driven by the perception that Third World development is a requirement for worldwide economic recovery. With hunger identified as a product of poverty, more emphasis is needed on accelerating per capita income growth and its equitable distribution. This necessitates better world economic policies, together with Third World macro-economic and sectoral policies that foster agricultural and rural development. Such policies should focus on the needs of small farmers, and on rural and urban poor. They should be supported by the ongoing application of science and technology in food production, by research, and by better co-ordination at the level of IMF, GATT and other multilateral agencies.

David Hopper of the World Bank, summarizing the origins and background of the Green Revolution, indicated that in Asia, where the technology has been widely used, the effects of drought have been reduced and much of the continent has been removed from the food crisis list, although extensive under-nutrition persists. In Latin America, problems are largely institutional and infrastructural. In Africa, the technology for the Green Revolution does not yet exist, and research on African soils and conditions remains inadequate. In all developing regions, governments which are faced with intense competition for limited resources, encounter serious dilemmas in allocating funds among the various agricultural and rural interests. These pressures will increase in future as environmental concerns, to which little priority is now assigned, demand greater investment.

Sartaj Aziz, Minister of State for Food, Agriculture and Co-operatives, Pakistan, contended that a program of global food security must include trade liberalization and stabilization of grain market prices. At the national level, he noted the need for improved production, particularly in African countries, which would lead to an accompanying focus on women as the primary producers of food on that continent.

Concentrating on myths about the world food situation, Vaclav Smil, of the University of Manitoba, criticized the Western misconception that some developing countries lack the capacity to provide their own food. This in his view has created false expectations concerning the need for food exports by the West.

Muni Anandakrishnan, from the U.N. Center for Science and Technology for Development, focussed on the needs of the marginalized poor, who in developing societies are easily pushed from subsistence to crisis. There is a requirement in many countries for deliberate programs to examine problems of marginalized populations, and to develop appropriate policies and structures.

The large number of questions from the audience ranged from the need for import substitution, to queries as to how poor farmers can have input into political systems in order to address issues of food security.

Panel Number 2: Science and Technology in the World Food System

Moderator: Carl-Goran Heden, Professor Emeritus, Karolinska Institute, Stockholm

In his introductory remarks, Heden struck the *leitmotif* which was to pervade much of the conference discussion. Asking how the tools of science could be focussed on the world food problem, he stated:

"Framing the question holistically reveals that the successful introduction of novel production technologies is functionally dependent on the social, cultural and political milieu. For the present, malnutrition is less a problem of food production than one of education, distribution and waste."

Nevin Scrimshaw, of the United Nations University, referring to both long and short term issues, recognized the interrelatedness of socio/political as well as scientific/technological dimensions, and indicated some of the negative results that can arise from exclusive concern with increasing food production per se.

Discussing the connection between famine and "lack of entitlement" that Third World populations have over national resources, he contended that the introduction of capitalist marketing practices has resulted in the decline of indigenous food production capacity and loss of local control over food supply and demand. Future approaches will require more sensitivity to second generation effects caused by the Green Revolution, and to "entitlement" issues, with a stronger emphasis on the social sciences, and on more practical use of the appropriate technology that already exists. In short, new directions in agricultural development should be more balanced, with productivity seen as only one component in a comprehensive social and political process.

Noting that the world's food is becoming cheaper and more plentiful, Gelia Castillo of the University of the Philippines dissented from the widespread myth that there is a world crisis of supply. Instead she considered that lack of employment among Third World people, which limits their ability to purchase food, is causing the food "crisis." She outlined the potential short-comings of conventional research when applied to Third World agriculture, posing the question, "Does the prescription fit the ailment?" What is needed is fine tuning of existing technology, based on genuine understanding of indigenous or traditional cultural practices.

She also criticized the assumption, frequently implicit in the introduction of new technology, that small farmers have access to the necessary facilities. This is not possible without an effective extension network. She further proposed that the descriptive nature of most social science studies on the role of women in agriculture should be replaced by more functional analysis — that is, understanding why women do what they do and in what order they do it? Since science and technology, so important in the developed world, can be virtually unknown in the developing world, she suggested that problem solving may require an entirely different approach.

The need for more funding and renewed public faith in the scientific community's ability to overcome technical limits to food production were major points raised by Dennis Greenland of the International Rice Research Institute. Discussing current research on biological pest control, he contended that, possibly coupled with more selective chemicals, it may provide an ecologically acceptable and profitable alternative to conventional pesticides.

Idriss Jazairy, from the International Fund for Agricultural Development, focussed on the need for appropriate technology. He outlined the "ideal" technology, which a) is low cost, b) is location specific, c) fits within prevailing practices, d) encourages sustainable gains, e) improves the environment, f) increases employment, and g) enhances the role of the local populace as decision makers. He indicated that technological advances are often unavailable to those who most need a means of escaping the poverty trap, while the technology that is available is

51

frequently inappropriate to their actual conditions. Noting the failure of Asian rices and Indian millets when introduced into Africa, he contended that there are no universal applications of inputs that can solve all of a region's problems. Development of indigenous research capacity is essential, in particular research on indigenous foods as distinct from export crops.

Panel Number 3: The Carrying Capacity of the Planet

Moderator: John Mellor, Director, International Food Policy and Research Institute, Washington

Mellor, in preliminary remarks, contrasted the high production and surpluses of western agriculture with continuing food shortages in LDCs and increasing pressures on fragile environments.

Alexander King of the Club of Rome, referring to effects of population density on the world environment, noted that population is a main element in the food situation, with significant and increasing geopolitical implications. He stressed that countries require population policies, since choices must be made between high populations with low standards of living, and low populations with high standards of living. Measuring the carrying capacity for human beings, is, however, difficult, and may involve such factors, as agricultural policies, available resources, water usage, and energy input and output. For national planning, the major consideration must be the desired level of living standards vis-a-vis existing resources. Relations between population, resources and energy thus require much more study.

Naima Al-Shayji of the International Fund for Agricultural Development, examining inter-related factors that put stress on the relationship between carrying capacity and environment, contended that as population increases, people will continue to destroy the environment in order to guarantee their own survival. Population increase thus necessitates careful planning and stewardship of natural resources. The roots of the problem reside in a non-sustainable model, both practically and ethically, characterized by being capital intensive, hierarchical in decision making, large project oriented, and with no real participation by women in decisions concerning their lives. A sustainable model would preserve the environment, make peasant agriculture economically viable, and emphasize local labour, crops and inputs for independent food production, thus assuring the national sovereignty of each country.

Pat Mooney of Brandon University, addressing the politics of carrying capacity and their effects on genetic resources, stated that developing countries need assistance with agricultural technology, yet they end up making major contributions to international genetic preservation at the expense of their own development. Criticizing agricultural aid missions, he noted that Canadian soil scientists and farm credit advisors go to developing countries as experts in a range of problems while at home Canadians face the same problems and find no solutions. Referring to the "reverse aid flow," he reported that the United States gives about 12 million dollars per anum to IRRI and CIMMYT, but gets back an annual farm gate value from those institutes of some 2 thousand million dollars.

In contrast to other speakers, A.R.E. Sinclair of the University of British Columbia, contended that carrying capacity depends on technological advance, which, however, leads to further problems not easily resolved. World demographic patterns in his view have proved Malthus correct: population grows until it outstrips production. Technological advance allows an increase in population by only a temporary respite. Attention should thus turn from technology to focus on population problems. In conclusion, he called for sustained use of fixed resources, international planning to replace short term approaches, and education.

Panel Number 4: The Politics of Food: Some Revealing Cases

Moderator: O.P. Dwivedi, Chairperson, Department of Political Studies, University of Guelph

The panel, concentrating on the experiences of countries that have made clear decisions regarding development strategies and food policy, began with an overview of Chinese agriculture by An Min of Beijing Agricultural University, who noted that China feeds 22.7% of the world population with only 7% of the world's arable land. Until recently, the Chinese food structure was based mainly on plant production (grains, cereals). In 1982, animal food production accounted for only 6% of the food supply, compared to the world average of 17%. Efforts to increase this figure are now underway, requiring parallel increases in feed grain production.

Improvement of Chinese agriculture relies firstly on policy development, followed by the application of science and technology. Since 1978, foreign contact, together with liberalized market policies, has enhanced farmers' demands for science and technology inputs. This is likely to increase the unit area yield, since it is difficult under Chinese conditions to expand the total amount of arable land under tillage. Future Chinese agriculture is expected to combine traditional organic farming with newer inorganic farming techniques.

The value of well designed agricultural policies was reinforced by Abdul Mallek Bin Isshaq Al-Alsheikh of the Educational Mission for Saudi Arabia, Ottawa, who outlined agricultural developments in Saudi Arabia during the past two decades. Since oil revenues were not enough to guarantee economic self-sufficiency, the government instituted an ambitious agricultural development program to foster private sector capability. From 1969 to 1970, this concentrated on basic infrastructural development. In 1979, modern farming techniques were introduced with advanced technologies designed to increase yields. Large scale production has now replaced traditional agricultural patterns, where small holdings had previously limited the use of farm machinery. This has led to significant progress in a variety of agricultural crops. Saudi Arabia is thus closer to food self-sufficiency, an achievement of great importance since the country cannot remain dependent upon a non-renewable resource (oil) indefinitely.

Kenneth King of the United Nations Development Program contrasted the worldwide increase in malnutrition with the more widely publicized incidence of famine and starvation. He considered that politicians from the North and the South share the blame for food emergencies, rather than planners and policy makers. He also noted that, in the most recent African food emergencies, the flight from the land by small scale farm families has shifted the locus of hunger from rural to urban settings. In his view, the causes of famine include inadequacies of development planning, lack of a local scientific base and a research capacity, inadequate use of modern technology and poorly devised aid programs.

Development and food production are ultimately political questions in the view of David Hopper of the World Bank, who stated that in the past decade the world has become more aware of food problems as global perspectives on food crisis have developed. In most cases, however, policy making in the area of resource development is not yet clear and ramifications of programs and projects are not well defined. Lower death rates and higher birth rates in developing countries have also resulted in a continuing increase in resource constraints. Development thus becomes more difficult each year.

Questions from the audience, mainly dealing with political aspects of food production and food crisis, reflected a mistrust for the involvement of politicians in development programs, together with a belief that North/South progress and co-operation will be most productive when politics are minimized.

Panel Number 5: Options for the Future

Moderator: Bernard Wood, Director, North/South Institute, Ottawa

Introducing the topic, Bernard Wood, panel moderator, suggested that the task was to find a way out of the current problems of poverty which have led to the hunger crisis. He asked how we can make sense of the situation in which Japanese farmers receive three times the world price for rice while in Europe, farmers are paid not to grow wheat. He identified the need for long term attention to the problem of food supply, stating that the issues are complex, inter-related and multifaceted.

Nat Colletta, on secondment from the World Bank to the government of Indonesia, saw the death of 3.5 million people and the malnutrition of 100 million adults and children annually as a crisis in food distribution, not in food production. Growth in production since the 1950s has doubled food availability, with increases in yields outstripping population growth. This overall food sufficiency, attributable to the achievements of science and technology, has so far resulted in abundance in some places and shortages elsewhere. The root cause of the problem, Colletta contended, was disparity in the production and reproduction of knowledge. He saw the resolution lying in the twin themes of human resource development and knowledge production. The first world dominates in knowledge production; developing countries tend to reproduce knowledge from the North. There is need for development of human resources in the South, to facilitate the creation of an indigenous knowledge production capability. North/South disparities in this field are revealed by the proportion of GNP spent on research, which, in 1980, was 2.3% in the North, compared to .34% in the South.

Emerging from this growing emphasis on knowledge production, Colletta predicted, would be a major concern for intellectual property rights during the next decade. Unless underlying policies influencing the production and use of knowledge are put in place, he predicted an accelerated brain drain from developing countries.

Vandana Shiva from India spoke critically of the effects of the Green Revolution in her country. The watershed in forty centuries of sustained agriculture, she said, came in 1968 with the introduction of intensive cultivation. This had degraded the ecosystem, while new varieties of crops had reduced the overall biomass, producing less straw and interrupting the recycling of nutrients. The hybrids introduced during the Green Revolution, in many cases, had brought new diseases, damaging indigenous varieties and wiping them out. The hybrids were less efficient users of water and had resulted in a reduced food source for livestock.

Of critical concern to Shiva was the commercial value placed on food as a commodity, leading to its use as a source for wealth for some while others suffer poverty and starvation. In the process the ecosystem is being degraded, and pervasive hunger continues to plague the most disadvantaged. In the Punjab, she contended, the dislocations caused by failures of the Green Revolution lay at the root of social unrest and terrorist activities. She concluded with a call to get nature, women and children back into the food production system, to look to the soil as a natural reservoir and to stop thinking of fertilizers and irrigation systems as the answer to the food crisis.

Joseph Hulse of IDRC spoke critically of the system of technology transfer to solve problems in developing countries as "grossly over-engineered and grossly excessive of need." Technology he saw as existing before science, and as fundamentally a domestic craft. The basic crafts of food, shelter and textiles had experienced a critical break between the development of the steam engine and the electric motor. Technology, which once proceeded science, now drives science. Good science, he contended, does not generate good technology without thinking of the consequences of technological development. Science should look to the pressing needs of farmers and find out what farmers already know.

IV. Closing Statement

Linking Labs and Life

Margaret Catley-Carlson, President, Canadian International Development Agency

In a challenging presentation, Catley-Carlson called upon participants to project their minds to the year 2000, and to imagine that the world food crisis had been resolved and hunger and malnutrition eradicated. By using a rearview mirror and assessing the problems that had been overcome, she mapped out how we should proceed in efforts to find lasting solutions to global food insecurity by the end of the century.

Enumerating major factors involved — population growth, decline of arable land, ecological damage, poor development planning, desertification, deforestation, overemphasis on the application of technology without consideration of social and cultural realities — she proposed a broad-based scenario.

As a first step, she envisaged that governments had changed their agricultural policies, a process already underway by 1986. For developing countries, this included raising prices paid to farmers, selling off state-owned business, cutting government spending, devaluing currencies, giving increased emphasis to small farmers and decentralizing control of agricultural programs. In developed countries, policy reform had encompassed abandonment of agricultural protectionism and thereby allowing market discipline to take effect. Aid bureaucrats for their part had begun to use food aid less as a means of disposing of crop surpluses and more as an element of development policy in conjunction with plans for stepping up Third World food production.

Meanwhile, we had become aware that science and technology must be better linked with the social and cultural aspects of development, that we must be more willing and able to disseminate scientific knowledge and to make it appropriate for the real life circumstances of those people who need it. This meant practical realistic programming for rural women and more determined applications of medical knowledge to eliminate preventable disease — based on a determination to see that progress does occur, rather than waiting for it to happen spontaneously.

In Africa, she envisaged that development had been given a chance by making necessary resources available to allow a Green Revolution to occur there too. At the level of technology, needs and production methods were determined through appropriate research and, at the social level, through adequate funding for extension services, literacy training, health care and other measures designed to improve the quality of life of marginalized populations.

To accomplish these measures by the end of the century, she stressed that those involved in science and technology need a holistic view of the factors that shape actual results when their work is put to use in the real world — particularly the Third World. Scientists and development planners must take time to listen to the people whom they are trying to help. They must ask the right questions. Are things getting better or worse? What need is most urgent? What help would be most useful? By listening closely, they will find answers from "the quiet people whose lives and futures are at stake."

In conclusion, prescribing an agenda for science and technology for the rest of the century, she said: "First, give us more of what you have already given us, including better ways to grow more food; second, help the developing countries strengthen their own science and technology and agriculture and all the other vital fields; and, third, help us build all those linkages that I mentioned earlier between your work and the Third World farmer, between labs and life."

NOTE:

Those who wish to receive a more complete summary of the conference, including brief synopses of the fifteen workshops and a list of all discussants can write to the Centre for International Programs, University of Guelph, Guelph, Ontario, N1G 2W1, Canada.

Chapter 1

FOOD INSECURITY:
DYNAMICS AND ALLEVIATION

Truman P. Phillips and Daphne S. Taylor

ABSTRACT

This paper examines the dynamics of food insecurity and the role of governments in lessening food insecurity. It is argued that regional or national food insecurity is an aggregation of the food insecurity state of households. For this paper, three types of households are defined: the food self-sufficient non-market oriented household; the wage-earning household; and the market-oriented commercial household. The types of food insecurity faced by these households are classified as: temporary food insecurity; cyclical food insecurity and chronic food insecurity. The assessment of a household's food insecurity depends on three concepts: the food insecurity risks faced by the household; the food insecurity insurances available to the household; and the effectiveness of these measures in lessening food insecurity. The paper contains a discussion of these concepts as they relate to different types of households and food insecurity.

The paper also contains a discussion of the role of governments (local, national and international) in combatting food insecurity from both the demand and supply side. Governments that have made a commitment to food security have a number of alternative policy paths from which to choose. However, policy decisions are often made on the basis of very limited and questionable knowledge as to the possible repercussions and side effects of such action. The challenge for analysts and decision makers alike is to integrate food security objectives and activities at all levels (national, international and local) to improve and protect food security at the individual and household level.

1 INTRODUCTION

Food insecurity is a worldwide problem. It is estimated that in 1980 between 340 and 730 million people suffered from under-nourishment, owing to inadequate incomes. Eighty percent of the people are located in countries with very low per capita average incomes. By regions, about two-thirds live in Asia and twenty percent in Sub-Sahara Africa (World Bank, 1986b).

During the 1970s it was widely believed that food insecurity was a result of declining food availability per capita. Subsequently, policies were aimed at using resources to increase agricultural technology and production. In contrast, the 1980s have seen increasing global food stocks accompanied by severe regional famines suggesting that increased world, regional and even national food production alone is not sufficient to ensure food availability for everyone. It is now recognized that problems of food insecurity originate from the demand side as well as the supply side of the market.

Ensuring an adequate level of food security entails ensuring that the supply of and the demand for food interact at a level which provides an adequate diet for all people. Food security in general is a much broader concept than food self-sufficiency and a much narrower concept than agricultural development (Rukuni and Eicher, 1987). This paper examines the dynamics of food insecurity and the role of governments in lessening food insecurity.

2 HOUSEHOLDS AND FOOD INSECURITY CLASSIFICATIONS

A state of food security ensures that all members of every household in a nation have access throughout the year to a diet that is adequate for leading a continued, healthy and active working life. Conversely, a state of food insecurity exists when members of a household have an inadequate diet or face the future possibility of an inadequate diet. Within these definitions two points should be highlighted. First, food security at a national level is an aggregation of household food security. Second, for a household to be food secure it must be food secure now and in the future.

Food security at a national level is often defined in terms of national food supplies, or per capita production or consumption. Unfortunately, this measure camouflages problems of household or individual food insecurity. A more accurate description of regional or national food insecurity can be found by aggregating households by the types of food insecurity that they experience. Such an aggregation would reveal the percentage of households (or population) which face food insecurity, as well as the percentage that are food secure. Depending on the quantity and availability of household data, the aggregation could also reveal the geographical locations of those facing severe food insecurity and the characteristics of food insecure households. Programs and policies could then be directed to lessen food insecurity at household and community levels which would then lessen food insecurity at regional and national levels.

To facilitate our discussion of food insecurity, three types of households and three states of food insecurity are defined.

2.1 Classification of Households

Households can be classified as either market oriented or non-market oriented. A market oriented household is any household that exchanges resources such as cash, services, goods or food with other market oriented households and/or enterprises. The market oriented household can be further broken down into those households which exchange their labour in return for goods or wages and those households which sell goods or produce for cash income or resources. A non-market oriented household is a household that does not exchange household resources and is, by definition, a self-sufficient and self-sustaining economic unit. This grouping of households is useful because the factors which influence household food insecurity are similar for each type of household. For this reason three household classifications can be distinguished: the food self-sufficient, non-market oriented household; the wage-earning household; and the market-oriented commercial household.

A **food self-sufficient, non-market oriented household** (to be referred to as a self-sufficient household) is a rural household which produces and consumes its own food. This household behaves as a self-sustaining economic unit and normally has a "limited" income base and a "small" land base.

A **wage-earning household** is a rural or urban household of wage earners and dependents who sell their labour, services and talents in exchange for food, cash income or resources. This household represents the complete range of wealth entitlements, from resource rich to resource poor households.

The **market-oriented commercial household** (to be referred to as a commercial household) is a rural or urban household which has access to land and/or capital and specializes in and markets products to earn income to support household food purchases. This household also represents the complete range of households from those with a small land and/or capital base to those with a large land and/or capital base. The distinguishing feature of this household is that it must sell its products in return for cash income or resources and thus is a commercial operation (regardless of the scale of operation). A rural market oriented commercial household producing agricultural products may or may not produce sufficient food to meet it's needs, but is in a position to use income earned from the sale of agricultural produce to purchase food from the marketplace. Although the discussions to follow are directed more toward commercial agricultural households, the marketing issues which concern this type of household can also be applied to market oriented households which are engaged in non-agricultural activities.

2.1 Classification of Types of Food Insecurity

Again for purposes of analysis three types of food insecurity are identified. These are: temporary food insecurity; cyclical food insecurity; and chronic food insecurity.

Temporary food insecurity exists when a household lacks an adequate diet at some time during the year because of *random* factors. The common characteristic is that the food shortage is *unforeseen and unpredictable.*

Cyclical food insecurity exists when a household repeatedly lacks an adequate diet at specific times during the year. Cyclical or seasonal food insecurity arises because of *reoccurring* factors. The common characteristic is that the shortage of food is *repetitive, foreseen and predictable.*

Chronic food insecurity exists when a household lacks an adequate diet for substantial portions of the year. Chronic food insecurity is a state of *persistent* shortage of food, and exists because the household can neither purchase nor produce enough food to meet its needs.

3 THE DYNAMICS OF FOOD INSECURITY

Identification of problems of food insecurity requires a conceptual framework which is comprehensive enough to be consistent across time and space. Food security at a given moment does not necessarily imply food security in the future. Similarly, food security at the national level does not guarantee that every individual in that nation has ensured access to an adequate diet.

Based on the above classifications, households may remain in a given category or move between categories. Currently food secure households may remain food secure or may experience varying states of food insecurity in the future. Each household has some likelihood of an improvement or worsening of its food security state. The probability of change depends on, among other things, the wealth entitlement of, and resources available to each household type. For instance, chronically insecure households, relying solely on their own resources, will likely have a low probability of improving their status.

While the current state of a household's food security depends on its present food consumption, the future state of a household's food security is a function of three factors: 1) the food insecurity *risks* faced by the household; 2) the food insecurity *insurances* available to the household; and 3) the *effectiveness* of these measures in lessening food insecurity.

The dynamic nature of food insecurity is incorporated in the concept of food insecurity *risks* because risk is a measure of the possible damage caused if a particular event occurs given some probability that the event will occur. The concept of food insecurity *insurance* incorporates the idea that people can take specific action to decrease the likelihood of the event happening and/or the magnitude of the damage if it does happen. The concept of *effectiveness* incorporates the idea that some food insecurity insurance options are better than others as each insurance measure may have beneficial effects as well as unintentional harmful effects.

In the case of household food insecurity, damage is defined as inadequate food consumption. Events which may cause such damage may be production shortfalls, unemployment, price increases, etc. Insurance actions which decrease the likelihood that such events will occur may include adoption of new food production techniques, job training, creation of co-operatives or government food pricing schemes. Insurance actions which decrease the resulting damage given that the event occurs may include the use of household food stocks, income supplement programs or the introduction of national and international food aid programs.

Examples of food insecurity risks, insurance strategies, and the effectiveness of such strategies for different classes of households are discussed below and summarized in Tables 1 to 3. The examples discussed below do not represent a comprehensive list of factors that effect household food insecurity. The intention is only to illustrate the concepts and definitions previously defined.

3.1 Food Insecurity: Risk Factors

Temporary food insecurity exists when a household lacks an adequate diet at some time during the year because of *random* factors. Temporary food insecurity may be experienced because of shortages in food supply owing to unforeseen conditions, or because of sharp declines in household wealth. The risk of temporary food insecurity, for the *self-sufficient household*, results primarily because of food production shortfalls. Such production shortfalls may be owing to the unforeseen occurrence of poor climate conditions, pests, disease, civil strife or war. For the *wage-earning household* temporary food insecurity risks may arise because of temporary food shortages in the marketplace or temporary declines in income owing to unforeseen unemployment, unexpected layoffs or exceptional increases in food prices. The *commercial household* may encounter temporary food insecurity owing to unexpected production shortfalls or unexpected income shortages owing to food price increases, unexpected increases in production costs or temporary marketing problems owing to transportation or infrastructure failures.

Cyclical food insecurity exists when a household repeatedly lacks an adequate diet at specific times during the year. The risk of cyclical food insecurity, for the *self-sufficient household*, could result if the household is not able to produce and/or store enough food to meet its requirements during non-harvest periods of the year. Limited production capacity coupled with variations in climatic conditions may also lead to food shortages in some seasons or years. As a non-market oriented household, there may be insufficient cash income or resources available to exchange for needed food, or markets for exchange may not be accessible. For the *wage-earning household* cyclical food insecurity risks may arise from seasonal unemployment which is common if the members of the household are employed as agricultural labourers. Cyclical risks may also arise if food supplies in the market are cyclical. Cyclical food insecurity risks may arise for the *commercial agricultural household* because of the seasonal nature and marketing vagaries of food production. Cyclical food insecurity may also occur at times of the year when expenditures are predictably high and income is predictably low.

Chronic food insecurity exists when a household lacks an adequate diet for substantial portions of the year. Chronic food insecurity is normally a symptom of poverty. Unfortunately, chronic food insecurity can also contribute to poverty to the extent that poor nutrition causes poor health, which limits the ability of household members to improve their quality of life. The risk of chronic food insecurity for the *self-sufficient household*, arises primarily because of an inadequate production base, lack of access to production inputs, or a decline in productive capacity. An additional risk faced by this type of household is that of a diet which is nutritionally inadequate, owing to a lack of food variety. For the *wage-earning household*, chronic food insecurity risks are usually owing to poverty because of persistent unemployment, low wages, or rising prices relative to wage rates. This household also faces food insecurity if the local food system is incapable of supplying a variety of high quality foods at reasonable prices on a continuous basis. For the *commercial household*, chronic food insecurity may exist if the production base is too small. Chronic income shortages owing to the continuous sale of produce at below-cost prices will also result in chronic food insecurity. Low market prices may arise because of overproduction, declining quality in the produce, or government pricing controls which do not offer producers a profitable return for their labour. Chronic food insecurity may also result because of marketing risks which entail not being able to move produce to marketing centres, loss of quality in the produce as a result of marketing delays and exceptional costs incurred in marketing produce.

For commercial agricultural producers chronic food insecurity may exist if access to agricultural inputs or markets is limited, or productivity and yields continually decline. If food market prices are continuously below the costs of production, agricultural producers will tend to switch to more profitable commodities (which may be non-food commodities). If agricultural households diversify their production to satisfy their own needs, such action can collectively reduce the supply of food available in commercial markets, thus increasing food insecurity for market dependent households.

3.2 Food Insecurity: Insurance Strategies

Food insecurity insurances are actions which can be taken to decrease the likelihood that specific events will occur that result in food insecurity or given that such events do occur, decrease the impact of food insecurity for the household. In the former case, food insecurity insurance strategies necessitate improving productive capacities and incomes. In the latter case, food insecurity insurances necessitate improving access to food. Although food insecurity is primarily viewed as a household problem, insurance strategies may require assistance from community groups, or national and international agencies. Insurance strategies will be discussed in terms of what can be done at these different levels.

At the **household** level, food insecurity insurance strategies for non-food producing households may include increasing and improving the capacity to store food; acquiring additional income in times of emergency through loans, credit, charity or selling household resources; increasing the ability to earn income through new, seasonal or self-employment opportunities, establishing household co-operatives or migrating.

The food producing household (whether self-sufficient or commercial) may prevent the occurrence of chronic food insecurity by using production-enhancing agricultural inputs: fertilizers, pesticides, new varieties, tools, new techniques and extension services. These households can also prevent chronic, seasonal and temporary food insecurity though some diversification of agricultural production to offset risks of production loss. The commercial food producing household may also offset the risk of declining commodity prices by taking advantage of marketing opportunities in food-deficit rural and urban areas in times of regional overproduction.

At the **community** level, food insecurity insurance strategies may include community services and facilities which provide job training and employment opportunities, education or improved infrastructure. The community may also provide facilities for households to form co-operatives which can improve agricultural production, storage, processing, marketing and credit. Depending on the nature of the community, it may even provide food security related training and educational programs at the household and individual level.

At the **national** level, food insecurity insurance strategies include setting the price of food items, both for the producer and consumer, increasing or decreasing national food supplies through imports from or exports to world markets, or transferring or redistributing resources from one segment of the economy to another. Governments may also hold buffer stocks of food, not only as a means of regulating price and supply, but also as an insurance against temporary and cyclical food shortages. Governments can develop temporary employment schemes, such as Food For Work programs, which provide seasonal employment in exchange for food. Or, governments can target certain groups within society for preferential treatment, regarding their access to food. Finally, governments can introduce policies to stimulate national food supplies and improve distribution through increased domestic production, trade or foreign aid programs. (Additional issues and concerns which impact on government insurance strategies and their effectiveness are discussed more fully in Section 4.)

Donor agencies can also contribute to food insecurity insurance strategies in two important ways. First, they can provide food and assistance to counteract food insecurity in emergency situations. Second, they can support programs which address the root causes of food insecurity. Donors can also support national programs in terms of the provision of resources and technical expertise.

3.3 Food Insecurity: Effectiveness of Strategies

Although some insurance strategies may be helpful in the short term for reducing food insecurity they may also create long-term problems. For example, for food producing households, seeking off-farm employment during times of cyclical food insecurity may eventually lead to permanent migration of the younger and more productive members of the household to urban centres, thereby endangering the long-term food production capacity of the household. Also, the sale of household resources may lead to future reductions in food production, because the household may not be able to re-purchase the needed productive resources once the temporary food insecurity passes. Additionally, insurance strategies which promote techniques for increased food production which are not sustainable may eventually lead to greater food insecurity risks in the future.

Potential problems associated with measures to offset the food insecurity risks faced by commercial agricultural households are numerous. Use of production enhancing techniques may be thwarted by the producers' lack of liquid income to purchase the required inputs and tools or subsidized inputs may be unavailable at the required times. Government programs which include price schemes which support one commodity while ignoring others may encourage an over-supply in those commodities, increasing the cost of price support schemes to such an extent that the schemes cannot be financed. Excessive diversification may lower profits and gains from specialization, and resources may not be capable of being diversified. Expanding markets may not be viable owing to inadequate transportation vehicles, roads, storage or loading facilities. The sale of food to international buyers may deplete national food supplies, and taking land out of agricultural food production may depress regional food supplies and consumption.

Insurance strategies used by wage-earning households also have caveats which may decrease their effectiveness against food insecurity in the long run. Household savings could be exhausted in meeting temporary or cyclical food shortages, leaving the unit less able to cope with the next shortage. Excessive long-term indebtedness to creditors (private and state) could arise. Collective or union activities, or minimum wage programs, could reduce employment opportunities and encourage mechanization within industries. In addition if union activities are unacceptable they could result in dismissal, repression or imprisonment. Job migration could place the household at greater risk because of physical displacement and severing of local ties. In addition, government supported strategies, such as broad price subsidy programs, not only create dependencies but could become so expensive that the government is forced to curtail or discontinue them. Consumer subsidies may place stress on national food production by increasing demand; or the distribution system may become overburdened and incapable of providing food to needy households.

Although households can take specific actions to increase their food security status, the power of governments to lessen food insecurity is often greater than the aggregated power of households. Thus the role of governments in altering the risks of food insecurity faced by households merits special attention. The following section is devoted to a general discussion of some of the more common policies which governments use to decrease food insecurity.

4 ROLE OF GOVERNMENTS IN LESSENING FOOD INSECURITY

The primary food security objective facing most governments is to facilitate the movement of food insecure households to increasingly food secure states. In general, developing nation governments attempt to do this by 1) increasing the ability of market oriented households (whether wage-earning or commercial) to acquire food, 2) increasing the productive capacity of food producing households (whether self-sufficient or commercial) to supply food and 3) by improving the food marketing system's capacity to provide a variety of high quality foods at reasonable prices on a continuous and nationwide basis.

4.1 Increasing the ability to acquire food

There are a number of ways in which governments can increase the ability of market oriented households to acquire food. Five of the more common programs are; 1) general price subsidies,

2) targeted price subsidies, 3) cash transfers, 4) direct food transfers, and 5) food rationing.

4.1.1 General price subsidies

It has long been documented that developing countries favour food price subsidies to enhance household food security. This type of food policy is consistent with broader economic development policies that use low labour and food costs as a means to encourage industrialization. However, a number of problems can make this type of policy very costly and inefficient in the long run.

In Mexico, the government supports a two price policy to increase food security. Agricultural producers receive artificially high support prices for their produce while consumers pay artificially low subsidized prices for their food. For example, a government agency buys wheat and corn from farmers at an artificially high support price and sells it to the producers of tortillas and bread at an artificially low price. The Mexican government covers the difference.

Three potential problems arise from this policy (Kehoe and Serra-Puche 1986). First, the support price is intended to encourage production by ensuring a minimum of profits. However, there are many farmers in rural communities that do not produce enough for their own consumption. Since average rural market prices are bid up by the support prices offered by government agencies, these deficit producers are made worse off as they are forced to purchase food and feed grains at artificially high prices.

Second, consumer subsidies are intended to provide commonly purchased goods to the poorest groups of society at low prices. However, every agent in the economy, regardless of income level, has access to subsidized food. This lack of targeting to those in need adds to the cost and inefficiency of the program and can create serious misallocations in resource use. For example, livestock producers have been known to use subsidized processed food (tortillas) as animal feed. Third, the cost of the program is borne by the Mexican government which increases the national deficit.

Although alternative programs could be introduced to achieve the desired effect of food security, not surprisingly, poorer consumer groups in both the urban and the rural sectors prefer policies that retain all subsidies, while the richer consumer groups prefer that all subsidies be abolished, to lower their indirect tax rates. Reducing food subsidies has an adverse effect on the poorer consumer groups, yet maintaining general price subsidizes has a high opportunity cost.

The problems faced by Mexico owing to the use of general subsidies are common to other countries as well. Egypt and Sri Lanka have experienced similar problems related to high costs and lack of targeting. Although there are substantial economic costs associated with this type of policy, there are overriding political pressures that force these types of policies to remain unchanged.

4.1.2 Targeted food price subsidies

As the fiscal costs of maintaining general food price subsidies rise, governments have tried to restructure food subsidies so that they are targeted directly to those with the greatest need. By targeting food programs, governments hope to increase the cost-effectiveness of food security programs.

Targeted programs, such as food stamp schemes, are generally based on household incomes. However, food stamp schemes are very difficult to administer because income levels are often difficult to measure and leakages easily occur. Alternatively, the rationing shop system of targeting, places outlets for subsidized foods in neighbourhoods with a high proportion of poor households. These distribution centres may be public ration shops, private shops or a combination. In this way, high income groups are usually discouraged from purchasing subsidized foods, either because of time constraints waiting for purchases or because the food offered is of a lower quality than they desire.

Many studies have indicated that ration shops improve income distribution and raise both the nutritional and consumption levels of the poorest households (Kumar, 1979; Ahmed, 1979). However, some inefficiencies can still occur. To prevent these inefficiencies, governments must choose commodities that reflect the nutritional needs of the targeted population, that are readily available, that command a large share of the food budget, and provide relatively inexpensive energy (Pinstrup-Andersen, 1987).

73

Rationing shops also have a strong bias toward the urban poor because of higher distribution and transportation costs in rural areas. Since the poorest households are usually in rural areas, rationing programs have to be accompanied with rural infrastructure and extension services if food security is to be improved for everyone.

4.1.3 Cash transfers

The purchasing power of low income households can also be improved by tied or untied cash compensations for losses in real incomes, owing to high food prices. However, cash transfers are not widely used. It is common to hear that such transfers are costly and difficult to control because of excessive leakages to non-targeted groups and non-food commodities (Pinstrup-Andersen, 1987). It is also argued that income supplements do not necessarily increase the nutritional levels of the targeted population if income transfers are made to the male heads of households (Tobisson, 1980). Additional research, however, is needed to determine the true effectiveness of cash transfers toward food security. If additional food supplies were available in the marketplace, additional income to low income households would appear to be a very cost-effective and efficient food security program.

4.1.4 Direct food transfers

As a means to increase targeting of food security to those in need, direct food transfers are becoming increasingly popular. Such transfers provide food supplements or direct feeding programs for selected groups, such as children, and pregnant or lactating women. Since malnutrition and infectious diseases are generally found together, direct food transfers are also administered through health and nutrition clinics. Direct food transfers focus on malnourished individuals and integrate social assistance with health care, education and food supplements (Leslie, 1987). It appears, however, in some cases these programs have had only limited success.

An extensive survey by Beaton and Ghassemi (1982) concluded that the benefits of supplemental feeding programs, while having a positive and significant impact on participating women and children, only filled 10 to 25% of the apparent energy gap in the target populations. The explanation given for this was that donated food was substituted for other food that normally would have been consumed, or that the donated food was sold or traded. Therefore, if the objective is to improve the nutrition of certain target groups and not to transfer real income, these programs may not be very successful and are usually very costly to administer. An alternative to government programs for feeding children and mothers may be found if more emphasis is placed on improving technologies that will increase the efficiency of or reduce the time spent in the competing demands on women's time.

A major deterrent to the proper feeding of young children is the need for frequent feedings of energy dense foods that are free from bacterial contamination. Decreasing the preparation time of weaning foods would greatly enhance the ability of women to improve child care. Community kitchens are another approach to meet the feeding needs of children while reducing the time requirements of mothers (Ram and Holder, 1978). With greater freedom from time consuming chores such as fuel and water gathering and food preparation, women can be expected to participate more actively in literacy, health and nutrition education classes, as well as increasing their time and energies in household food cultivation or income earning activities (Huffman, 1987).

4.1.5 Food rationing

Food rationing is generally used to ensure that the poor are not penalized by scarcity and that priority groups such as the young, the old and the sick are served first.

Rationing is generally criticized as costly to administer, encourages black markets and usually requires the same type of subsidization plan from public revenues as other food policies. Rationing is also extremely costly both to administer and for the recipients who must line up daily at distribution centres. Nevertheless, in Cuba, food rationing has been seen as a way to ensure that everybody shares the available food equally (Michael Redclift, 1986, pp. 203).

While the pendulum has swung in favour of associating food security problems with the inability of people to acquire food, it must be remembered that if household purchasing power were to increase because of redistributive policies and was added to the extra demand caused by population and economic growth, the supply of food in such countries as Bangladesh, India and many African nations would be inadequate to meet these new demands for food (Reutlinger, 1985). Food security in developing countries requires an appropriate mix of policies involving both demand and supply considerations.

4.2 Increasing the capacity to produce food

Until recently, increasing the productivity of small commercial agricultural producers in developing countries was believed to be unprofitable. It was argued that small commercial operators had low adoption rates to new agricultural techniques and that output increasing technologies would only cause substantial declines in commodity prices thereby discouraging producers from future expansions in output. It was also thought that small commercial operators were averse to risk and had little or no access to inputs or credit facilities required in the adoption of new varieties. A number of the studies now suggest that these concerns are not entirely valid.

The contention that the adoption of production increasing technologies leads to a drop in price, and hence a drop in income for small farmers was recently examined by Behrman and Murty (1985). Their study on changing sorghum technology suggests that while sorghum prices would decrease, on average, small sorghum producers would receive greater gross revenues from the technological improvement, since gains from production increases would be much larger than losses due to price declines. However, not all farms would be affected equally, owing to differences in land quality, water control and management capabilities. Lower sorghum prices however would make consumers of sorghum undoubtedly better off and these benefits would accrue relatively more to the poorer members of society (Behrman and Murty, 1985).

In a similar vein it has been argued that the Green Revolution emphasized improvements in productivity on larger commercial farms, and discriminated against small farmers. Studies of the Green Revolution in Southeast Asia now indicate that low-income farmers have adopted high-yielding varieties to the same extent as larger farms but adoption is at a slower pace because of institutional obstacles. It has been found that for adopters of new technologies the net gains per unit of land tend to be larger on smaller farms (Prahladachar, 1983; Blyn, 1982;

Chaudhry, 1982; Herdt and Capule, 1983).

To increase the adoption rates of technological improvements by small commercial operators, technological innovations should be combined with policy measures and institutional changes that focus on land reform, development of infrastructure and irrigation facilities, improved marketing facilities, access to extension services, credit and health facilities, and a series of other government interventions which would change the socio-economic environment and strengthen the resources of small agricultural producers (Pinstrup-Andersen and Hazell, 1987).

Farming Systems Research is now being suggested as a means of developing technologies which are applicable and adopted by small commercial operators. The objective of Farming Systems Research is to generate technology for individual farms while taking into account the biological, social, cultural, economic, and institutional environments in which the farming system operates. In this way, research has a better capacity to increase the overall productivity of the farming system and therefore the welfare of individual farming households. Support for such research examines the subsystems of agricultural activities such as crops, animals, and households. These subsystems are then integrated with the economic, social and institutional environments of the community and the nation.

To date, the household subsystem has been long neglected in agricultural technology research. However its importance is becoming increasingly visible as research into this area unfolds. In examining household subsystems, the role that women play in agricultural production has come to the forefront. Between 25 to 35 percent of the developing world's households are headed by women because of divorce, death, desertion, long-term migration of husbands or because they were never married (Tinker, 1979; Youssef and Hetler, 1983). Female headed households are among the poorest in developing countries.

Women in developing countries spend the majority of their time on home production, including child care, food production, water and fuel supply, and market production in subsistent or cash crops. Food production includes cultivation, harvesting, processing and preparation. In most parts of Africa, women traditionally are involved in subsistent production, while men are involved in cash crop production. Since women cultivate most of the food consumed for the household with additional food supplies generally purchased from extra income earned by women, in many households, women are the sole providers of food (Dey, 1981).

A study of women's roles in Tanzania observed that although women are responsible for agricultural tasks, they lack authority in decision making and resource allocation. With limited access to the cash incomes earned by their husbands, they are often unable to buy additional food for their families, which increases the importance of their own agricultural production (Tobisson, 1980). Agricultural technologies that are not accessible to women and their food production needs, will always have limited success in achieving food security, since women play such a crucial role in the food production system.

In the past, government policies have not emphasized increased productivity for the small commercial or subsistent agricultural producers. Rather they have favoured large agricultural producers. However, the survival of the small agricultural producer and the reliance of so many households on subsistent agricultural production should suggest that future agricultural research be directed towards the limited resource producer. Such aims however must be coupled with improvements in human resource development, indigenous knowledge and access to extension services. While it is obvious that advanced agricultural technologies, such as those used in the Green Revolution, can provide a vehicle for long run food security, its short run impacts can be negligible if it is not accompanied by appropriate public policy and institutional changes favouring a more equitable distribution of assets and incomes.

4.3 Improving the food marketing and distribution system

In addition to policy and institutional changes which increase food production, transportation bottlenecks must be overcome if the benefits are to be retained. In many circumstances where malnutrition and famine exist, there is a problem of transportation and distribution of food commodities. This problem is most evident between rural and urban communities. Inadequate infrastructure and transportation facilities inhibit many small domestic producers from selling their production to the more populated urban centres. Likewise, rural communities often suffer from food shortages because imported foods are not easily transported into the rural areas of the nation.

A number of problems inhibit the marketing of food surpluses, especially for small producers. The inability to transfer foods from surplus areas to deficit areas results in depressed prices, discouraging production. As near-subsistent producers expand their production, their surpluses must compete with producers who use more formal marketing institutions in larger urban centres. Smaller individual traders with very little capital cannot afford to deal with long expensive marketing processes on their own. As a result, traders become part of a chain of intermediaries, making only a small profit but using relatively little capital (Bromley, 1971). Although some marketing institutions for agricultural producers encourage improved profitability for producers and guaranteed access to food for consumers, marketing institutions have also been known to create many disincentives for small producers and price distortions for other sectors of the economy.

It has been widely reported that marketing institutions often discriminate against smaller producers and do not promote fair distribution and service to consumers. Government controlled export marketing boards are generally set up to promote price stability, revenue collection and maximization of foreign exchange earnings. However, marketing boards also suffer from alternative objectives such as maximizing their own profits from selling and buying operations. Profits can then be used to increase board member salaries, grant concessionary loans for privileged growers or finance board owned plantations at the expense of individual farmers (Pollard and Graham, 1985, pp. 1067).

Government controlled boards may find it hard to deal with the sheer complexity of markets dominated by small output operations, and therefore become ineffective in achieving the objectives for which they were established. Controlled marketing boards do provide some useful services to producers, such as assuring quality control, arranging shipping and providing producers with technical advice and information. However, private and co-operative exporters' and producers' associations may be just as efficient in accomplishing many of these tasks (World Bank, 1986a, p. 86).

Well designed food systems not only move physical food products from farm to final consumers, they also perform a host of associated economic activities such as pricing, merchandising and financing through the system. Economic development necessitates many changes in the institutions, facilities and procedures for accomplishing food security. But unless the food system responds to the challenge, neither the development goals which are consumer oriented, nor those which are producer oriented, have the ability in isolation to achieve these goals.

4.3.1 The role of food imports

In times of limited domestic production, domestic food supplies may be enhanced by procurements of commercial food imports. The primary role of such imports is to supplement domestic food supplies and/or increase the variety of foods available to consumers. Food imports may also provide a cheaper and more efficient mechanism to supply food to remote areas within a nation that may not be easily accessible though national transportation facilities.

Food imports may also provide food supplies at lower prices than could be produced domestically. However, in many countries distorted monetary policies which overvalue domestic currencies artificially reduce the cost of food imports and thereby discriminate against domestic agricultural producers competing in the same market (Taylor, 1989). Similar pricing policies which discriminate against domestic agricultural producers in order to provide cheap food for urban consumers have been widely cited in development forums as a cause of agricultural stagnation (Bale and Lutz, 1981; Peterson, 1979 and 1983; and World Bank, 1982).

Factors that influence a nation's ability to purchase commercial imports are numerous and often outside the control of the many developing countries' governments. Factors include the domestic policies in industrial nations that affect the world price of basic trading commodities and international trade policies that affect the extent that industrial nations import from or export to specific developing countries. Volatile international prices and trading patterns, combined with high costs of importing and low profits from exporting, increase the difficulties for the developing nation trying to provide food security through food imports.

Alternatively, developing countries such as the newly industrialized countries have implemented intensive industrial development through industrial export incentives and have been able to increase national food supplies through imported food purchases on world markets using the foreign exchange earnings from their industrial exports. By using the agricultural sector as a resource reservoir, trade, exchange rate and other macroeconomic policies are designed and implemented to extract resources from agriculture for the development of manufacturing and its infrastructure. Industrial development policy, if successful, can provide food supplies through international food purchases; however there are substantial social costs and international risks that must also be faced.

4.3.2 The role of food aid

An effective food marketing and distribution system should have the capacity of regulating and maintaining food stocks and imports to meet year to year fluctuations in domestic production. Emergency and reserve stocks should also be maintained in case imports cannot be acquired in a timely fashion or as a means of price stabilization. For a country that is experiencing excessive debt, low foreign exchange reserves and political and infrastructural barriers to trade, this type of food marketing system is impossible to maintain without financial assistance or food aid.

Food aid can conveniently be divided into three categories: emergency food aid, program food aid, and project food aid. Emergency food aid is the immediate short-term provision of food in times of emergencies. Program food aid is the long-term provision of food oriented and designed to address the root causes of hunger. This category of programs includes food loans and grants which provide a country with funds to import food at concessional or no-cost terms. The domestic funds generated from the sale of this food ("counterpart funds") are in turn used to support agricultural and development projects. These programs are intended to provide additional imported food, and are not to replace normal food imports. Project food aid is targeted food aid assistance, such as Food for Work projects or supplementary feeding projects.

Initially, food aid was founded on the principle that food aid should be provided from the agricultural surplus stocks of donor countries and should directly feed hungry people. Over the past 30 years however, food aid has evolved whereby food aid is now given under longer term commitments and is used mainly to facilitate broad agricultural and industrial development objectives (Hopkins, 1987).

Even though the principles and objectives of food aid have evolved through analysis and evaluation of previous food aid projects, debate about the goals and the practice of food aid are still on-going. Most concerns revolve around issues of targeting, efficiency, cost-effectiveness, distribution and transportation. The use of food aid as a development tool also raises concern regarding the "tied" conditions placed on food aid by specific donor countries and international organizations. The increased reliance on food aid by many developing countries further increases the need to examine the nexus between food aid and food security objectives as well as general agricultural, industrial, and economic development goals.

5 SUMMARY

A state of food security ensures that all members of every household in a nation have access throughout the year to a diet that is adequate for leading a continued, healthy and active working life. A state of food insecurity exists when members of a household have an inadequate diet or face the future possibility of an inadequate diet. Therefore to determine regional or national food insecurity one must understand household food insecurity. To facilitate such a task three types of households and three types of food insecurity were defined: the dynamics of food insecurity were described though illustrations of the food insecurity risks faced by the different types of households; the food insecurity insurance options available to these households; and the effectiveness of these options in lessening food insecurity.

Although households can take specific actions to increase their food security status, the power of governments to lessen food insecurity is often greater than the aggregated power of households. Thus the policies and resources available to governments to alter the food security states of households were also discussed. Such actions on the part of governments include increasing the ability of market oriented households to acquire food, increasing the productive capacity of food producing households to supply food and improving the food marketing system's capacity to provide a variety of high quality foods at reasonable prices on a continuous and nationwide basis.

Co-ordinated food security policies are required to avoid the possibility that one set of policies increases food security while others inadvertently decrease food security. Governments are frequently pressured into adopting food security programs which lessen the symptoms of food insecurity (hunger and malnutrition) and in so doing often neglect programs which would lessen its causes (poverty, civil strife, etc.). Nations that have made a commitment to food security have a number of alternative policy paths from which to choose. However, policy decisions are often directed at national level food security with limited understanding of their possible impact on household food security. The challenge for analysts and decision makers alike is to integrate food security objectives and activities at all levels (international, national and community) to improve and protect food security at the individual and household level.

REFERENCES

Ahmed, Raisuddin. 1979. *Foodgrain Supply, Distribution, and Consumption Policies within a Dual Pricing Mechanism: A Case Study of Bangladesh.* Research Report No. 8. Washington, D.C.: International Food Policy Research Institute.

Bale, M.D. and E. Lutz. 1981. "Price Distortions in Agriculture: An International Comparison." *American Journal of Agricultural Economics.* 63(1): 8-22.

Beaton, G. H. and H. Ghassemi. 1982. "Supplementary Feeding Programs for Young Children in Developing Countries." *American Journal of Clinical Nutrition.* 35: 864-916.

Behrman, Jere R. and K.N. Murty. 1985. "Market Impacts of Technological Change for Sorghum in Indian Near-Subsistance Agriculture." *American Journal of Agriculture Economics.* 67 (8): 539-549.

Blyn, George. 1982. "The Green Revolution Revisited." *Economic Development and Cultural Change.* 31(4): 705-725.

Bromley, R. J. 1971. "Markets in the Developing Countries: A

Review." *Geography*. 56(2): 129-130.

Chaudhry, M. Ghaffar. 1982. "Green Revolution and Redistribution of Rural Incomes: Pakistan's Experience." *The Pakistan Development Review*. XXI (3): 173-205.

Dey, P. 1981. "Gambian women: unequal partners in rice development projects?" *Journal of Development Studies*. 17(3): 109-122.

Herdt, R. W. and C. Capule. 1983. *Adoption, Spread, and Production Impact of Modern Rice Varieties in Asia*. Manila: International Rice Research Institute.

Hopkins, Raymond F. 1987. "The Evolution of Food Aid: Toward a Development-First Regime." *Food Security: Integrating Supply, Distribution and Consumption*. (ed. J. Price Gittinger, Joanne Leslie and Caroline Hoisington). Washington D.C.: John Hopkins: 246-259.

Huffman, Sandra L. 1987. "Women's Activities and Impacts on Child Nutrition." *Food Security: Integrating Supply, Distribution and Consumption*. (ed. J. Price Gittinger, Joanne Leslie and Caroline Hoisington). Washington D.C.: John Hopkins: 371-384.

Kehoe, T. and J. Serra-Puche. 1986. "A General Equilibrium Analysis of Price Controls and Subsidies on Food in Mexico." *Journal of Development Economics*. 21(1): 65-87.

Kumar, Shubh K. 1979. *Impact of Subsidized Rice on Food Consumption and Nutrition in Kerala*. Research Report No. 5. Washington, D.C.: International Food Policy Research Institute.

Leslie, Joanne. 1987. "Interactions of Malnutrition and Diarrhea: A Review of Research." *Food Security: Integrating Supply, Distribution and Consumption*. (ed. J. Price Gittinger, Joanne Leslie and Caroline Hoisington). Washington D.C.: John Hopkins: 355-370.

Martinez, Olga and E.A. Cebotarev. 1989. "Food Aid, Food Security and Quality of Life in Poor Households: A Review." *The World Food Crisis: Food Security in Comparative Perspective*. (ed. Hans Bakker). Toronto: Canadian Scholars' Press.

Peterson, W.L. 1979. "Introductional Farm Prices and the Social Cost of Cheap Food Policies." *American Journal of Agricultural Economics*. 61(1): 12-21.

_____. 1983. "International Farm Prices and the Social Cost of Cheap Food Policies: A Reply." *American Journal of Agricultural Economics*. 65(4): 827-8.

Pinstrup-Andersen, P. 1987. "Food Prices and the Poor in Developing Countries." *Food Security: Integrating Supply, Distribution and Consumption.* (ed. J. Price Gittinger, Joanne Leslie and Caroline Hoisington). Washington D.C.: John Hopkins: 282-292

Pinstrup-Andersen, P. and Peter B. Hazell. 1987. "The Impact of the Green Revolution and Prospects for the Future." *Food Security: Integrating Supply, Distribution and Consumption.* (ed. J. Price Gittinger, Joanne Leslie and Caroline Hoisington). Washington D.C.: John Hopkins: 106-118.

Pollard, S. and D. Graham. 1985. "Price Policy and Agricultural Export Performance in Jamaica." *World Development.* 13(9): 1067-1075.

Prahladachar, M. 1983. "Income Distribution Effects of the Green Revolution in India: A Review of the Empirical Evidence." *World Development.* 11: 927-44.

Ram, Eric R. and Vasant M. Holder. 1978. *Assignment Children.* July-September. 43: 47-56.

Redclift, M. 1986. "Radical Food for Thought." *Food Policy.* 11(3).

Reutlinger, Shlomo. 1985. "Food Security and Poverty in LDCs." *Finance and Development.* 22(4).

Rukuni, M. and C.K. Eicher. 1987. "The Food Security Equation in Southern Africa." *Food Security Issues in Southern Africa.* (ed. M. Rukuni and Carl K. Eicher). East Lansing: International Development Reprint No. 5, University of Michigan State: 3-39.

Taylor, Daphne S. 1989. *A Cross Country Analysis of Food Grain Price Differentials.* unpublished M.Sc. Thesis. Guelph: Department of Agricultural Economics and Business, University of Guelph.

Tinker. I. 1979. *New Technologies for Food Chain Activities: the imperative of equity for women.* Washington, D.C.: Office of Women in Development, Agency for International Development.

Tobisson, E. 1980. *Women Work, Food and Nutrition in Nyamwigura Village, Mara Region Tanzania.* Report No. 548. Dar es Salaam: Tanzania Food and Nutrition Centre.

World Bank. 1982. *World Development Report 1982.* New York: Oxford University Press.

World Bank. 1986a. *World Development Report 1986.* New York: Oxford University Press.

World Bank. 1986b. *Poverty and Hunger Issues and Options for Food*

Security in Developing Countries. Washington D. C.: World Bank Policy Study.

Youssef, Nadia and C. Hetler. 1983. *Rural Households Headed by Women.* Geneva: International Labour Organization.

Table 1:
Temporary Food Insecurity: Risks, Insurances, Problems and Policies

TYPES OF HOUSEHOLDS	RISKS	INSURANCES	POTENTIAL PROBLEMS	POLICY/PROGRAM
I, III	unforeseen production shortfalls owing to climate, pests, disease, civil strife.	adequate storage from previous year's harvest.	storage facilities and post harvest techniques may be inadequate.	assist in post harvest techniques to prolong the life of stored foods.
II	unforeseen income shortages owing to temporary unemployment or sudden food price increases.	use of household savings to support current expenditures.	prolonged unemployment may deplete savings.	collective or co-operative unemployment insurance schemes.
III	unforeseen income shortages owing to production shortfalls, temporary marketing setbacks, temporary low prices, unexpected loss of markets.	access to income earning employment and markets to purchase foods.	labour supply may be lost, if the younger more productive household members migrate to urban centres in search of employment.	encourage alternative temporary employment opportunities in rural areas and access to food supplies.

Table 1 (Continued):
Temporary Food Insecurity: Risks, Insurances, Problems and Policies

TYPE I - THE SELF-SUFFICIENT, NON-MARKET HOUSEHOLD
- a rural household of dependents and labourers which produces and consumes
its own food. This household behaves as a self-sustaining economic
unit.

TYPE II - THE NON-FOOD PRODUCING HOUSEHOLD
- a rural or urban household of wage earners and dependents which sells
its labour services in exchange for food and/or income to purchase food.

TYPE III - FOOD PRODUCING COMMERICAL HOUSEHOLD
- is a household of dependents and labourers that has access to land and
agricultural production opportunities. This household specializes and
markets produce to earn income to support household food purchases within
the marketplace.

Table 2:
Cyclical Food Insecurity: Risks, Insurances, Problems and Policies

TYPE OF HOUSEHOLD	RISKS	INSURANCES	POTENTIAL PROBLEMS	POLICY/PROGRAM
I	seasonal production shortfalls owing to climate, pests, labour supply.	charity from neighbouring households or communities.	neighbouring households may also be faced with production shortfalls or may not have excess food available to assist.	assist in the establishment of emergence community or regional storage facilities, co-operatives or collectives.
III	seasonal production shortfalls owing to shortage of labour, investment capital.	access to loans to support household expenditures.	repayment of loans may result in excessive debt and poverty.	regulation of interest rates and credit facilities.
II	seasonal income shortages owing to seasonal unemployment or seasonal food price increases.	access to alternative or high income employment opportunities.	alternative employment may not be available or may require alternative skills, re-location or migration.	encourage diversification in local production activities and industry. Provide re-training and education opportunities.
III	seasonal income shortages owing to seasonal low market prices, loss of markets,	sale of productive resources to purchase food.	selling assets and resources may undermine future production levels if such resources cannot be repurchased.	discourage the sale of productive assets by providing temporary assistance through government programs and projects.
II,III	seasonal market food supply shortages, or seasonal lack of variety.	government policies which regulate food prices, safety and quality of foods, accessibility of people to the foods they	problems in such policies are numerous — inability to finance, lack of targeting, insufficient national food supply to	establish policies which encourage an increase in national food supplies, either through domestic production, or trade and

Table 2 (Continued):
Cyclical Food Insecurity: Risks, Insurances, Problems and Policies

need either through subsidies or distribution centres.	meet the demand at subsidized prices, inadequate distribution and communications capabilities.	foreign aid opportunities. Practice appropriate structural adjustments to decrease deficit and curb inflation.

Table 2 (Continued):
Cyclical Food Insecurity: Risks, Insurances, Problems and Policies

TYPE I - THE SELF-SUFFICIENT, NON-MARKET HOUSEHOLD"
- a rural household of dependents and labourers which produces and consumes
its own food. This household behaves as a self-sustaining economic unit.

TYPE II - THE NON-FOOD PRODUCING HOUSEHOLD
- a rural or urban household of wage earners and dependents which sells
its labour services in exchange for food and/or income to purchase food.

TYPE III - FOOD PRODUCING COMMERICAL HOUSEHOLD
- is a household of dependents and labourers that has access to land and
agricultural production opportunities. This household specializes and
markets produce to earn income to support household food purchases within
the marketplace.

Table 3:
Chronic Food Insecurity: Risks, Insurances, Problems and Policies

TYPE OF HOUSEHOLD	RISKS	INSURANCES	POTENTIAL PROBLEMS	POLICY/PROGRAM
I, III	declining yields owing to inadequate land and water base, soil and water quality, labour supply, seed quality.	access to production enhancing agricultural inputs, fertilizers, pesticides, new varieties, tools, new techniques and extension services.	the cost of agricultural inputs and the producer price of agricultural commodities may not warrant increased production.	co-ordinate government pricing policies such that price incentives exist for expanded agricultural production.
			lack of income prevents the use of purchased inputs and tools. The prolonged overuse of land and water resources may inhibit future productivity levels.	provide credit facilities to assist producers using production enhancing techniques.
			Purchased or imported inputs may not be delivered at the appropriate time.	assist in the development of transportation, storage and rural infrastructure.
			the prolonged overuse of land and water resources may inhibit future productivity levels.	encourage self-sustaining agricultural techniques which uses indigenous or re-generating inputs.
		sale of household resources to acquire food.	selling household assets and resources may undermine future production levels if such resources cannot be repurchased.	discourage the sale of productive assets by providing temporary assistance through government programs and projects.

Table 3 (Continued):
Chronic Food Insecurity: Risks, Insurances, Problems and Policies

	Risks	Insurances	Problems	Policies
	sell or use land in non-agricultural capacity.	land and labourers may have no other productive uses. Taking the land out of agricultural use may deplete regional food supplies and consumption.	retain the profitability of productive agricultural land by maintaining appropriate pricing policies which encourage agricultural production and a guaranteed level of income to producers. Encourage self-sustaining agricultural techniques which use indigenous or re-generating inputs.	co-ordinated pricing policies which stabilize yearly price variability as opposed to set prices. Operation of buffer stocks to stabilize yearly price fluctuations.
III	chronic shortages of income owing to the continued sale of agricultural products at below cost prices, inability to access markets.	government price supports for food commodities such that producers, prices are seasonally stabilized.	inappropriate price supports may encourage an over supply in specific commodities while discouraging the production of other crops.	
		diversification of agricultural production to offset price risk.	excessive diversification may lower profits and gains from specialization. Resources may not be capable of diversifying.	establish co-operatives and crop price stabilization insurance schemes.
		use commercial agricultural production for home consumption. Move from a market oriented food producing household to a	removes or decreases the level of national food supplies available to non-food producing households.	establish an efficient and equitable marketing system which encourages agricultural producers to market produce.

Table 3 (Continued):
Chronic Food Insecurity: Risks, Insurances, Problems and Policies

		self sufficient household.		
II, III	persisent lack of income owing to unemployment, underemployment, low wages, wages in kind, rising prices relative to wages.	access to income earning employment and markets to purchase foods.	labour supply may be lost, if the younger more productive members migrate to urban centres in search of employment.	encourage alternative temporary employment opportunities in rural areas and access to food supplies.
		supplementing income from self employment opportunities.	entrepreneurial skills and investment income requirement may not be available.	encourage entrepreneurial skills and business education. Provide credit opportunities to viable businesses.
		create or monitor minimum wage rate.	may discourage employment opportunities and encourage mechanization within industries.	provide income supplements to low income households.
		unionized labour to provide job security.	may discourage employment opportunities and industrial development.	encourage co-operative or collective employment opportunities.
		financial assistance from other household members or neighbouring households.	prolonged assistance may not be available.	collective or co-operative financial assistance programs.
	insufficient market food supplies.	access to loans to support household expenditures.	repayment of loans may result in excessive debt and poverty.	regulation of interest rates and credit facilities.

Table 3 (Continued):
Chronic Food Insecurity: Risks, Insurances, Problems and Policies

Risks	Insurances	Problems	Policies
limited access to a variety of high quality foods owing to high food prices, shortage of foods in the marketplace, long distance marketplace, payments in kind.	government policies which regulate food prices, safety, quality and variety in foods, as well as accessibility of people to food supplies. Policies that link food deficit and food surplus regions.	inadequate and high costs in transportation and communication facilities may inhibit the flow and quality of food distribution.	encourage rural transportation, storage and marketing infrastructure. Co-ordinate and monitor price policies that encourage variety in agricultural food production.
	access to markets to exchange foods with other households to increase the variety of food consumption by each household.	knowledge of food preparation may be inadequate to prepare different varieties of foods for consumption.	encourage training and eduction of food nutrition and preparation techniques.
inability of access markets owing to long distance, lack of transportation facilities.	expand marketing opportunities to food deficit rural and urban centres within the nation.	may not be viable due to inadequate transportation facilities, roads, storage, etc.	encourage transportation, communication and distribution facilities.
	expanded marketing opportunities through international trade.	the sale of food to international buyers may deplete national food supplies.	co-ordinate trade activities such that the export of food supplies is not done at the expense of domestic food consumption. If national food supplies are not in surplus, exported food supplies

should be matched with an equal or greater quantity of imported food supplies.

Table 3 (Continued):
Chronic Food Insecurity: Risks, Insurances, Problems and Policies

TYPE I - THE SELF-SUFFICIENT, NON-MARKET HOUSEHOLD'
- a rural household of dependents and labourers which produces and consumes its own food. This household behaves as a self-sustaining economic unit.

TYPE II - THE NON-FOOD PRODUCING HOUSEHOLD
- a rural or urban household of wage earners and dependents which sells its labour services in exchange for food and/or income to purchase food.

TYPE III - FOOD PRODUCING COMMERICAL HOUSEHOLD
- is a household of dependents and labourers that has access to land and agricultural production opportunities. This household specializes and markets produce to earn income to support household food purchases within the marketplace.

Chapter 2

FOOD SYSTEMS AND FOOD SECURITY IN LATIN AMERICA:
A SYSTEMIC APPROACH TO POLITICS, IDEOLOGY AND TECHNOLOGY

Jorge Nef and Jokelee Vanderkop

1. INTRODUCTION

This chapter is an attempt to understand and explain the political economy of food production, distribution and exchange in Latin American and the Caribbean. This will be done by concentrating on the concept of "food security." We regard the term food security as a conceptual device for the study of the complex interrelationships between economy, society and polity in the context of the development process. This chapter is a condensed version of a monograph which contains more detail and fuller documentation (Nef and Vanderkop, 1989).

A superficial glance at the general food situation in Latin America and the Caribbean makes it clear that it is set apart from most of the rest of the Third World. For one thing, the ratio of cultivable land to population in Latin America and the Caribbean is the most favourable in the developing world, especially in comparison with parts of Asia (Cohan, 1982: 27). Not only are there some of the richest, yet unexploited agricultural lands, but in terms of food production and food consumption per capita, Latin America and the Caribbean (the LAC countries) rank only below the Atlantic community and Eastern Europe, and well above Africa, Asia and most of the

Middle East.

The paradox, however, is that despite this apparently exceptional endowment, in 1980 over fifty million of its three hundred and fifty million inhabitants were unable to reach the level of food consumption that is widely considered to be required for a normal life (Rodríquez, La Grá and Bastidas, 1985: 6). Moreover, since the 1960s, Latin America as a whole has become a net importer of food, a phenomenon that has coincided with an overall strengthening of foreign dependency (Tuomi, 1976: 11). These tendencies to food inaccessibility, pauperization, malnutrition and food dependency have increased dramatically during the last decade as declining values of exports and a soaring foreign debt have wreaked havoc in the region. In this sense, Latin America and the Caribbean are faced with a food crisis and, therefore, are faced with a situation that is similar to that characteristic of other Third World countries. However, the causes of the net result are somewhat different.

The paradox referred to above raises serious doubts about the possibility of explaining such crises through conventional theories which concentrate on environmental, technological or population factors. While those factors may play a role in Latin America and the Caribbean, it is also true that the LAC food problem differs from that in the rest of the Third World in certain key respects. The LAC region, for example, has an important agricultural sector producing grain, meat, coffee and other foodstuffs for the world market.

The problem of food insecurity in LAC is related to the fact that there is an inequitable distribution of benefits resulting in a highly polarized yet integrated socio-economic structure. Here, a numerically large labour-intensive traditional subsistence sector co-exists beside a large-scale capital-intensive commercial sector. More often than not, the latter provides the main source of employment income for the peasantry. Seventy percent of the families in the region live in poverty and some fifteen percent suffer from malnutrition (Swift, 1978: 101-119; RAWOO, 1986: 13-14).

It is a commonplace today that poverty rather than insufficient food production lies at the core of food insecurity. The poor do not have access to adequate food supplies. That is coupled with inadequate policies to ensure credit, market accessibility, know-how, and — most importantly — income. It perpetuates and even enhances "the vicious cycle of poverty" for producers and consumers alike.

What is a less common analytical approach than the analysis of the vicious circle of poverty is what might be termed a "holistic" analysis of food insecurity from a perspective which focusses on such aspects of food insecurity as the relationship between poverty, income and unemployment. In such an analysis the economic, political and social welfare factors related to food insecurity would all have to be examined. Food insecurity, even in countries characterized by the most severe cases, does not affect everyone in the entire population in the same way and to the same degree of intensity.

Transitory versus Chronic Food Problems

Such a holistic analysis would require more analysis of underlying causes. In order to initiate such an analysis a distinction should be made between *transitory* and *chronic* food problems (RAWOO, 1986: 6). The former refers to inadequate food consumption levels due to intra- or inter-seasonal fluctuations in supply or effective demand. The latter occurs when the **means** to assure an adequate diet are persistently lacking.

These concepts must, first of all, be considered with reference to another important analytical distinction, the notion of *heterogeneity* of the population. Within any country, there will always be those (often a minority) whose permanent level of income is high and secure enough to satisfy their own food needs. Their only requirements are those of physical supply. Secondly, there is another segment of the population with sufficient income levels to acquire food, but with a propensity to experience a deterioration of their purchasing power. This is a partially vulnerable group which requires not only physical supplies, but also compensatory mechanisms to stabilize incomes in times of emergency. Last, there is the rest of the population which cannot satisfy their basic food needs through existing socio-economic structures. This is undoubtedly the most affected group, for whom the food crisis is a concrete and permanent reality.

1.1 The Framework: Key Concepts

Food security is an analytical construct that belongs both to the realm of development studies and to the realm of security studies. It is our conviction that, since its onset the term has been eminently political and value-laden. Far from being a neutral and purely technical notion, what might be called the "food security paradigm" entails explicit policy options and solutions to handle normatively defined socio-political problems. Not everyone would agree that the term "food security" is value-laden in this manner, but often the manner in which international organizations utilize the term in official documents turns out to be far less neutral than the scholarly use of the term in academic journals.

The definition of what the problem of food security is, whose problem it is, what its root causes are, and what the assumptions and likely forms of management are — or in Lasswell's terms, "Who gets what, when and how?" (Lasswell, 1936) — are intrinsically political questions.

Three concepts are central in our analysis: **food system, food regime**, and **food security**.

These are largely derived from the pioneering work done by Hopkins and Puchala (1978). We have drawn as well from other authors (e.g., Kent, 1984; Chisholm and Tyers, 1982; Valdés, 1981; Balaam and Carey, 1981; Warnock, 1987; Bennet and George, 1987).

Food system implies the interconnection of several functions. It "refers to the whole complex of human/natural interactions relating to food production, processing, exchange and consumption. It stresses the interactions and feedbacks between component elements and thus is not linear. It is concerned with the place of ... food ... within larger environmental resource and social contexts" (UNACSTD, 1986: 6). The UN definition concerns the local, national, regional and international levels. It further denotes a broader and more analytical construct than the concept of food security. In fact, food system encompasses the notions of food self-sufficiency and self-reliance. In systemic terms we are talking about the "shaping, and sharing" (Lasswell, 1936: 3-25) of food as well as its circumstances.

Within this framework, the global, regional, national and local levels possess, in various forms and degrees, a "set of rules, norms or institutional expectations" (Hopkins and Puchala, 1978: 20) that govern the system. These sets of institutionalized practices constitute what we call the *food regime*. Food regimes vary in form, substance and institutionalization. Some are very loose and decentralized (e.g., a "classical" perfectly competitive market); others are largely unipolar (i.e., monopolistic, whether hegemonic or by imposition). In the first case, the boundaries of the system and the regime are basically the same. In the latter case, the larger system is clearly subordinated to the regime which becomes the real power locus. In sum, the food regime is where political will, policies (both decisions and non-decisions), planning, agencies and managerial practices are formulated and instrumentalized. In other words, a "loose food regime" is a decentralized system in which market forces determine the distribution and exchange of food, while a "monopolistic food regime" is one that moves away from a perfectly competitive market situation for various reasons.

The nature of the food system and the food regime is closely correlated with the degree to which individuals and households enjoy relative food security.

Food security can be defined as the ability of a society and its members to have stable and reliable access to the basic foods needed. This can sometimes be accomplished through a series of policies, as well as by production, trade, purchase and barter measures and practices oriented to ensure an adequate level of food quality and variety for all its members. The aforementioned combination of instrumentalities varies according to a country's resource endowments and its comparative advantage in agricultural production, both food and non-food, and its level of industrialization (Johnson, 1985: 67; UNACSTD, 1986: 6).

In addition to the terms food system, food regime and food security we also need to consider two other terms. National food security is not synonymous with food self-sufficiency nor self-reliance. *Food self-sufficiency* can be defined as the absence of net food imports while food self-reliance means the determination and capacity of a country to feed itself by utilizing and mobilizing its own resources. Food security must also take into consideration the patterns and levels of the food system — regional, national, sub-national, community and household. Thus, the attainment of food security at one level may be accompanied in practice by increased insecurity at other levels. Therefore, it cannot be assumed that having reached acceptable regional or national levels of food security will automatically translate into food security for everyone. Shortages, price fluctuations, threats and punishments (i.e., the use of "food power"; Balaam and Carey, 1981: 2) will certainly increase food insecurity.

By the same token, other than meeting basic conditions of survival what is an acceptable level of food security for one country, is not necessarily acceptable for another. In the developed countries, for instance, food security entails a broader range of choice for the household, while in the less developed countries choice is subordinated to fundamental availability and accessibility. Hence, food self-reliance is quite different in the two situations.

Food security involves two basic conditions. One is a conscious decision by actors in the system to reach certain desirable levels of performance (a food security policy whether explicit or implicit). The other is the existence of favourable circumstances for its operation and reproduction. Often, the failure of a food policy stems from the fact that policies have been exclusionary, or have addressed a misperceived problem. The political will or circumstances may not be conducive to goal attainment or the means may be inappropriate. By the same token, a system may achieve a significant and circumstantial degree of food stability, predictability and need satisfaction even in the absence of an explicit food security policy.

In those countries where the food system is weak and unstable, an explicit food security policy is most pressing. One source of insecurity is that these countries are often faced with the inability to generate adequate supply to meet actual needs through the domestic productive system. A second source of food insecurity is the incapacity of the economy to generate sufficient income for individuals to buy food. A third source is the extent to which externally generated food supplies will be contingent upon restrictive conditions, the latter connected to food dependency (FAO, 1986 b: 7).

The relevance of these factors varies from society to society. For some, growing food becomes the utmost obstacle. For others, it is the inability to earn enough foreign exchange to purchase food abroad or to combat poverty. Still for others, the issue of possible blackmail places a premium on self-sufficiency and the shifting of suppliers. The most prevalent source of food insecurity for all countries is, however, inaccessibility to food by individuals and households.

2. FOOD SYSTEMS AND FOOD REGIMES

2.1 The Context of the LAC Food System

Any understanding of food systems and regimes (and their dysfunctions) in the LAC countries has to start with three contextual characteristics. These pertain to the: 1) diversity, 2) pattern of development, and 3) "penetrated" nature of LAC societies.

2.1.1 Diversity

The very term Latin America is an abstraction that refers to twenty republics with diverse profiles, histories and levels of development. On the whole, they are not "emerging" nations in the sense commonly used to refer to the Third World. Most of them have been in existence as recognizable entities since at least the time of the Congress of Vienna (when most of the present European nation-states came into being). The Caribbean region, made up of recently independent "emerging" nations, has had little interconnection with "Latin America." Moreover, separate developments, including the establishment of colonial and neo-colonial export economies, have accentuated tendencies of relative isolation among the countries. Thus, it is more common in the region to hear about Argentinians, Brazilians or Mexicans than about Latin Americans, the term mostly used in North America.

The same generalized appellation is used by the multilateral institutions, bilateral agencies and the Western media. Reference is usually made to regional parameters such as Latin America, the Caribbean and Central America as regions as opposed to individual countries. It is perhaps not an exaggeration to say that the LAC countries as a grouping are a creature of these international organizations and the discourse of analysts and bureaucrats.

Internal trade and exchanges within the area, despite such initiatives as LAFTA (Latin American Free Trade Area), the Andean Region or SELA (the Latin American Economic System) have been far weaker than those between individual countries and the centres of world power. The basic pattern of interaction between the countries of the hemisphere and the North has been bilateralism, the latter immersed in an extremely asymmetrical interamerican system. The North means, at least since World War I, an overwhelming American presence; Western Europe and Canada play a less important role. In fact, the North-South system in the Western hemisphere involves a juxtaposition of two quite different sub-systems. One is the Latin American system of nation states where more or less classical nineteenth-century "balance of power" (Morgenthau, 1985: 185-240) interactions predominate. The result is a loose bundle of very independent, nationalistic, sovereign countries vis-a-vis each other. The other sub-system is a basically unipolar interaction between each individual country and the US. In the case of Central America, this is the result of a long tradition of US "quasi-colonial domination" whereas in South America, British hegemony mitigated these tendencies until the 1920s. The English-speaking Caribbean finds itself in a different geopolitical pattern altogether. The retreat of the British empire shortly after decolonization left a power vacuum which was quickly filled by American — and to a lesser extent — Canadian presence.

2.1.2 Pattern of Development

Economic, social and political development in the LAC countries has been quite disjointed. While most of the LAC economies and societies are distinctively "underdeveloped" by comparison to North America, Europe or Japan, they occupy as a whole the upper cluster of the Third World.

(i) South America and Central America

Since the Great Depression, the relatively more advanced economies in the area (Argentina, Brazil, Uruguay, Chile, Mexico) experienced an accelerated industrial expansion under the aegis of its so-called "import substitution industrialization" model (ISI) in the 1930s and 1940s. This entailed a Keynesian approach to demand-side economic management by the state sector and its parastatals. It was oriented to reducing the heavy dependence on manufactured imports present in their traditional export economies. ISI policies were also attempted two decades later (late 1950s and early 1960s) in the Central American region as well as in Venezuela, Colombia and Peru. By the 1960s, this approach to induced development had exhausted its economic and political possibilities. This exhaustion was a direct consequence of the inherent limitations of Latin American reformism: the maintenance of the traditional socio-economic order, while increasing mobilization, the inability to deal with the problem of rural and urban poverty and the socio-political dislocations brought about by modernization. Most important, import substitution industrialization was fundamentally reliant on the maintenance of traditional exports and deficit financing as vehicles to pay for ambitious development programs. Moreover, its heavy industrial and urban bias resulted in a serious neglect of the agricultural sector with the peasantry subsidizing, in a manner of speaking (through their super-exploitation), food production for consumption in the urban areas.

Rising expectations and mobilisation combined with shrinking capabilities and the ever present tendency of deteriorating terms of trade resulted, in the long run, in growing social and political polarization, stalemate, hyperinflation and political instability (Nef, 1983: 371-385). This phenomenon, which has been referred to by political analysts as a crisis of hegemony (Nun, 1968: 154-185), paved the way to a proliferation of repressive, national security regimes (Rockefeller, 1969) with strong international encouragement. Authoritarian capitalism, in this context, was an attempt by a transnationalized alliance of military officers and the business community to restructure dependent capitalism through unrestrained "supply-side" and monetarist policies.

The effects were not only a dismantling of the Keynesian administrative state, but most importantly, an overall denationalization, privatization and deindustrialization of import-substitution. This subsequently was accompanied by structural adjustment policies oriented to undoing existing agrarian reform schemes and fragmenting labour organizations.

The uncontrolled expansion of a military and police state was the costly corollary of "liberalization." The main thrust of these policies was to encourage unbalanced growth based on existing comparative advantages to bring about national development through unrestricted market mechanisms. The early success of this liberalization could be measured in impressive growth rates of the GNP referred to by many as "economic miracles." However, such miracles brought about an extremely unequal distribution of income further exacerbating rural and urban poverty and making the economies more vulnerable to external price fluctuations and imports (e.g., energy, technology, capital and foodstuffs). These miracles also fuelled (in the absence of political restraints) an irresponsible public and private attitude among the dominant economic actors enticed by easy foreign credit. Indebtedness grew faster than the economy to the point that the latter soon overshadowed any real growth of the GNP.

Increased food dependency in the 1970s was largely a legacy of over-reliance on comparative advantages, the "strategic hamlet" logic of military planners, expanding exports and the illusion of easy credit. Until the early 1980s, most countries experiencing apparent economic expansion found it cheaper to import food, mostly grain, from the US, than to grow it domestically. In some cases, the import of cheap foodstuffs ended up changing existing dietary habits. Where pulses, roots and corn once served as the major staples, particularly for the poor, these crops were now displaced. Bread and other wheat products as well as beef were particularly important in the consumption of the "modern" urban sector. Paradoxically though, overall agricultural production expanded with an emphasis on exports and Green Revolution packages while food production for the domestic market declined. Conversely, reliance on imported foods also increased. However, most imported foodstuffs were consumed by those with the capacity to pay, that is the wealthier socio-economic sectors. In fact, in the cases where aggregate nutritional standards – measured in per capita calorie consumption as percentages of nutritional requirements — increased, the increase did not represent an overall improvement for the entire population but mainly for the well-to-do. Socio-economic, quality of life and health indicators highlight this inequitable distribution. Most severely affected were the rural poor, the unemployed and within these, the most vulnerable groups (poor women and children).

The economic policies outlined here were not only pursued by bureaucratic authoritarian regimes (O'Donnell, 1973) such as those of Brazil, Argentina, Uruguay or Chile. Other more patrimonial authoritarian regimes, such as those of Central America, also adhered to this neo-conservative orientation. Even competitive, semi-competitive and populistic regimes (Venezuela, Colombia, Costa Rica, Ecuador or Mexico) for quite different reasons, applied monetarist, privatizing and unbalanced growth measures to a greater or lesser extent. The common denominators were also heavy international borrowing and dependence on food imports. For instance, the oil producing countries (Venezuela, Mexico and Ecuador) attempted to utilize the comparative advantage of their newly found petro-power to pursue a deepening of import substitution industrialization while neglecting food production for domestic consumption. When the OPEC bubble burst in 1982, they were saddled with unmanageable debts and a crippled food producing sector; a situation that continues to this day.

(ii) The Caribbean

The Caribbean region, for our purposes, comprises the so-called "West Indian" nations of Belize, the Guyanas (Suriname, Cayenne and Guyana), as well as the multitude of islands, excluding the Dominican Republic, Cuba, Haiti and Puerto Rico. As an off-shoot of the plantation economies of the seventeenth and eighteenth centuries, the political economy of the region now experiences the same poverty, population problems, inflation, unemployment and small domestic markets as other Third World countries. Less than twenty years ago, the overall population was generally food self-sufficient, with rural dwellers in particular, having access to the natural food resources of the land and sea. Agriculture consisted mostly of a two-tier system — small farm production (many of an acre or less) and the aforementioned plantations. Small farm production for domestic consumption was well diversified, efficient and plentiful. Today, there is a pronounced food problem with the area not only being a chronic importer of food, but also suffering growing malnutrition among large segments of its population.

With independence in the 1960s, urbanization, modernization and the growth of government, there came a conscious drive on the part of the local political elites to expand commodity production (cash crops), to commercialize fishing and create a massive tourist industry. As a result, their economies became even more export-oriented with sugar, bananas, bauxite and tourism becoming vital to their foreign currency earnings. This has further entrenched dependency linkages with the West (especially the US and Canada) making these nations extremely vulnerable to such pressures as fluctuating commodity prices, protectionist practices by the developed countries and foreign indebtedness.

(iii) The Common Regional Pattern

In spite of all the structural dysfunctions present in the LAC region, measured by standards of income, urbanization, literacy, industrialization and life expectancy, most of the countries could be placed in a middle category of nations within a system of international stratification. For instance, the overall level of manufacture, extractive industries and the proportion of the population in the tertiary (service) sector puts most of Latin America and the Caribbean well above Africa, Asia and even the Middle East. Comparatively speaking, only the "four little tigers" of the Far East (South Korea, Taiwan, Singapore and Hong Kong) surpass Latin America in this respect.

To say that the LAC countries are underdeveloped basically means that their large mono-producing economic structures are extremely vulnerable to "boom and bust" cycles. They also lack the resource, administrative and managerial capacity, and to some extent, the political will to address and deal with the root causes of poverty. Vast sectors, both urban and rural, of their societies are marginalized and live in permanent squalor alongside affluent "islands" of prosperity. The patterns of distribution of wealth, power and privilege are not only extremely unequal, but have progressively worsened over time. All this results in extreme polarization between "haves" and "have-nots," city and countryside, "modern" incorporated and "traditional" marginalized sectors. Generalized frustration combined with a lack of mobility opportunities confers on the political process endemic characteristics of violence and instability. This results not only in weak, unstable and often repressive and corrupt governments, but also, in great difficulties for national planning and policy continuity.

2.1.3 The Penetrated Nature of the LAC Societies

LAC development has historically been the consequence of the insertion of the region's economies in an international division of labour dominated by a Western core. As such, these nations are **"penetrated"** polities and societies, a phenomenon which has created conditions for structural underdevelopment. This more classical form of economic dependency has been reinforced by an increasing process of transnationalization of the state (Nef, 1986: 279-306) with the latter expressing itself in an integration of crucial politico-military and technocratic structures dominated by a US centred interamerican security network. Similarities can be drawn between this relation of complex dependency (both economic and military) and the pattern of satellitization observed within the Eastern bloc countries. In this context, the possibility that Latin American and Caribbean elites may implement independent political projects (e.g., Arbenz, Arosemena, Goulart, Bosch, Allende, Manley, Bishop or present day Nicaragua) is severely curtailed by external constituencies with veto power. The instruments of this coercive diplomacy range from the use of discriminatory trade policies (e.g., the Hickenlooper amendment regarding US sugar import quotas), to the denial of foreign aid, pressures on foreign private lenders and multilateral agencies to refuse credit (e.g., the role of the IMF), embargoes, destabilization — both covert and overt — and even to direct invasion (e.g., Dominican Republic, Grenada).

A crucial dimension reflecting the international vulnerability of the Latin American nations today, in both structural and historical terms, is the aforementioned soaring debt. In fact, out of the seventeen most indebted countries in the world, twelve are in the LAC region (World Bank, 1988a: xiv). The neo-liberal policies pursued by most regimes during the seventies combined with heavy borrowing from private and public sources of international finance have brought about a per capita **debt** of $946 in 1986. This compares to a regional per capita **income** of approximately $1543. The annual interest service of the debt alone averaged well over 33 percent of total export earnings for 1986/87. The total debt for the same period represented about four times the export earnings while the annual growth rate of debt between 1986 and 1987 was 4.3 percent (World Bank, 1988 a:

18), well above the average growth rate of the GNP.

(i) The Problem of Food Insecurity

The Latin American and Caribbean region, as a whole, does not appear to have a "typical" Third World food problem. A comparative study of per capita world daily calorie consumption from 1966 to 1980 shows that the region's consumption of daily calories is around the world average (Huddle, 1987: 10). On a country-by-country basis, however, an analysis of dietary energy supplies between 1969 and 1983 indicates either a general stagnation or a relative decline of nutritional standards (FAO, 1986: 19, 183-184) with nearly half of the countries still exhibiting nutritional profiles below their own recommended minimal requirements (e.g., Bolivia, Ecuador, El Salvador, Guatemala, Haiti, Honduras, Panama, Peru, Uruguay and Venezuela). Among these, Bolivia, Ecuador, Haiti and Peru have remained the most affected cases.

If one takes a more micro perspective and concentrates on **social sectors** within countries, it is possible to see that even the most affected countries have population groups which enjoy relative affluence. As we said earlier, access to food is not evenly distributed. Chronic hunger relates to the inability of having enough income to buy food. In the LAC countries, the "problem of malnutrition does not arise primarily from insufficient production of food. It mainly reflects the distortions prevailing in the distribution of income and wealth and therefore in the access of various population groups to food" (FAO, 1986 b: 31).

An important factor affecting the accessibility of food is the overall rate of inflation, and more specifically, the increase in the cost of the typical food basket. It should be noted, however, that what represents a "typical" food basket for the better-to-do is not the same as for the poor. Inflation in the Latin American region has been the most persistent and accelerated in the world. Three and even four digit annual increases of consumer prices have not been rare though the bulk of the Caribbean exhibits much lower rates.

Since salary adjustments for the wage earning sectors do not keep pace with price increases, low income groups are most seriously affected (Hirschman, 1964: 84). As most of the population in Latin America is urban and thus salaried, the wage price spiral has a direct effect on their standard of living. This also holds true for the rural population, most of which is semi-proletarianized (i.e., selling labour for wages). In many countries, food prices have increased faster than the overall cost of living index, thus reducing still further, food accessibility (FAO, 1986: 181).

If one looks at the production side, grain production, especially wheat, experienced a declining trend since the 1960s with the most serious downturn in per capita grain production occurring after 1982, the year when the debt crisis surfaced. (Brown, 1986: 15). Up until then, grain could be imported more cheaply from the US and Canada which had abundant surpluses and easy credit resulting from excess petro-dollar liquidity in Western banks. Since then, the debt crisis has tightened the LAC country's credit worthiness despite continued Western grain surpluses.

The resulting decline of Latin America in the world grain trade raises the question of the relationship between national and regional food security and food dependency. The latter means, for the most part, having to rely on North American grain exports (Wise, 1987: 306).

The present conjuncture has created pressures to reduce grain dependency and pursue policies of regional and national food security. However, a long-range, macro analysis of the LAC regional food system points in the direction of the persistency of a pattern of structural dependency.

2.2 The Cultures of Food Security

By culture we mean the different orientation, perceptions, ideologies, goals and analytical modes pertaining to the food problem and its solutions which guide the actions of various groups, actors and institutions in the system. In practical terms, it is impossible to separate these patterns of orientation from the actors themselves. Thus, this distinction is merely analytical. Within any food system there are several and often conflicting views. The greater the consensus around a modal pattern, the nearer a system is to becoming a **food security community**. The existence of a food security regime entails, undoubtedly, a fundamental consensus as well as accepted rules of the game by those who control the system. But, this does not automatically confer on the system, as a whole, the degree of generalized consensus among subordinate actors characteristic of a community. Consensus makes the governance of a system easier by legitimating the regime. The international food regime, as described by Hopkins and Puchala, is not necessarily legitimate but this does not impede its **de facto** functioning in allocating values.

The "food security paradigm" is by no means unambiguous nor unified. In fact, a careful examination of the literature and official documents indicates that there exists within it two quite different and identifiable discourses (World Food Council, 1979: 2). For the sake of simplification, we will call them respectively the **conventional** and **critical** views. These two ideologies underpin the various existing positions and orientations pertaining to food security in the inter-american system.

2.2.1 The Conventional Approach: Growth Economics and Neo-Malthusianism

The roots of mainstream thinking on food security are to be found in both domestic experiences in rural development in the West and in modernization theory. Since its very origins, this perspective has tended to have a pragmatic, project-oriented, apolitical and technocratic focus. This is not to say that the paradigm in question lacks a theoretical and ideological base, as is often pretended. Quite to the contrary, for all its "instrumentalist" and micro focussed proclivities, mainstream thinking is grounded in an orthodox, reformist and culture bound conception of development (modernization = Westernization = stability = development) privileging the international and domestic status quo. The analytical framework is based upon a conservative structural-functional epistemology (Almond, 1968: 55-66) where systems maintenance, social integration and gradual evolution are contrasted with undesirable radical change.

The central role of externally induced development, foreign aid, cultural diffusion and the like is to close the gap between rich and poor and to bring progress along Western lines to the Third World. Development, here, is eminently seen in terms of economic growth with "trickle down" effects. At the political

112

level, it is geared to the prevention of Third World insurgencies (Dwivedi and Nef, 1982: 60).

This perspective focusses largely on **production dysfunctions** in the food system which create insecurity at the international, regional and national levels. Although the causes of food insecurity in developing countries are seen primarily as stemming from Third World conditions (technological, environmental and political but mostly demographic), the solution is defined in the context of a broader global-international, regional and ultimately North American perspective. The antecedents of such a project are found in the grain surplus policies of PL 480, "Food for Peace" with the use of grain as an instrument of foreign policy and its subsequent mutation, the US "Food Security Act of 1974" (U.S. Congress, 1974). Its most direct international expression is the creation of a grain insurance scheme by the name of "Cereal Import Facility" established in 1981 under the control of the IM

> The facility has provided credits of at least SDR 300.million to ... LDCs; however, drawings are restricted to the country's credit standing with the IMF... The facility goes part way toward a system of world food insurance (Manghas, 1985: 4).

However, due to the restrictive nature of the facility, few LDCs have made use of its credits preferring to rely on regular bilateral supplies of foreign aid.

The conventional approach or mode of rationalization is rooted in orthodox development theories where international co-operation, Western technology and population stabilization measures play a fundamental role. It also focusses on a neo-Malthusian view where growing population, diminishing resources and systemic entropy are regarded as the central problems of food insecurity (Warnock, 1987: 29-58). This approach rests upon an assumption of comparative advantages, mutuality and complex interdependence between the North and the South. In fact, the issue of food security constitutes one of the central aspects of the North-South dialogue and the structuring of the International Economic Order (Brandt, 1980: 113; Brundtland, 1987: 118-146).

The UN World Food Council has referred to this approach as having a "narrow focus" definition of both the problem and the solution to food security. In an operational sense, food security means, first and foremost, "the stability of the international wheat market" (World Food Council, 1979: 2) controlled by a few First World wheat producers, mainly the United States. The model also questions the viability of self-sufficiency articulated by UNCTAD (the United Nations Conference on Trade and Development) and concentrates basically on three major components: a) the liberalization of trade barriers in agricultural products, b) the establishment of grain reserves throughout the world, especially in the producing countries, and c) the creation and expansion of insurance schemes and financial facilities underwritten by the industrialized nations. All this confers, whether by design or default, a large amount of metapower to industrial, grain producing nations over grain deficit countries. As Balaam and Carey have argued:

> ... there exists a type of "food power" relevant to inter-national relations ... [As] the relative positions of various states change with the waning of the Cold War and new issues and forms of wealth emerge, food security provides many with a source of power (Balaam and Carey, 1981: 2).

2.2.2 The Critical Approach: The Primacy of Economics, Society and Politics

Contrary to the orthodox approach, this "counter discourse" contains an amalgam of positions around one common perspective ranging from radical revolutionary approaches, theology of liberation, basic needs, ecologism to self-interested nationalist pragmatism on the part of Latin American elites. The central unifying feature of this alternative rationalization is the perceived need to solve Latin American and Caribbean problems from within the region. That is, Latin American and Caribbean food security, and that of the specific countries is first and foremost an internal matter. This does not generally preclude purely instrumental transfers of technology and capital from such institutions as the World Bank, the IMF or bilateral assistance. However, this position stresses political autonomy and endogeneity of decision making without the imposed prescriptions and interference of these bodies. In one pole of the spectrum, this heterogeneous "non-aligned" position is represented by the stance of Cuba and Nicaragua, whose governments perceive food security as a fundamental survival strategy vis-a-vis the US. This involves food security as part of a war economy.

At the other pole, there is the "pragmatic" (and perhaps opportunistic) view represented by nationalist, conservative governments and agricultural interests which see some form of protectionism, export promotion and incentives to agricultural production as a necessity for their survival as a class. In both cases, self-sufficiency and self-reliance are key words of this counter-discourse.

In its most puristic manifestation, the critical perspective sees distribution dysfunctions as having a relative autonomy from production. This is to say that increases in production will not automatically translate into a reduction of food insecurity. The central issue here is poverty, the latter resulting from socio-economic and political structures which render the poor powerless and poorer. Food insecurity, though having a material base, is essentially a **political** problem; so is its solution.

This approach is much "broader" (World Food Council, 1979: 2) in its definition of food security than the conventional approach. It looks at food as a basic human right (an "objective freedom" or "liberty from"), not as a **commodity**. Its focus of attention is mainly the **household**. The analysis centres on a redefinition of development theory: basic **needs**. Need orientation, self-reliance and autonomy are fundamental tenets of "another development." Unlike Western orthodoxy, the critical approach perceives the international system, not as the solution to Third World problems but rather as a major cause of dysfunctions. The solutions, however, are generally seen by necessity as coming from within Third World societies. By emphasizing macro-policy aspects, the critical approach focusses on fundamental systemic — social, political and economic — reorganization ("social technologies") to address the food problem. Unlike the orthodox approach, internal demographic and technological factors are not viewed as the central causes of food insecurity.

The underlying theory of International Relations present in this analysis is derived from both dependency theory and world systems theory. The critical approach, therefore, challenges the assumptions of mutuality and "antiseptic" comparative advantages extant in complex interdependence. Food power and conventional food security schemes are perceived as instruments that provide the "centre," especially the US, with a powerful weapon in the North-South conflict (Tuomi, 1976: 16).

Food security is viewed critically as an inextricable part of national and international security, in particular with regards to Western wheat exports and food aid. From this perspective, one of the major perceived problems of food insecurity for individual Third World countries is food dependency — especially the reliance on wheat imports.

The critical approach is permeated by a generalized distrust towards Western, particularly American, policies and intentions. This is especially the case in Latin America where a long history of American intervention, both disguised and overt, has defined a kind of North-South monologue. This "metaphysical pathos" should not be overlooked as an important component of the critical model (the same way as with the "do-gooder" and missionary attitude of the orthodox paradigm).

2.3 The Structures of Food Security

The regional food system of Latin America and the Caribbean does not possess within itself a single and highly institutionalized food regime. The latter is made up of a web of international organizations, national governments, transnational corporations, NGOs (both national and international), domestic commercial producers and merchants (large and small), peasant farmers, consumer groups and community self-help associations. However, this complex conglomerate is interlinked to an "external" actor, the US, through a circuitry of power networks which give the latter a position of clear paramountcy. In this sense, the regional de facto food regime is a specific variation of the global sets of rules, norms and institutional expectations which govern the global political economy of food. Its main characteristics are: a) the externality and transnationalization of decision making, rule formation, capital and technology, b) the internal and fragmented nature of production and distribution, c) pervasive scarcity, dependency and vulnerability, in particular for the weaker social sectors, d) limited mass accessibility conditioned by low incomes and marginalization (chronic poverty), e) weak organicity and, f) lack of integration as well as internal and external discontinuities (e.g., from nation to household and from nation to region).

2.3.1 Transnationals

These networks encompass **unofficial power structures** through major global corporations and agribusiness which in turn influence agricultural and trade policies at the centre. Among these corporations, two American-based and family owned super giants — Cargill and Continental Grain — in conjunction with three other firms, Bunge (Argentina), Dreyfus (France) and Andre-Garnac (Switzerland) have "an almost total monopoly of the US grain trade... [For instance] Cargill is the largest single contributor to the US balance of payments" (Bennet and George, 1987: 177). It is also the most widely diversified of these transnationals, operating in 36 different countries and covering practically the whole gamut of agricultural production, processing, storage, transportation, commercialization and R&D (Bennet and George, 1987: 177-179). In many cases, these transnationals have penetrated into Latin American rural areas through the purchase of large haciendas. The Amazon region of Brazil has been particularly favoured by such corporations as Volkswagen, Georgia Pacific, Anderson Clayton, Goodyear, Nestle and Mitsubishi, to mention but a few (Miró and Rodríguez, 1982: 57).

Over the last decade, these same cosmo-corporations (in conjunction with petrochemical enterprises) have made decisive inroads into biorevolution-type technologies and have acquired proprietary rights to new plant varieties (Mooney, 1987: 31-32). Their greatest impact is not only felt in shaping internal and external US agricultural policies but through the **de facto** control of the regional and global political economy of food.

2.3.2 Official North-South Channels and Policy Instruments

In terms of economic strength, agripower and diplomatic presence, it would appear that the United States and Canada would both be the most influential actors within the hemispheric food system. Canada, however, plays only a minor role in relation to its southern counterpart. This is due in part to two fundamental and interrelated reasons. Firstly, Canada lacks, by and large, an entrenched historical presence in Latin America because of a predominately American hegemony since the turn of the century (Nef, 1987: 170-183). Secondly, Canada's subordinate and dependent position in relation to the United States has made her take a back seat to American interests in the LAC region. In this, Canada's objective position shares structural similarities with some of the area's "subparamount" powers (Brazil, Argentina or Mexico) who remain primary commodity producers with little influence in the regional political economy of food despite their huge amounts of agricultural exports, most of which are sold

outside the LAC region. Canada's influence, however, is more significant in the Caribbean where it has had a financial, industrial and diplomatic presence since the early 1950s.

At a **manifest** level, American foreign policy, including aid and development assistance packages (as with any country's foreign policy), conveys the "official" bilateral position vis-a-vis the governments of the LAC region. Institutions such as USAID, the US Department of Agriculture or the EXIMBANK act as channels for the expression of American agricultural policies in Latin America and the Caribbean. Particularly important here are the operation of food aid programs, grain sales at both commercial and concessionary prices, bilateral agricultural co-operation and credit. The most important channel of US influence in the regional food system, however, is what could be referred to as "disguised" bilateralism (i.e., by proxy). This involves the indirect but effective control by the US government and dominant economic interests of seemingly multilateral agencies. Three such key international bodies are the IMF, the World Bank and the GATT. All three fall under the legitimating mantle of the United Nations System and are among the few, yet crucial, UN agencies to remain under US and Group of Seven control. Their influence on the food regime lies in their capacity to define the financial and trade matrix (i.e., the rules of the game) within which the Latin American and Caribbean food system operates. This confers upon these bodies a significant degree of "metapower."

Their regional and relatively less "hegemonic" counterparts are the IDB (Interamerican Development Bank) and the OAS (Organization of American States). The latter also lay the institutional groundwork for the operation of the regional food system. The IDB does so through the financing of development projects (with US veto) while the OAS, other than its involvement in hemispheric defence, co-participates with the UN in the management of two fundamental regional-international agencies (IGOs) dealing respectively with health/nutrition and food/agriculture. One is the Pan American Health Organization (PAHO) which acts as the linkage between the World Health Organization (WHO) and the OAS. The other is the Interamerican Institute for Agricultural Cooperation (IICA) which links the FAO to the OAS.

The importance of these organizations lies in their normative and technological capacity to formulate standards, plans and policy orientations regarding the food system. Unlike the case of the World Bank group, the OAS and the IDB, American interests do not guide to any large extent the policy direction of the PAHO and even less so that of IICA. In fact, a significant involvement by most of the UN agencies receptive to the non-aligned movement severely reduces the ideological hegemony of the US and that of the orthodox paradigm. The contradictory orientations within PAHO and IICA due to the UN-US (OAS) rift, emanate from conflicting views on development. This tends also to affect consensus in policy-making, the financing of these organizations and often creates administrative paralysis.

2.3.3 Official South-South Channels and Policy Instruments

Besides the above discussed lattice of interactions which constitute the centre of gravity of the regional food regime, there are other secondary, although also important, regional and international actors which make up the structure of the food regime. Among these, the UN Economic Commission for Latin America and the Caribbean (ECLAC), as well as ILPES (the Latin American Institute of Socio-Economic Planning) provide intellectual orientation for regional and national initiatives in the area of food. On the operational side there are a number of trade arrangements. These include, among others, CARICOM (the Caribbean Community), LAFTA (the Latin American Free Trade Area), the Andean Region Pact, SELA (the Latin American Economic System) as well as the initiatives of regional and sub-regional co-operation such as the Brazilian/Argentinian/ Uruguayan agreement of 1986 and the more recent meeting of Presidents in Acapulco (The Acapulco Commitment for Peace, Development and Democracy).

More specifically, several efforts have been undertaken to achieve higher levels of food self-sufficiency and security throughout the area. In 1983, the Action Committee on Food Security (CASAR) was created as part of SELA with a comprehensive mandate, leading more recently to the formulation of national food plans. Initially, CASAR oriented its activities toward food and food marketing strategies in Latin America. This involved technical co-operation on food policies and plans, mechanisms for food aid, and the creation of a regional information network. Since 1986, CASAR's efforts have concentrated on supporting national food plans, trade in basic foods and emergency food protection. Likewise, in 1983, the Board of the Cartagena Agreement (The Andean Treaty), with the support of FAO, created the Jose Celestino Mutis Andean System regarding agriculture, food security and environmental conservation. Its fundamental objective has been the formulation and adoption of measures facilitating the protection of member countries against food shortages and as a means of meeting nutritional needs of the whole Andean sub-region. The Board of the Cartagena Agreement has worked in conjunction with FAO to promote policies within member countries to establish national food security systems as the instrumental basis of a broader Andean System (FAO, 1986).

All these agencies vary in degree of formalization and provide at present, to a greater or lesser extent, a potential though intermittent institutional vehicle for the establishment of a Latin American and Caribbean food security system. The unifying feature of these agencies is their being active components of a North-South and South-South dialogue oriented to restructuring the international and regional economic order, under the terms of reference laid down by UNCTAD and the "Group of 77." It is here that resides the potential regional capacity for LAC to deal with its own food problems.

2.3.4 National Initiatives

Since the time of the 1974 World Food Conference, a growing

number of Latin American and Caribbean governments have begun formulating national food policies and food security programs. In 1976, the Panamerican Health Organization produced a methodology for the formulation of intersectorial policies of food and nutrition emphasizing five major aspects: a) strengthening primary health services related to nutrition at the household level, b) monitoring the nutritional status of the population, especially high risk groups (mothers and children), c) preventive measures to control nutritionally related diseases, d) reinforcing the administrative and technical capacity of nutritional services in schools, hospitals and so forth, and e) personnel training programs (PanAmerican Health Organization, 1976: 4, 9). Since then, nearly all the countries in the region have adopted and continue to implement specific intersectorial food programs centred on nutrition and health. Some of these programs have been inserted within broader plans for socio-economic development. Others have been specifically oriented to food relief to handle emergencies or endemic critical poverty. Still others, have emerged from strategies of national defence to cope with external aggression to national security. In varying degrees, the notion of food self-sufficiency, however, is already present in most Latin American and Caribbean food programs.

2.3.5 Entrepreneurs and Peasants

The central actors in the national and subnational food systems can be classified into two fundamental segments: the entrepreneurs and the peasantry (Moore, 1966). The interplay of these two groups determines the internal processes of the food system. Their often conflicting relationship affects the very definition of the region's social and political structures (e.g., land tenure). The process of concentration and deconcentration of land ownership resulting from such interactions has a direct impact upon the emergence of intermediary, farmer groups in society. The "middle class" (petty capitalist) type family farm, as known in the West, with very few exceptions (e.g., Costa Rica) has never been a dominant feature of Latin American agriculture. The entrepreneurial sector refers to those forms of agriculture which are often called "modern commercial agriculture." This includes agro-industry, plantations and large farms. These are capitalist forms with varying levels of development, technical efficiency and mechanization (Cordovéz, 1982: 21).

The peasant sector is equally heterogeneous. It ranges from relatively well-to-do owners, to small producers, to poor peasant farmers, to settlers, sharecroppers and itinerant labourers. Their common characteristic is the use of family labour as well as the small size of their holdings.

(i) The Leading Sector

The dominant and faster expanding sector throughout Latin America is the capitalist sector. Its most discernible traits are the growing utilization of advanced Green Revolution technologies, capital intensiveness, cash crop production — mostly for export markets — integration into an agroindustrial "modern" sector and the proletarianization or semi-proletarianization of the peasantry in the form of wage labourers (Miró and Rodríguez, 1982: 51-71). Thus, this sector has a most decisive impact in altering the nature of peasant agriculture from **minifundistas** to salaried farm workers; from being small producers for local markets to marginal buyers of processed foods. Brazil serves as a prime example of such modernizing tendencies. The most dynamic agricultural states of the southern region (Sao Paulo, Paraná and Rio Grande do Sul)

> have one fifth of the total area farmed, but four-fifths of the tractors in the country. The use of fertilizers is in practice concentrated on export items ... [In] 1970, while national average consumption per hectare was only 29 kg, the figure was 73 kg in Saõ Paulo... [The] government finances up to 80% of investment in specific production lines for export...[Moreover, the] southern region in 1970 absorbed 65% of total credit granted. (Gómes and Pérez, 1979: 69).

Needless to say, the profitability of this modern sector is substantially higher than that in more traditional agriculture. The bulk of this production is in bananas, coffee, sugar cane, cotton, oilseeds and soybeans which are not directly consumed but are produced for export markets.

When dealing with the entrepreneurial sector, a fundamental distinction should be drawn between those areas which constitute traditional exports (e.g., wheat and cattle in Argentina, bananas in Central America) and those engaged in the so-called non-traditional exports (soybeans, grapes, apples, poultry, etc.). The former are characterized by classical latifundia and plantation type farming where land concentration is essential, though the level of technological inputs is often relatively low. The new form of agribusiness is represented at its uppermost level by the agro-industrial complex. Here the use of high tech methods of production (HYVs mechanization, sophisticated irrigation, intensive use of pesticides and fertilizers etc.) is by far more important than extensive land ownership. The common denominators of the traditional and modern components of agricultural enterprise in Latin America are capital, not unit size, and its overall insertion in the structure of dependent capitalism.

(ii) The Subordinate Sectors

With regards to the peasant economy, it encompasses that sector of domestic agricultural activity in which family-type units engage in the process of production with the aim of ensuring, from one cycle to another, the reproduction of their living and working conditions. The peasantry, despite the capitalization of agriculture discussed above, is still the most decisive though decreasing component in Latin America's production of food for internal consumption.

Peasant units are not limited, though, to internal markets. In many countries, other than local production, peasant agriculture also accounts for a significant share of certain export products, particularly coffee, cocoa, and livestock (not to mention the thriving illegal economies in Bolivia, Peru and Colombia).

2.3.6 Nongovernmental Organizations (NGOs)

NGOs as voluntary and non-profit organizations are composed of relief organizations, church groups and other development groups which support projects in the Third World. They are generally participatory, non-bureaucratic agencies configurating what has been referred to as a "third system" (Nerfin, 1986).

The role of NGOs in the Latin American and Caribbean food system is quite extensive and complex, though generally not very well known. One type of NGO encompasses First World private agencies which do research and carry on programs in the Latin American and Caribbean region. In general, they all serve as linkages between the international (Western) system and the domestic (Third World) setting through interfaces with local NGOs and governments. CARE, the Red Cross, Oxfam, WUS, Save the Children Fund are examples of worldwide organizations which are active in the LAC countries. Such Canadian NGOs as CUSO, WUSC, CANSAVE, Canada World Youth, the Canadian Catholic Organization for Development and Peace, the Canadian Hunger Foundation and the Inter-Church Fund for International Development have a notable presence in the poorer countries of the region. These First World NGOs approach food problems from both conjunctural and structural perspectives and are thus geared to meet specific emergency cases with food relief and welfare activities through the provision of clothing, medical supplies etc.

In Canada, NGOs are moving toward longer term development work bringing these agencies to introduce an on-going "project-centred" approach (Brodhead, Herbert-Copley and Lambert, 1988: 12-13). This is as much a result of increased levels of CIDA funding and its subsequent demands for accountability and measurement of outputs as well as the realization that small self-contained operations (e.g., charity) have limited developmental effects.

In recent years various forms of NGOs in the LAC countries themselves have proliferated. Two of these forms are particularly important. One type has been the Latin American and Caribbean based "independent research centres." These are organizations made up of local experts (generally counter-elites) presenting alternative, and sometimes critical, analyses to the prevailing models of development (e.g., the Fundacion Bariloche in Argentina, GIA – the Group of Agricultural Research in Chile, DESCO – Centre for the Studies and Promotion of Development and the Fundación Amauta in Peru). The development and expansion of these "centres of excellence" have been a direct consequence of the climate of political repression combined with fiscal austerity. The neo-conservative trend in Latin American governments has severely compromised academic freedom and restricted professional employment opportunities in the universities and the civil service for those who hold critical views. Most of these centres depend upon First World financial sponsorship and contacts with First World NGOs for their survival.

The other type of NGO is a more amorphous expression of non-elite survival strategies to cope with crisis situations and political repression. The bulk of these organizations has emerged in the margins of society, in the rural and urban communities of peasant farmers, villages, squatters and shantytown dwellers. Their members are mostly women, the young and the unemployed (Nef, 1987: 14-23). Their administrative style is generally participatory, antipatrimonial and non-bureaucratic. They involve the so-called "base" communities (CEBs in Brazil), popular economic organizations (OEPs in Chile), self-managed urban communities (CUAs in Peru), peasant associations, and the like. Most of them are involved in food distribution, but a good number also comprise co-operatives and embryonic forms of self-government: **poder popular**.

Interaction between these and more "elite" NGOs is not infrequent though they are both quite independent from each other. Other than financing, there is one important difference between the base organizations and their more "technical" and "professional" counterparts. Base communities rely heavily on popular political participation to change the rules of power relations that govern the food system at the community and potentially at the national levels.

2.4 The Functions of the Food System

2.4.1 Processes and Effects

By processes, we refer to the input/output and feedback interactions (Easton, 1957: 384-385) among and within different structures and sectors of the food system as they pursue their goals and orientations. In general terms, the food arena is characterized by a combination of conflictual and co-operative behaviours. The predominance of one over the other depending on

> the nature of the products, efforts, and influence of interest groups, parties in power and intervening political purposes and interests (e.g., strategic). Within some regions ... cooperation tends to be dominant as mechanisms for conflict resolution exist, are effective, and are used quite often. Interregional trade tends to display more conflictual

behaviour ... but at this level mechanisms to create the rules of the game do exist in GATT and UNCTAD (Balaam and Carey, 1981: 5-6).[1]

The expanded commercialization of agriculture has had, by and large, a negative effect in regional food security. Growing agricultural export markets have provided a source of foreign exchange for the exporting countries and profits for the landowning elites. This has also resulted in a growing reliance on imported technological and agricultural inputs while simultaneously depressing peasant agriculture. In fact, the much hailed modernization of agriculture in Latin America has meant the expansion and strengthening of the capital intensive sector (capitalists and landowners) yet the underdevelopment and marginalization of peasant agriculture. The persistence of these tendencies, combined with the phenomenal growth of urban centres, has increased the fragility of national food systems. A recent FAO report on the LAC countries has pointed out that "urbanization and the expansion of agro-industry [has] induced significant changes in the pattern of food consumption. This has had two main implications: an increase in food dependency, and a market-induced discrimination against peasant producers" (FAO, 1986 b: 21).

The current economic depression has heightened the marginalization of the rural peasant economy turning scores of peasants into dependent, semi-proletarianized labour, if not an outright displaced sub-proletariat. In fact, with 39% of all peasants owning less than 2 hectares, this results in peasant agriculture becoming a shelter for the surplus labour force. The effect of this sub-proletarianization leads to migration to the cities. The outcome is a growth of slum settlements and widespread urban poverty. This reinforces political demand overloads on the food system. Government policies oriented to attacking social disparities have been for the most part ineffectual. As Figueroa has pointed out: "the social crisis in the agricultural sector...could not be resolved within the rural setting. Instead, the nature of the problem changed and shifted to the marginal zones of large urban centres; with very few exceptions, this has been the modern manifestation, thus far in this century, of the long-standing and unresolved rural social problem" (1985: 112).

By the same token, peasant production has the greatest incidence on the overall level of food availability. It is also geared to more traditional dietary habits with price levels generally within the reach of popular consumption. A decline of peasant production has had, therefore, a serious effect on the steady decline of per capita food production in Latin America and the Caribbean. It has also affected the "internationalization" of prices of foodstuffs which excludes many former consumers from market accessibility with dysfunctional effects on food security.

Export agricultural production, in particular the non traditional exports, has been articulated in a new development model which implies a reinsertion of the Latin American economies in the world system as exporters of raw materials. The idea behind this "neo-classical" development policy has been that of comparative advantages: increased revenue from exports could be used to strengthen internal weak links such as food production for the domestic market. Cheaper imported food appeared to be more advantageous than growing it domestically. The problem with this reasoning is two-fold. First, it creates a discontinuity, if not a contradiction, **within** the system between production and distribution, making the system extremely vulnerable to uncontrollable price fluctuations determined by the international market. Secondly, it assumes — as it turns out to be, quite erroneously — that the income level of the population, as in most developed countries, would be able to secure food accessibility. That is, that the majority of the population is gainfully employed, that the fruits of development miracles are equitably distributed and that the surplus population generated by the decline of the peasant labour force would be absorbed by urban industrial and service employment. Since the model also stressed extreme concentration of wealth for capital generation, deindustrialization, denationalization and the undermining of collective bargaining mechanisms, none of the above assumptions could be met. Thus, the logic of systemic development tends to break down under the pressure of poverty and unemployment. This dysfunction appeared long before declining prices for raw materials and the foreign debt came to a head. Its consequence was, and remains, food insecurity which ultimately leads to hunger, malnutrition and their related health problems in most of the countries in the region. Growing dependence on external, mostly Western food supplies, becomes in this context the key compensatory mechanism to deal with internal shortages.

Nevertheless, the acuteness of the economic recession has had a number of unexpected and potentially positive countervailing consequences. For instance, many food dependent, especially grain dependent countries, have become, out of necessity, relatively self-sufficient. The examples of Brazil and Chile are cases in point. Indeed, this newly acquired status is fraught with dangers and uncertainties. These countries face a temporary, yet dire, import crisis due to insufficient foreign credit. Moreover, no concerted long range attempt has taken place to restructure the food system in order to meet the needs of its population. The fact remains, however, that an initial step towards food independence has been taken.

3. CONCLUSIONS

It would appear that the Latin American and Caribbean food system is presently at a crossroads. New objectives and priorities of necessity will have to be formulated. It is important to remember that systemic change, whether adaptive or revolutionary, is not beyond the objective parameters or capabilities of the Latin American and Caribbean system. For instance, the already mentioned fact regarding the extremely favourable land/population ratio combined with a significant concentration (12%) of the world's proven oil reserves contrasts rather sharply with contextual circumstances of other areas of the globe. Therefore, political intervention and political will acquire paramountcy. Without ignoring systemic constraints, the region is still far from reaching its objective "limits to growth" (Meadows and Meadows, 1972). In this sense, food security in Latin America and the Caribbean is both attainable and sustainable. A new internationalism in Acapulco, and a generalized "rebellion in the chorus" are the agents for change reflecting a new mood, a new "consciousness" in Paolo Freire's terms.

3.1   Concluding Remarks: The Quest for Food Security

The study of the Latin American and Caribbean food system points to a complex relationship between micro and macro levels of explanation for its functioning. The common characteristic which intersects both aspects is the presence of a food crisis. On the one hand, the food crisis refers to the current level of insecurity for vast sectors of the region's population. On the other hand — assuming that present trends and structural characteristics persist — the crisis refers to the growing inability of the present food system to adequately feed its population in years to come (projected insecurity).

The most striking macro aspect of the Latin American and Caribbean food system is a combination of somewhat contradictory trends. The first such tendency is the noticeable weakening of what former Canadian Minister of Agriculture Eugene Whelan referred to as "food sovereignty" (Whelan, 1981). Such erosion is historically and structurally related to the decline of peasant production for domestic consumption and its relative displacement by "modern" large-scale production and agribusiness. Unlike the Western world where farming evolved with significant continuity into agribusiness through increased infusions of capital and technology; in the LAC countries, agricultural modernization has meant the supplanting of peasant production by large commercial international and transnational concerns.

The weakening of food sovereignty has been presently countervailed by a second tendency. This involves efforts to institute food security policies emphasizing self-sufficiency, intra-regional trade and co-operation and a subtle detachment from the present unipolar food regime. This counter tendency may augur a new wave of multilateral protectionism and concerted action to deal with the region's problems — food security and regional trade included — as part of a unified Latin American and Caribbean position. Time and circumstances permitting, the end result could be the emergence of a food security community.

The possible role of Canada in this on-going restructuring process involves a balancing of divergent tendencies. Many Latin Americans and West Indians perceive Canada as a "shield" as well as a back entry into American type technology and capital without the "imperialistic" designs attributed to the "colossus of the North." For the US, Canada could perform quite an opposite task: a friendly and acceptable "Trojan horse" to further facilitate penetration into the Latin American and Caribbean markets. In all likelihood, Ottawa has yet another agenda. That is, one more connected with enhancing Canada's "honest broker" role, its international image as a peace maker and middle power, as well as strengthening its presence in multilateral institutions. From all three perspectives, Canada's role in the LAC countries at the bilateral, multilateral, and most importantly, at the NGO levels is bound to increase. Given Canada's expertise, much of this involvement would be concentrated in the areas of food and agriculture.

At the micro level, the clearest generalization of this study is that food security in Latin America is far from being a technical problem related to resource scarcity or overpopulation. The main cause of food insecurity is poverty while poverty itself is the most explicit symptom of marginalization and powerlessness. The major impediment to food security is the natural and induced process of marginalization resulting from the inequalities in the present socio-economic and political structures.

The tackling of these problems together with the still unresolved land tenure question is part of the difficult menu that national elites, their governments and various other national and popular political forces will have to grapple with in order to bring food security to its citizens.

Policy interventions oriented to bringing about food security in the region could only be successful if a number of basic conditions are met. One is that of **integration**. By this we mean the convergence of micro and macro (Piñeiro, 1987: 3) levels of food security policies leading to a viable and expanded regional trade regime through clearance accounts and a tariff system ultimately oriented to the creation of a food security community. A second condition is **equity** — meaning that food security in the LAC countries must concentrate first and foremost on fighting poverty. Without this, increases in production, no matter how spectacular, would remain discontinuous with improvements in consumption because inaccessibility to food would still persist. Food security in this sense, has to be understood as a foundational component in any effort to bring peace, human rights and democracy to the region. A third condition is **comprehensiveness**. This refers to the insertion of a food security policy based on a realistic assessment of the systemic interconnections between contextual factors (e.g., the foreign debt, energy, land tenure, population, urbanization, water and technology) and food production and distribution. It also means a treatment of food security as an integral part of a development strategy where various aspects of the food production system (e.g., crops, horticulture, livestock, fisheries, ecology and even the drug trade) must be addressed in an interrelated fashion.

Finally, there is the question of a **technological frontier**. By this we mean far more than physical factors (land, water) and gadget technologies. We include here, as most important, socio-political technologies as part of complex technological functions. The possibilities of horizontal and vertical expansion of Latin American food security is contingent upon policies able to provide for an "optimal and appropriate" technological mix. In fact, "basic food items which are not oriented to exports have shown so far a reduced degree of general technological dynamism" (Cohan, 1982: 27). This is an area where technological improvements have a potentially high payoff. Technology transfers may play an important role. However, it is only with the possibility of developing an autonomous, scientific and technological capacity geared to studying the problems and formulating solutions to deal with those problems that appropriate technological breakthroughs in critical areas can occur. The lure of importing easy but costly solutions, such as Green Revolution packages in the recent past and some of the emerging biotechnologies in the present, must be clearly assessed in light of the region's real food needs and problems. They should also be assessed in terms of the impact on peasant and small holder farmers. Canada's research centres, official technical co-operation agencies and NGOs have an extremely important role to perform in contributing to the mutually beneficial task of bolstering such regional scientific and technological capability.

In the technological frontier of food security, social technologies are not just one component. They are the foundational components of food security. It is here that frontiers of knowledge as well as frontiers of imagination (Cohan, 1982: 27) are of prime importance. Management, planning, organization — and above all, politics — are central components of food systems, food regimes and food security. However, social technologies remain, so far, the least developed of the technological arsenal to deal with underdevelopment and its offspring, food insecurity. There is a need to know more and "know better." In our capacity to study and explain reality lies the key to bring about the rational, predictable and compassionate change of that reality.

REFERENCES

Almond, Gabriel. 1968. "Comparative Political Systems." In Macridis, Roy and Bernard Brown (eds.). *Comparative Politics: Notes and Readings*. Third Edition. Homewood, Illinois: Dorsey Press: 55-66.

Balaam, David and Michael Carey (eds.). 1981. *Food Politics: The Regional Perspective*. London: Allenheld, Osman.

Bennet, Jon and Susan George. 1987. *The Hunger Machine*. Toronto: CBC.

Brandt, Willi. 1980. *North-South: A Program for Survival*. Cambridge, MA.: MIT Press.

Brundtland, E. 1987. *Our Common Future*. New York: Oxford University Press.

Brodhead, Tim, Brent Herbert-Copley and Anne-Marie Lambert. 1988. *Bridges of Hope? Canadian Voluntary Agencies in the Third World*. Ottawa: North-South Institute.

Brown, Lester R. 1986. *State of the World 1986*. New York: W.W. Norton & Co.

Carey, Michael. 1981. "Introduction." In Balaam and Carey, op. cit.

Chisholm, Anthony and Rodney Tyers (eds.). 1982. *Food Security: Theory, Policy and Perspectives from Asia and the Pacific Rim*. Lexington, Kentucky: D.C. Heath & Co.

Cohan, Hugo. 1982. "Seguridad Alimentaria; Desarrollo Agrícola y Rural." *Desarrollo Rural en las Americas*. XIV (1).

Cordovéz, Luis López. 1982. "Trends and Recent Changes in the Latin American Food and Agricultural Situation." *CEPAL Review* (August).

Cox, Robert. 1983. "Gramsci, Hegemony and International Relations: An Essay on Method." *Millenium. Journal of International Studies.* 12 (2): 163 ff.

Dwivedi, O.P. and Jorge Nef. 1982. "Crises and Continuities in Development Theory and Administration: First and Third World Perspectives." *Public Administration and Development.* 2.

Easton, David. 1957. "An Approach to the Analysis of Political Systems." *World Politics.* 9 (3): 384 ff.

Editorial. 1982. "Another Development and the Third Development Decade." *Development Dialogue:* 1-7.

FAO. 1986a. "Background Paper on Food and Agricultural Situation in Latin America and the Caribbean." *FAO Regional Conference Background Papers.* Rome: FAO 19th Regional Conference for Latin America and the Caribbean, held on Barbados 5-13 August, 1986.

FAO. 1986b. *The State of Food and Agriculture 1985: Mid-decade Review of Food and Agriculture.* Rome: FAO Agriculture Series, No. 19.

Figueroa, Manuel. 1985. "Rural Development and Urban Food Programming." *CEPAL Review.* 25.

Galtung, Johann. 1981. "Global Processes in the World in the 1980's." In Hollist, Ladd and James Rosenau (eds.). *World Systems: Structure, Continuity and Change.* Beverly Hills, California: Sage: 110-138.

Goodwin, Paul. 1988. *Global Studies: Latin America,* Third Edition. Guildford: Dushkin Publishing Group.

Gómes, Gerson, and Antonio Pérez. 1979. "The Process of Modernization in Latin American Agriculture." *CEPAL Review* (August).

Hirschman, Albert. 1964. "Alternatives to Revolution." In Randall, Laura (ed.). *Economic Development: Evolution or Revolution?* Boston: D.C. Heath & Co.

Hopkins, Raymond and Donald Puchala (eds.). 1978. *The Global Political Economy of Food.* Madison, Wisconsin: University of

Wisconsin Press.

Huddle, Janet Marie. 1987. *Production and Distribution of Food: A Study of the Green and Blue Revolutions.* Guelph, Ontario: unpublished M.A. thesis.

Huddle, Janet Marie. 1989. "The Blue Revolution: The Modernization of Fisheries." Guelph, Ontario: unpublished manuscript. [See the Chapter by Huddle in this book.]

Johnson, Gale. 1985. "Alternatives to International Food Reserves." In FAO (compilers) *World Food Security: Selected Themes and Issues.* Rome: FAO Economic and Social Papers, (53).

Lasswell, Harold. 1936. *Politics: Who Gets What, When and How?* New York: McGraw Hill.

Kent, George. 1984. *The Political Economy of Hunger: The Silent Holocaust.* New York: Praeger.

Keohane, Robert and Joseph Nye. 1977. *Power and Interdependence: World Politics in Transition.* Boston: Little, Brown & Co.

Manghas, Mahar. 1985. "Relative Emphasis on Domestic Food Self-sufficiency and Trade-oriented Self-reliance." In FAO (compilers) *World Food Security: Selected Themes and Issues.* Rome: FAO Economic and Social Papers, (53).

Meadows, Donella H. and Denis Meadows. 1972. *The Limits to Growth.* New York: Universe Books.

Miró, Cármen A. and Daniel Rodríguez. 1982. "Capitalism and Population in Latin American Agriculture." *CEPAL Review.* 16 (April).

Mooney, Pat. 1987. "Plant Breeding Rights Legislation." *Fate of the Earth: Prairie Network News* [Special Edition]. 4 (Summer).

Moore, Barrington, Jr. 1966. *Social Origins of Dictatorship and Democracy: Lord and Peasant in the Making of the Modern World.* Boston: Beacon Press.

Morgenthau, Hans. 1985. *Politics Among Nations: The Struggle for Power and Peace,* Sixth Edition. New York: Knopf.

Nef, Jorge. 1983. "Stalemate and Repression in the Southern Cone: An Interpretive Synopsis." *New Scholar.* 8: 371-385.

Nef, Jorge. 1987. "Alternatives to Development in Contemporary Latin America: An Interpretive Essay on Politics, Ideology and Social Change." *Cahiers GRAL.* (5): 14-23.

Nef, Jorge and O.P. Dwivedi. 1981. "Development Theory and Administration: A Fence Around An Empty Lot?" *Indian Journal of Public Administration.* 27 (1): 42 ff.

Nef, Jorge and Jokelee Vanderkop. 1989a. *Food Systems and Food Security in Latin America and the Caribbean: Politics, Ideology and Technology.* Guelph: Centre for Food Security Research Report Series #1, University of Guelph. [The present chapter, which is Nef and Vanderkop 1989b, is a condensed and edited version of this monograph, which appeared earlier in 1989.]

Nerfin, Marc. 1986. "Neither Prince Nor Merchant Citizen: An Introduction to the Third System." *CEPAL Review* (August): 69 ff.

Nun, José. 1968. "A Latin American Phenomenon: The Middle Class Military Coup." In Petras, James and Maurice Zeitlin (eds.). *Latin America: Reform or Revolution.* New York: Fawcett: 154-185.

O'Donnell, Guillermo. 1973. *Modernization and Bureaucratic Authoritarianism: Studies in South American Politics.* Berkeley, California: Institute of International Studies, University of California.

PanAmerican Health Organization. 1976. *Políticas Nacionales de Alimentación y Nutrición.* Washington, D.C.: Discusiones Tecnicas de la XXIII Reuinión del Consejo Directivo de la OPS. (328).

Piñeiro, Martín. 1987. "The Role of Agriculture Must Be Bolstered." *News IICA.* 4 (3).

RAWOO. 1986. *Food Security in Developing Countries: General Recommendations.* The Hague, Netherlands: RAWOO [Advisory Council for Scientific Research and Development Problems].

Rockefeller, Nelson. 1969. *The Rockefeller Report: U.S. Presidential Mission for the Western Hemisphere.* Chicago, Illinois: Quadrangle Books.

Rodríguez, César, Jerry La Grá, and América Bastidas. 1985.

Formulación de un Plan de Acción a Corto Dentro de un Marco de Seguridad Alimentaria: Marco Teórico. Dominican Republic: IICA.

Swift, Jeannine. 1978. "Food, People and Unemployment: Reasons for Food Problems." *Economic Development in Latin America.* New York: St. Martin's Press: 101-119.

Tuomi, Helena. 1976. "On Food Imports and Neocolonialism." In Harle, Vilho (ed.). *Political Economy of Food.* Tampere: Tampere Peace Research Institute Research Reports, (12). [Proceedings of an International Seminar.]

UNACSTD. 1986. "Technology Applied to Agricultural Development and Related Development Areas." *General Assembly of the United Nations.* New York: UN, Sixth Session, 3-12 February, 1986. United Nations Advisory Committee on Science and Technology for Development.

U.S. Congress. 1974. "Food Security Act of 1974." Washington, D.C.: Joint Hearing, House Committee on Foreign Affairs, 96th Congress, First Session.

Valdés, Alberto (ed.). 1981. *Food Security in Developing Countries.* Boulder, Colorado: Westview Press.

Warnock, John. 1987. *The Politics of Hunger.* Toronto: Methuen.

Wallerstein, Immanuel. 1983. "Crises: The World Economy, the Movements and the Ideologies." In Bergesen, Albert (ed.). *Crises in the World System.* Beverly Hills, California: Sage: 21-36.

Whelan, Eugene. 1981. "Speech at World Food Council Meeting, July, 1981." *Canada Weekly.* (9): 27.

Wise, Timothy. 1987. "The Current Food Crisis in Latin America: A Discussion of de Janvry's `The Agrarian Question.'" *Latin American Perspectives.* 14 (3): 306-312.

World Bank. 1988a. *World Debt Tables: External Debt of Developing Countries, 1987-1988 Edition.* Vol. I. Analysis and Summary Tables. Washington, D.C.: World Bank.

World Food Council. 1979. "World Security for the 1980s." *Report by the Executive Director of the United Nations World Food Council.* New York: United Nations, April 26, 1979.

Part II

COMPARATIVE REGIONAL CASE STUDIES

"THE HARVEST"
A family participates in the rice harvest in Indonesia as part of a traditional communal effort. Such joint work is becoming less frequent due to "proletarianization" and "mechanization."

Photo courtesy of IDRC.

Chapter 3

SOCIO-ECONOMIC AND DEMOGRAPHIC DIFFERENTIATION AMONG SMALLHOLDERS:
IMPLICATIONS FOR TECHNOLOGY DEVELOPMENT AND TRANSFER[1]

Michael D. Schulman
Patricia Garrett

ABSTRACT

This paper examines how socio-economic characteristics differentiate smallholders in a regionally specific segment of small farm strata. Data are based on a sample of ninety smallholders from three North Carolina Piedmont counties. Respondents were predominantly male, black, and involved in growing flue-cured tobacco. Factor analysis revealed five major dimensions of internal stratification: scale, off-farm labour and income, on-farm family labour, demographic characteristics of the farm operator, and land tenure. Four major types of smallholders are distinguished in this sample, and their needs for agricultural technologies are identified. These results challenge the assumption of socio-economic homogeneity that underlies much of the farming systems literature and speak to a major debate in the theoretical literature concerning peasant economy.

A central objective of farming systems research is to develop agricultural technologies appropriate for small-scale producers. Smallholders, however, are a heterogeneous group. To the extent that they are internally stratified and differentiated, they have different needs for agricultural technologies.

Scholars and practitioners long have been aware that available technologies were adopted by some groups of farmers and rejected by others. During the 1950s and 1960s, the diffusion of innovation paradigm was dominant. Differential adaptation (i.e., "early adopters" versus "laggards") was explained by the personal characteristics of producers (Rogers and Burdge, 1972: 349-375). More recently, however, concern has shifted from the social psychology of the user to the characteristics of the technologies themselves (Ashby and Coward, 1980). An increasingly influential thesis is that technologies developed by national and international institutions may be inappropriate for small-scale agriculturalists (Gilbert et al., 1980; Shaner et al.,1982). Consequently, innovations are rejected not because smallholders are "traditional" but because they recognize technologies to be inappropriate.

The contemporary farming systems literature emphasizes the distinction between small-scale and medium-/large-scale producers. This is entirely appropriate. Scale is related not only to how farmers with varying resources combine different crops and animals but also to how they organize the production of the same commodity. Although scale is certainly a fundamental distinction among farmers, it is not the only one. Smallholders who are homogeneous with regard to scale may be differentiated. There is an emerging consensus in the U.S. literature (Buttel, 1981; Carlin and Crecink, 1979; Heffernan et al., 1982; Thompson and Hepp, 1976) that both scale and demographic characteristics are important dimensions along which smallholders differ.

This paper examines how socio-economic characteristics differentiate smallholders in a regionally specific segment of small farm strata. Data are based on a sample of ninety smallholders from three North Carolina Piedmont counties. Respondents were predominantly male, black and involved in growing flue-cured tobacco. Factor analysis revealed five major dimensions of internal stratification: scale, off-farm labour and income, on-farm family labour, demographic characteristics of the farm operator, and land tenure. Four major types of smallholders are distinguished in this sample, and their need for agricultural technologies is identified. These results challenge the assumption of socio-economic homogeneity that underlies much of the farming systems literature. Moreover, the results address a major debate in the literature concerning peasant economy.

Conceptual Framework

In the peasant economy literature, a critical question is the relationship between social class membership and demographic characteristics. Contemporary scholarship is heavily influenced by the political debate between Lenin and Chayanov (Hussain and Tribe, 1981). With the increasing penetration of capitalism in the countryside and emancipation of the serfs, rural communities in Russia experienced new pressures for change. Lenin (1967) argued that the long-term consequences would be polarization of communities and the eventual development of two classes—landless labourers and capitalist farmers. Increasing orientation to commercial or commodity production would encourage the reorganization of agriculture, specifically leasing land and hiring labour. Market involvement with concomitant indebtedness would make producers vulnerable to economic and/or climatic variations. Under these circumstances, impoverishment and land loss could be rapid. At the community level, these changes would restructure social relations and destroy traditional levelling mechanisms that redistributed resources from the affluent to the needy. Polarization along class lines would occur within communities.

An opposing interpretation was provided by Chayanov and the Russian populists (Chayanov, 1966; Shanin, 1972). A central thesis was that the rationale of peasant economies differed from that of capitalist firms. The assumption was that peasants organize production to meet consumption needs. Consequently, how much peasants produce is determined principally by the number of mouths to be fed. After basic consumption needs are met, peasants weigh the drudgery of labour against the value of increased production and decide whether to produce a surplus. In this argument, demographic factors, notably the number of household members and the amount of household labour, are critical.

Chayanov (1966) argued that communities like the Russian

mir periodically redistributed productive resources to households that needed more land. Consequently, access to land changed in a predictable pattern over the domestic life cycle, as households received lands consistent with the number of able-bodied workers. Superior access to productive resources, therefore, was a temporary rather than a permanent aspect of rural social organization.

The influence of both Lenin and Chayanov is reflected in contemporary theorizing (Harrison, 1977; Hussain and Tribe, 1981; Shanin, 1973, 1974). Those whose principal concern is with proletarianization tend to work in the Leninist tradition (e.g., de Janvry, 1980), emphasizing the penetration of capitalism as a mode of production, with the attendant consequences of differentiation and class formation. By contrast, those who are impressed with the persistence of the peasantry (e.g., Shanin, 1973, 1974) and the resilience of petty commodity production (e.g., Friedmann, 1980) typically cast the argument in recognizably Chayanovian terms (Hunt, 1979). Others (e.g., Banaji, 1976; Lehmann, 1980) search for a synthesis.

At a theoretical level, one can argue that a process of differentiation and class formation is occurring and that this process varies throughout a demographic cycle. To make such an argument, one would need evidence that demographic composition and household labour can be empirically distinguished from characteristics of the farming enterprise and off-farm employments. These dimensions are empirically distinguishable in data collected from smallholders in three Piedmont counties of North Carolina.

METHODOLOGY

Samples of smallholders in three North Carolina Piedmont counties were selected via a complex multistage procedure.[2] A total of 107 smallholders fell into the sample, and 90 operator interviews were completed. Male and female heads of household were interviewed, and the questionnaire covered crop production, allocation of labour on-farm, off-farm employment, contact with extension, and attitudes. All data pertain to the 1981 agricultural year.

This is an extremely interesting sample because it represents a subset of North American smallholders rarely studied. It includes full- and part-time farmers, the vast majority of whom are black (82%) and male (95%). On the average, the sample is middle-aged and poorly educated. As Table 1 illustrates, the mean number of acres farmed, both owned and rented, was 30.4 and a majority of respondents (77%) reported that they farmed some land they did not own. Tobacco, which is labour-intensive, was the predominant crop.[3] The majority (92%) of respondents grew tobacco, which occupied 22 percent of owned and leased land.

Although tobacco production is labour-intensive, approximately half (54%) of the farm operators had an off-farm job, mostly in operative and craftsmen/kindred worker occupations. Thirty-five operators (39%) reported having a spouse with an off-farm job, primarily in operative or service positions. Children worked off the farm in many (25%) sample households. More than 70 percent of smallholders reported that children and spouses worked on the farm. Hired labour was relatively unimportant.

Sixty-two percent of the smallholders reported that wages or salary were a source of family income. Average gross farm income (1981) was $14,759, and average net farm income was $2,520. Ten respondents reported that costs exceeded income, and sixteen reported that they broke even. Mean total off-farm family income was $9,103, and mean total family income from farm and non-farm sources was $14,135. Average farm debt was $9,017, and the vast majority (84%) of respondents used some form of credit during the 1981 agricultural year.

In summary, the sample has several characteristics generally recognized to be important issues for smallholders anywhere in the world — ethnic minorities with limited landbases and resources choosing labour-intensive crops and earning cash income by combining cash crop production and wage labour. The data obviously exhibit a specificity that derives from the historical experience of sample households in North Carolina Piedmont. Nevertheless, data analysis provides a rare opportunity to raise, if not answer, questions central to the analysis of small-scale agricultural production.

Data Analysis

Factor analysis is used to delineate the dimensions of internal stratification for the smallholder sample. This procedure is a technique by which the regularity and order in phenomena can be discerned. It identifies distinct patterns of relationships among a set of variables. Each pattern appears as a factor depicting a distinct cluster of interrelated data. The number of factors represent the number of substantively meaningful patterns of relationships and the factor loadings measure the degree and direction of variables within each pattern. Consequently, the first factor delineates the largest pattern of relationship in the data; the second factor represents the next largest pattern, etc. Oblique rotation (promax) is used because it does not force the factors to be orthogonal when they actually are intercorrelated (Rummel, 1970).

A set of variables, all with reference to the 1981 agricultural year, is utilized to measure internal stratification and is included in the factor analysis. Principal variables and their indicators are:

> Income: gross farm, total family, and total off-farm family income;
> Debt: money borrowed during agricultural year, total farm debt;
> Land tenure: total acres owned, total acres leased and rented;
> Dummy variable for tobacco allotment ownership: yes or no;
> Household's allocation of labour: days of on-farm and off-farm labour by operator and spouse; days of on-farm labour by other household members;
> Demographic characteristics: Total household size; education, years farming and age of farm operator.

Table 2 presents the results of the factor analysis. Five factors with eigenvalues of 1.0 or greater were identified.[4] The first factor represents the scale of the farm enterprise. Tobacco production variables load the highest, followed by gross farm income, money borrowed, total farm debt, and days worked on the farm by the operator. The second factor represents off-farm labour and income. Total off-farm family income loads the highest, followed by total family income and the number of days of off-farm work by the farm operator and spouse. The dummy variable measuring non-ownership of tobacco allotments has a moderate negative loading on this factor.

The third factor represents family labour on the farm. The number of days of on-farm labour by the spouse and by other family members load well, as does total household size. The fourth factor is demographic, and it represents the age, education, and years farming of the operator. The fifth factor represents land tenure. Total number of acres owned and total farm debt load the highest, followed by the dummy variable for tobacco allotment ownership and total acres leased/rented.

The five factors represent relatively independent dimensions along which the smallholders studied differed. As Table 3 demonstrates, inter-factor correlations are uniformly low. Variables measuring scale and off-farm income/labour load on different factors (1 and 2 respectively), thereby indicating that farm and family are relatively independent dimensions of work and income within the smallholder sample. Household labour can be analytically separated into off-farm (factor 2) and on-farm (factor 3) activities. All of these dimensions are distinguishable from the demographic characteristics of the operator (factor 4) and land tenure (factor 5).

Discussion

Data analysis demonstrated that the smallholders studied are a heterogeneous group. Moreover, this heterogeneity is itself complex, as reflected in the identification of five relatively independent factors. These results have important implications for farming systems research because they question the assumption of socio-economic homogeneity which underlies the concept of "recommendation domains" (Shaner et al., 1982: 215).

Scale is the first and most important dimension of internal stratification among the smallholders studied. Another factor is land tenure, and both relate to the access smallholders enjoy to productive resources. Other important dimensions along which smallholders differ reflect differences in household composition, off-farm and on-farm labour, and demographic characteristics of the operator. These dimensions affect the availability and allocation of labour, which, in turn, influence the adoptability of technology. It is not merely that each farm is unique. Rather, it is that systematic differences exist among farm families, which derive jointly from social class position and stage in the domestic life cycle. Such patterns have been objects of considerable theoretical inquiry by students of peasant economy because following the tradition of Lenin and Chayanov, a central intellectual concern has been to determine the relative importance of social class and demographic factors in the organization of agricultural enterprises.

This general concern has specific applied implications for work with the smallholders studied in the North Carolina Piedmont. Theoretical and empirical analyses provide the basis for creating a typology of smallholders, and detailed information on their current farming systems suggests appropriate interventions for each strata. Guidelines for research and extension emerge from this analysis.

In the North Carolina Piedmont sample, one identifiable category of smallholders has adequate land, secure tenure, ownership of tobacco allotments, and access to adequate family labour. These smallholders realistically can expect to remain in tobacco production, if the current allotment program is not dismantled. This defines the parameters for technical research and suggests that agronomic research focus on technologies that decrease the costs of production and maintain yields at approximately current levels. Males are principally responsible for tobacco cultivation, but the participation of women and children is marked, especially during periods of peak labour demand (Garrett et al., 1984). Consequently, a comprehensive evaluation of promising technologies would study the seasonality of labour, relating the labour demands of new cultural practices and the availability of jobs for all household members in the regional labour market. Initial analyses of the North Carolina agronomic data suggest that operators fail to perform tasks at the most opportune time, and this may be caused by off-farm commitments. To serve the needs of smallholders in Category 1, an ideal team would combine agronomic scientists specializing in tobacco production and agricultural economists familiar with production economics and regional labour markets.

The second category of smallholders identifiable in the North

Carolina sample has a less adequate landbase, no ownership of tobacco allotments, and adequate access to household labour. The central distinction between Categories I and II is socio-economic, because Category I has superior access to land in general and to land for tobacco production in particular. These differences are critical because they suggest that extension workers should facilitate the transition of Category II farmers from tobacco to alternative crops. Tobacco is both labour-intensive and high value, so viable alternatives must have similar characteristics. Vegetable and fruit production may be particularly attractive. For example, one acre of strawberries in North Carolina can provide almost the same income as one acre of flue-cured tobacco (Adams, 1981). Nevertheless, vegetable and fruit operations may pose the same problems of seasonality as tobacco, suggesting the importance of analysing labour availability in relation to the limits of tolerable variation for specific tasks and crops. Ultimately, an alternative that appears promising from a socio-economic perspective must be evaluated in an ecological context. Physical conditions like the ecology of the farm and its location in relation to market infrastructure are critical determinants of what is appropriate for individual growers. An ideal team of work with this category of smallholders would include crop scientists specializing in different vegetables and fruits, and agricultural economists specializing in production economics and marketing, including "You Pick" operations.

A third category of smallholders in the Piedmont sample is defined by the importance of off-farm employment to household income and the scarcity of family labour for farm enterprises. It is the availability of both labour and land that are critical factors limiting agricultural alternatives. Households with large and superior landbases might consider crops or livestock enterprises with low labor inputs. Limited resource households, however, would need to adopt a nonagricultural strategy. Both subgroups benefit greatly from programs that integrate farm and nonfarm alternatives. Especially beneficial are programs fomenting community development, employment generation, and job retraining. For young families, agricultural programs can complement community development programs, especially if they emphasize production of crops and/or livestock to be consumed on-farm. Work with youth, especially through 4-H, is also important, and home economists can complement the agriculture and youth components, emphasizing food preparation and nutrition education. Those serving Category III might define women and youth as their priority constituents, something that would be entirely inappropriate for teams service Category I and II households. An ideal team for Category III households would include professionals and paraprofessionals with expertise in gardening, animal raising, and food preparation/storage.

The fourth category of smallholder is elderly, with limited resource bases, and no dependable access to free labour. Income from agricultural production is likely to be relatively less important than income from social welfare programs like foodstamps or social security. Nevertheless, the farm is a resource, and it is particularly important that these smallholders be able to pass the legacy of farming to a new generation (Groger, 1983). The legalities of inheritance are critical. Smallholders in general and blacks in particular may not hold clear title to lands and may lack adequate wills (Browne, 1973). Land loss by blacks is a serious personal and social problem throughout the South (Salamon, 1976), and the unmet legal needs of elderly, black smallholders contribute to land loss. An ideal team to deal with smallholders in Category IV would include social welfare workers who can facilitate access to public services and lawyers who can clear land titles and prepare wills.

Comparison of these four categories of North Carolina smallholders illustrates that there is variation across categories not only in the emphasis of agricultural research and extension activities but also in the disciplinary composition of an ideal team. These principles can themselves be placed within a broader framework.

The theoretical literature from which this paper is derived is seldom cited by practitioners of farming systems research. Nevertheless, it is entirely germane because researchers need to consider the influence of the domestic life cycle and its interaction with social class to develop appropriate agricultural technologies. The results of this empirical analysis strongly suggest that social class and life cycle factors are independent and important dimensions along which smallholders differ. Further research must explore this relationship both theoretically and empirically before it is prudent to assume that recommendation domains with homogeneous socioeconomic characteristics can exist.

Table 1

CHARACTERISTICS OF THE NORTH CAROLINA SMALLHOLDER SAMPLE:

1981 Agricultural Year

DEMOGRAPHIC VARIABLE

Average Age	50.2 years
Average Education	8.9 years
Ethnicity	82% Black
Gender	95% Male

LABOUR VARIABLES

Mean days on-farm work, farm operator	229
Mean days on-farm work, spouse	135
Mean days on-farm work, other family	244
Mean days off-farm work, farm operator	127
Mean days off-farm work, spouse	135
Mean days off-farm work, other family	105
Mean days hired help	31

ACREAGE VARIABLES

Mean total acres farmed	30.4
Mean total acres tobacco (92% grow)	6.7
Mean total acres corn (68% grow)	7.1
Mean total acres small grains (41% grow)	9.7
Mean total acres soybeans (24% grow)	10.2

PRODUCTION VARIABLES

Mean tobacco yield	1706 lbs/acre
Mean corn yield	2294 lbs/acre
Mean small grain (wheat) yield	3573 lbs/acre
Mean soybean yield	2124 lbs/acre

INCOME VARIABLES

Mean money borrowed	$ 3,983
Mean total farm debt	9,017
Mean gross farm income	14,759
Mean net farm income	2,520
Mean total off-farm family income	9,103
Mean total family income (all sources)	14,135

Table 2

ROTATED FACTOR PATTERN*
SAMPLE OF NORTH CAROLINA SMALLHOLDERS
IN THREE PIEDMONT COUNTIES

	1	2	3	4		5
	Scale	Off-farm	Family Labour	Demographic	Land Tenure	h2
Gross farm income	(0.782)	-0.075	-0.050	0.020	-0.023	0.65
Total family income	0.050	(0.833)	-0.058	0.088	0.091	0.72
Total off-farm income	-0.118	(0.840)	0.033	-0.060	-0.080	0.75
Total farm debt (.456)	0.097	0.020	-0.221	(0.543)		0.63
Money borrowed (.673)	0.034	0.104	0.045	0.247		0.55
Total acres owned -.140	-0.231	-0.109	-0.147	(0.537)		0.32
Total acres rented .151	-0.044	0.010	-0.166	-(0.401)		0.20
Ownership of tobacco allotment (0=yes; 1=no)	-0.135	-(0.355)	-0.020	-0.269	-(0.450)	0.40
Total acres tobacco production	(0.945)	-0.029	-0.085	-0.046	-0.163	0.91
Total pounds tobacco production	(0.952)	0.009	-0.089	-0.004	-0.197	0.91
Education, farm operator	-0.075	0.036	-0.095	-(0.663)	0.201	0.51
Days off-farm work, farm operator	-0.109	(0.704)	0.136	-0.211	-0.103	0.60
Days off-farm work, spouse	0.025	(0.389)	-0.290	-0.161	0.035	0.31
Days on-farm work, farm operator	(0.383)	-0.200	0.222	0.030	0.032	0.31
Days on-farm work, spouse	0.046	0.114	(0.511)	0.140	-0.158	0.25
Years farming	-0.130	0.004	-0.136	(0.552)	0.148	0.38
Age, farm operator	0.010	-0.141	0.031	(0.686)	0.100	0.51
Household size	-0.052	0.008	(0.837)	-0.099	-0.010	0.73
Days on-farm work by other family members	0.061	-0.137	(0.730)	-0.064	0.057	0.64
Eigenvalues	3.93	2.40	1.82	1.14	1.00	

*Promax (oblique). Only factors with eigenvalues in excess of 1.0 were computed. Loadings greater than an absolute value of .350 are shown in parentheses. Loadings can be interpreted as standardized regression coefficients.

Table 3

INTER-FACTOR CORRELATION MATRIX

	Factor 1	Factor 2	Factor 3	Factor 4	Factor 5
Factor 1 Scale	1.0				
Factor 2 Off-Farm	-0.196	1.0			
Factor 3 Family Labour	0.137	-0.206	1.0		
Factor 4 Demographic	-0.045	-0.165	-0.187	1.0	
Factor 5 Land Tenure	0.043	0.167	0.073	-0.103	1.0

NOTES

1 Revised version of paper presented at the Farming Systems Research Symposium, Kansas State University, Manhattan, KS, October 7-10, 1984. This research received support from the North Carolina State University Title XII Strengthening Grant (AID/DSAN-XII-G-103) funded jointly by the U.S. Agency for International Development and the North Carolina Agricultural Research Service and conducted in collaboration with the North Carolina Agricultural Extension Service and the North Carolina A&T State University (Greensboro). Data analysis and interpretation were also supported by the North Carolina Agricultural Foundation. The opinions expressed are those of the authors, who would like to thank S. E. Szabo and R. Luginbuhl for assistance in data collection and analysis and C. B. Flora for substantive suggestions.

2 In Caswell County, the sample of smallholders is based upon those farmers who were participating in an Extension paraprofessional program during 1981. These were farmers who were under 65 and who had under $20,000 in annual gross farm sales. In Person and Granville Counties, samples of smallholders were drawn. First, census enumeration districts within each county were selected at random. Second, all farmers within each district were administered a short screening questionnaire. The sample of smallholders was drawn from the information collected by the screening questionnaire. A smallholder was eligible if he/she met the following criteria: 1) gross farm sales of $20,000 or less in 1981; 2) farm operator 65 years of age or less; 3) agriculture a significant part (20 percent) of total family income. A fourth criterion, working less than 100 days off the farm for pay, was dropped after the screening data revealed that farmers meeting the other criteria were bimodal with regard to off-farm work: one group had less than 100 days, but another group had more than 200 days. It was decided to keep in the sample the group working 200 or more days off-farm for pay. A total of 107 smallholders fell into the sample: 27 in Caswell, 41 in Person, and 39 in Granville County. Ninety interviews were completed: 21 in Caswell, 37 in Person, and 32 in Granville (Schulman and Luginbuhl, 1982).

3 According to USDA (1977), the average labour hours per acre required to produce tobacco was 281 (1971-75). In comparison, it was 5.1 for corn, 2.9 for wheat, 23.0 for cotton, and 161.5 for tomatoes.

4 Factor analysis should not be confused with an analysis of variance from a factorial experimental design. The five factor solution from the North Carolina smallholder data was an empirical result and was not determined or designed *a priori*. The eigenvalue rule of thumb, a scree test of the change in eigenvalues, and a chi-square test of a maximum likelihood factor solution all confirmed that the five factor solution was correct for the North Carolina data.

REFERENCES

Adams, Frank. 1981. "Vegetable and fruit crops: Viable alternatives for tobacco farmers." Pp. 93-102 in William Finger (ed.), *The Tobacco Industry in Transition*. Lexington, MA: Lexington Books.

Ashby, Jacqueline A., and E. Walter Coward, Jr. 1980. "Putting agriculture back into the study of farm practice innovation: Comment on status, knowledge, and innovation." *Rural Sociology*. 45 (3) :520-23.

Banaji, Jarius. 1976. "Chayanov, Kautsky, Lenin: Considerations towards a synthesis." *Economic and Political Weekly*. 9 (40): 1594-1607.

Browne, Robert S. 1973. *Only Six Million Acres: The Decline of Black Owned Land in the Rural South*. New York, NY: Black Economic Research Center.

Buttel, Frederick H. 1981. *Toward a Typology of Small Farms: A Preliminary Empirical Analysis*. Ithaca, NY: Cornell University. Rural Sociology Bulletin Series No. 116.

Carlin, Thomas A. and John Crecink. 1979. "Small farm definition and public policy." *American Journal of Agricultural Economics*. 61 (5): 933-939.

Chayanov, A. V. 1966. *The Theory of Peasant Economy*. Homewood, IL: Richard D. Irwin, Inc.

de Janvry, Alain. 1980. "Social differentiation in agriculture and the ideology of neopopulism." Pp. 155-168 in Frederick H. Buttel and Howard Newby (eds.), *The Rural Sociology of Advanced Societies: Critical Perspectives*. Montclair, NJ: Allanheld, Osmun.

Friedmann, Harriet. 1980. "Household production and the national economy: Concepts for the analysis of agrarian formations." *Journal of Peasant Studies*. 7 (2): 158-184.

Garrett, Patricia, Michael D. Schulman, and Damayanthi Herath. 1984. "Decision Making and Division of Labor in a Poor Tobacco Growing Area of North Carolina: A Male/Female Comparison." Unpublished paper presented at the Annual Meetings of the Rural Sociological Society. College Station, TX. August.

Gilbert, E. H., D. W. Norman, and E. E. Winch. 1980. *Farming Systems Research: A Critical Appraisal.* East Lansing, MI: Michigan State University. Rural Development Paper No. 6.

Groger, B. Lisa. 1983. "Growing old with or without it: The meaning of land in a rural community." *Research on Aging.* 5 (4): 511-526.

Harrison, Mark. 1977. "Resource allocation and agrarian class formation: The problem of social mobility among Russian peasant households, 1880-1930." *Journal of Peasant Studies.* (2): 127-161.

Heffernan, William D., Gary Green, Paul Lasley, and Michael F. Noland. 1982. "Small farms: A heterogeneous category." *The Rural Sociologist.* 2 (2): 62-71.

Hunt, Diana. 1979. "Chayanov's model of peasant household resource allocation." *Journal of Peasant Studies.* 6 (3): 247-285.

Hussain, Athar, and Keith Tribe. 1981. *Marxism and the Agrarian Question.* Vol. 2. *Russian Marxism and the Peasantry, 1861-1930.* Atlantic Highland, NJ: Humanities Press.

Lehmann, David. 1980. "Ni Chayanov ni Lenin: Apuntes sobre la teoria de la economia campesina." *Estudios Rurales Latinoamericanos.* 3 (1): 5-23.

Lenin, V. I. 1967. *The Development of Capitalism in Russia.* Moscow: Progress Publishers.

Rogers, Everett M., and Rabel J. Burdge. 1972. *Social Change in Rural Societies.* Second Edition. Englewood Cliffs, NJ: Prentice-Hall.

Rummel, R. J. 1970. *Applied Factor Analysis.* Evanston, IL: Northwestern University Press.

Salamon, Lester M. 1976. *Land and Minority Enterprise: The Crisis and the Opportunity.* Washington, DC: U.S. Department of Commerce. Office of Minority Business.

Schulman, Michael D., and Regina Luginbuhl. 1982. *The Small Farmer in North Carolina: Attitudes and Beliefs Toward Agriculture.* Raleigh, NC: North Carolina State University. International Programs Paper No. 4.

Shaner, W. W., P. F. Philipp, and W. R. Schmehl. 1982. *Farming Systems Research and Development: Guidelines for Developing Countries.* Boulder, CO: Westview Press.

Shanin, Teodor. 1972. *The Awkward Class: Political Sociology of Peasantry in a Developing Society: Russia 1910-1925.* London: Oxford University Press.

Shanin, Teodor. 1973. "The nature and logic of the peasant economy. Part I." *Journal of Peasant Studies.* 1 (1): 63-80.

Shanin, Teodor. 1974. "The nature and logic of the peasant economy. Parts II and III." *Journal of Peasant Studies.* 1 (2): 186-197.

Thompson, Ronald, and Ralph Hepp. 1976. *Description and Analysis of Michigan Small Farms.* East Lansing, MI: Michigan State University. Michigan Cooperative Extension Research Report No. 296.

United States Department of Agriculture (USDA). 1977. *Agriculture Statistics 1976.* Washington, DC: U.S. Government Printing Office.

Chapter 4

SAGO, LAW AND FOOD SECURITY ON AMBON

Franz von Benda-Beckmann

I. Introduction

> *In some parts of the archipelago, nature has distributed her gifts so freely that man can provide in his livelihood needs with a minimum of labour. This in particular holds true for those regions in which sago palms occur in such abundance that they provide the staple diet for the population. ... It is certain that the bad economic conditions are to a large extent due to the easy conditions of life which the Moluccans have thanks to the sago palm* (Ruinen, 1921: 24).

This statement, dating from colonial times, suggests a problematic relationship between food security and economic development, development understood as modernization and commercialization of agriculture leading to higher rates of productivity. Though it may be exaggerated to infer a rigid causal connection from the quotation, the suggestion is that the ecological and economic conditions that provide the Ambonese with a carefree life, at least a life without hunger, are also responsible for the "bad" economic conditions outside the sphere of food provision. And it is obvious that the Dutch commentator's value judgment inclines him to give priority to the improvement of the economic conditions; his further remarks on the potentials of a more commercially oriented exploitation of sago, and his references to more industrious Indonesian groups exporting sago to Singapore, make that clear enough.

Recent analyses of food security experts suggest the same problematic, albeit seen from the other end. Where there is economic development, food insecurity increases (Barraclough, 1986: 15). There are numerous examples showing that rapid expansions of agriculture and agro-exports have been accompanied by a spectacular growth of the GNP, but also by food insecurity for larger sections of the population (Barraclough, 1986: 12). Optimistic expectations about the general enhancement of the welfare of the poorer sections of the population through increased agricultural productivity seem to be unwarranted (ESCAP, 1985). There is even evidence to show "that malnutrition increases as cash-cropping cultivation increases and as farmers neglect subsistence food production for monetary incomes" (MacPhearson and Midgley, 1987: 46). Some analysts even tend to generalize "that the food systems that have maintained humankind throughout most of its history are disintegrating before other forms of economic activity are able to offer alternative means of livelihood to the displaced peasantry" (Barraclough, 1986: 15, Pearse, 1980).

While the general validity of such statements may be questioned, the suggestion that subsistence food production may be an important element in food security, and of social security in a more general sense, is an important one.[1] Yet subsistence food production has not been given much attention in the context of social security and food security policies. This is largely due to two closely related reasons.

1. Problems of food security and hunger in third world countries generally are addressed retrospectively. There is hunger, there are food shortages, and appropriate measures have to be taken in order to overcome the problem. Also in the wider field of social and social security policies, the major themes discussed in the field of food security are curative measures, and most attention is given to the devising of risk prevention systems that may cover such failures (see Savy, 1972; ESCAP, 1985).

2. Besides, agricultural policies are heavily biassed towards increasing productivity and income. The curative measures of social security policies and projects follow this trend. They are generally focussed upon income generating activities of the poor.[2] Projects are set up to overcome the thresholds of hunger and poverty by providing inputs for income generating activities for the poor (see Midgley, 1984; MacPhearson and Midgley, 1987;

Reidy, 1980; K. von Benda-Beckmann, 1988). Not only are such programs oriented towards the market economy, they also contribute to an increasing monetization of the relations of production through a grand scale infusion of money through financial credit. Social security policies thus are heavily biassed at raising the *general level of welfare,* and much less at redistributive activities on whichever level of welfare. Since most measures are directed at, and presuppose, persons who have sufficient physical and mental capacities to engage in income generating activities, those who lack those capacities will generally not be reached and will have to depend on the local non-state mechanisms of (food)help and redistribution (see F. von Benda-Beckmann et al., 1988: 19).

Where the large scale extension of state-regulated social security schemes for the rural population is planned, the schemes also presuppose a money economy. Most social security policies, like in Indonesia, are premised upon the idea that whatever social security measures may be devised for self-employed farmers or paid agricultural workers, the costs of the system will have ultimately to be carried by them.[3]

This emphasis on income generating activities leads, in analysis and policy, to a general policy preference for market-oriented economic activities. Little attention is given to situations where current food provision is not an acute problem, but where the maintenance of subsistence activities may be an important objective of economic and social security policy. Therefore, few social security strategies, and food security strategies in particular, make the protection or development of non-market activities their primary goal. In other words, there is little attention to subsistence production as an integral part of the economy which is particularly important for social security.

These economic policy preferences also find their reflection in legal policies. Here one also finds the attempts to introduce or to expand a legal framework which is considered to be particularly appropriate for a market-oriented economy, a framework in which emphasis is accorded to individualized property relations and to the creation of property forms which can be given as securities for credit loans.[4] Legal forms in which communality and obligations of reciprocity and redistribution are emphasized, are deemed an obstacle for market-orientated economic activities. New forms of communality and mutual help are invented which tend to stress communal forms of production and aim at raising the general level of welfare. Redistributive elements within the organization of production are then reduced to a newly created regulatory sphere of charitable matters. Social security policy becomes, as it were, the cleaning lady for the debris left by "economic" development. Even if Macarov's motto of the "Unholy alliance between work and welfare" (1980) still may not be completely fitting the intended conditions in rural areas, we can see that the general idea is at least one of "market production and welfare" — an alliance which may be as problematic as the coupling between wage labour and welfare schemes.

II. Sago and Food Security on Ambon

The case of food security on Ambon, which I shall discuss in this paper, is an instructive example that allows us to look at the problem of food security/insecurity from a different and more integrative perspective than is usually taken.

As the quotation above indicates, there has been little food insecurity on Ambon. The basic elements guaranteeing food security were the availability of sago and fish. This goes for the sago growing villages on the island Ambon itself, together with the availability of a huge sago reserve on the close by and sparsely populated island of Seram which has constituted the sago reservoir for the more densely populated islands of Ambon and Lease for centuries (see Ellen, 1979; Knaap, 1987; Krause-Katerla, 1986; Taale, 1988).[5]

This is not to say that the Ambonese village economy was one of pure subsistence only. Being one of the legendary spice islands, Ambonese villages have for centuries had a mixed economy in which subsistence activities, like fishing and the exploitation of sago palms, have been 'interwoven' (Elwert, 1980b) with the production of spices, cloves and nutmeg in particular, for non-regional commodity markets. The politico-legal frameworks for these productive activities have varied considerably, and so have the ways in which profits from clove production have been distributed over producers, traders, civil servants and state institutions. It has been carried out on the basis of tributory obligations, trade treaties under the monopoly of the Dutch East Indies Company, under the system of forced production and distribution (*cultuurstelsel*), free trade and trade via state co-operatives.[6]

Neither was the Ambonese food economy purely subsistence oriented. Rice and wheat flour, for instance, have been imported for centuries. Also for centuries, the demand for sago as a foodstuff has varied considerably with the availability of alternative food, such as rice and wheat flour, and, given the commercial character of these imported foodstuffs, with the capacity of the local population to buy these food stuffs. The varying income from tree crop sales, and the price of rice, have more or less always been of influence on the level of production and consumption of sago by the local population.

Within this mixed economy, the production and distribution of sago has largely kept its subsistence character throughout the centuries. Non-monetized access to sago on the basis of ownership or share-harvesting agreements has been the rule; excess production was accidental rather than intended. But there was usually a relatively secure supply of sago above the level necessary for the consumptive needs of the direct producers which could be used to cater for the needs of the "unproductive" members in the villages, a requirement for food security in subsistence-oriented food systems (see Schott, 1988: 101). Sago trade has played a changing role in the Central Moluccan region (see Ellen, 1979; Krause-Katerla, 1986; Knaap, 1987). But for villages on Ambon without permanent sago self-sufficiency, access to sago gardens on Seram has been based largely on inter-village friendship/kinship bonds (*pela*, see Bartels, 1977) or on large scale collective sago production expeditions of a group of villagers on the basis of share-harvesting.

In the contemporary Moluccas, sago still plays an important role as foodstuff. Recent estimates of the consumption of staple food by the Central Moluccan population give a general indication of the significance of sago in contemporary Ambon. Expressed in kg of rice equivalents per year, the per capita consumption in the Central Moluccas of 211 compares well with the average consumption in Indonesia of 187. However, of the 211 kg almost one half, i.e., 104 kg, is sago (NEI 1982: 18). This level of intake is just above the minimum requirements as established by the WHO (NEI, 1982: 18). Sago is rich in calories, but has hardly any protein and fats.[7] But served with other food added, fish in particular, it is no less nutritious than other food; there is no danger to the nutritional standard of the population.[8] Sago compares very well with all other crops in terms of energy produced per man-day and per hectare (LTA 72, 1983: 4.3).

Except for this relevance in actual food consumption, the availability of more sago than is currently consumed still constitutes a safety-net for times in which the acquisition of other foodstuffs may be more costly and difficult.

As far as it is based upon sago, the Ambonese food system to a high degree exhibits the five characteristics of food security specified by Barraclough (1986: 16):

1. The capacity to generate sufficient internal food supply;
2. Reliability, so that seasonal and cyclical variations are minimized;
3. A maximum of autonomy and self-determination, reducing its vulnerability to international market fluctuations;
4. Long-term stability; the production base — the ecosystem — must be conserved and improved;
5. The care for equity, the provision of a dependable access to adequate food by all social groups.

In my paper I shall examine the socio-economic characteristics of sago production and distribution. I shall try to pinpoint those elements in the system in which the food security is embedded. As I shall illustrate with material from the village of Hila,[9] this security lies in a specific form of subsistence production.[10] This specificity derives to some extent from the botanical and ecological character of sago and from the technology employed in sago production. But it also derives from the specific legal regime under which people have access to sago and under which sago is produced and distributed (Cf. Sen, 1981). In my analysis I shall try to elucidate the relation between the elements of food security and the normative system which structures food production, processing and distribution, and discuss the question how this relation would be affected by legal, economic or technical change.

III. The Importance of Sago in Hila

1. General socio-economic and political conditions

Location

Hila, the village where my wife and I carried out field research in 1985 and 1986, is situated at the northern coast of Leihitu, the northern peninsula of Ambon island.[11] The village territory comprises an area of 20 square kilometres. It includes a narrow, flat, coastal area in which the settlements are located. 2,407 ethnically Ambonese are living in the Ambonese core village, and another 1,700 Butonese immigrants[12] live in three separate settlements on the village territory (1985). In the coastal area one finds coconut and sago palms, and most of the gardens in which villagers grow vegetables, beans, cassava and groundnuts. A large part of the coastal area consists of clove tree gardens. The rest of the village territory is hilly, even mountainous, covered with secondary forest and newly cultivated gardens.

Political organization

Ever since the Dutch East Indies Company ordered the Ambonese population living in the mountains to settle in coastal villages during the second half of the 17th century, the political organization has been an amalgam of adat principles and government regulations. The most influential government institutions were, and are, the *raja*, the village chief, and the *kepala soa*, the heads of the *soa* (clan associations). Traditionally, the village chief was assisted by the village council, *saniri negeri*, consisting of the *soa* and *dati* heads (*dati* being land holding clan-segments), a village secretary and some other officials such as the *kewang*, the village forest overseer. Since Indonesia's independence, various local government reforms have followed each other, introducing new governmental bodies on the village level. Following the most recent local government legislation of 1979, the LKMD (*Lembaga Ketahanan Masyarakat Desa*) was introduced as the new official village council, with the LMD (*Lembaga Masyarakat Desa*) as a sort of first chamber. The *raja* and *kepala soa* have been integrated into these new governmental bodies as chairman and members of the LMD.

Social organization

The village organization is largely based upon kinship. Kinship is structured by the two overlapping principles of patrilinearity and bilaterality. The patrilineal principle is the dominant principle determining membership in the clan (*rumah tau* or *fam*), the *dati*, the *soa*-clan association and the village. For most other purposes, however, villagers' kinship relations are based upon bilaterlality. The descendants of all four grandparents are considered to be kin. Also important, if less extended, are affinal relationships. At least one's spouse's parents and their descendants are considered to be close kin.

Co-residence is mainly based upon relations of descent and marriage. Post-marital virilocal residence is the culturally and statistically dominant form; however, residence rules and arrangements are rather flexible. The size and composition of houses vary considerably. From a series of in-depth house-interviews[13] it appeared that the number of persons living in one house varied between 2 and 17.[14] In the 48 houses chosen for in-depth interviews, the composition of inhabitants was as follows:

Composition of houses	Frequency	
	Total	Percentage
one two-generation family	24	50.0%
two two-generation families	2	4.2%
three two-generation families	1	2.1%
one grandparent couple plus one two-generation family	13	27.0%
one grandparent couple plus two two-generation families	7	14.0%
two grandparent couples plus two two-generation families	1	2.1%

Consumptive units — a group of persons who use one kitchen for the preparation of food for themselves and who eat together[15] — are in most parts formed by a nuclear — parent-children — family living in one house. Thus 24 or 50% of the houses in our sample had one kitchen.

In those cases where more than one nuclear family live

together, e.g., two or more married brothers, sons and daughters with son-in-law, or married grandparents, they may or may not share one kitchen. The grandparents in those cases often share a kitchen with one of their children's nuclear family. Widowed grandparents living together with one of their children (married or unmarried) usually share their kitchen with them. Apart from close kin, foster-children, distant relatives living temporarily in the house join one of the kitchens. Of the 24 houses in which more than one nuclear family lived in one house, 8 (or 33%) had more than one kitchen: two kitchens in 6 houses, and three kitchens in 2 houses.

This is, however, a static picture which only gives a general indication of house composition and kitchen structure. Both house composition and kitchen structure, the structure of consumptive units, are flexible and change with the developmental cycle of the family members, and with the quality of social relations between them. The latter aspect usually plays a role in those cases where sons get married and the question arises whether a son's mother and his daughter(s) or daughter(s)-in-law are going to share a kitchen. Having one kitchen for 15 persons, including for instance three married couples, is seen as a sign of good relations. If sisters or daughters-in-law establish their own kitchen this indicates a strained relationship.

The number of kitchens per house usually expands and contracts over time. For an illustration, take the house of our neighbours, a grandparent couple with 6 children, two of whom were just married when they moved into their newly built stone house in 1978. During the first years they had only one kitchen, and this was maintained when the sons started to get their first children. When the third son married, the daughter-in-law moved in, but she had difficulties with her mother-in-law and the wives of her husband's brothers. The young couple therefore moved out into the original family house where the couple established their own kitchen. Gradually, the two remaining daughters-in-law established their own kitchen in a new kitchen building. A new kitchen was built with two fire places; later the kitchen was divided into two by a partitioning wall. The grandmother continued to use the old kitchen building for her husband, the two unmarried sons and their unmarried daughter. During our stay, the second son moved out, since he could live temporarily in the house of a relative.[16] There remained two kitchens. In 1988, another son finished high school, and the daughter got married and moved to a different village. Under these circumstances it may just be a matter of time before the two kitchens are fused into one again.

Social and economic co-operation, permanent or incidental, between the persons living in one house, sharing or not sharing a kitchen, is highy variable.[17] Just to give a brief illustration. In the house just mentioned, the three older brothers often processed sago together. They, and their parents, had separate vegetable gardens but helped each other occasionally. Each of the sons and the father engaged separately in various income generating activities, like fishing, working in construction, or producing sweets. The women, too, helped each other in economic activities, but acted both separately and jointly in e.g., baking and selling sago bread, or fruit, or in making and selling coconut-rice lunches.

Economic activities

Most Hila villagers are farmers. Cloves and nutmeg are the main cash crops. Since the early 1970s the clove price has risen dramatically and villagers had a great inflow of cash. Clove prices have dropped considerably, however, since the mid 1980s. Earnings from clove sales were for the greatest part spent on house building and extraordinary investments like the piligrimage to Mecca, the acquisition of machines, and extra clothing. Fish has become largely commercialized during the past 10 years. Among the Ambonese population of Hila there were only a few professional fishermen who operated with teams of about 20 helpers. Vegetables and fruit are partly grown for subsistence, partly brought to the market in Ambon at a distance of 42 kms, which has become more accessible for villagers since a tarred road connecting the northern coast with the city of Ambon has been built in the mid 1970s. Hila itself has no physical market. Most shopping is done in the 16 odd village stalls which sell all necessary items. Sago bread, sweets, fruit and vegetables are also sold along the road by women.

Food acquisition

Villagers acquire food in a variety of ways. For some food there is no alternative to buying. This holds true for rice, wheat flour, salt, refined sugar. For others there is the alternative of providing them by one's own labour, or the labour by one or more members of one's consumptive unit. The general data from the house interviews give a rough indication for the acquisition of some major non-imported food stuffs:

- Vegetables are usually cultivated or collected in the forest.

- 67% of the population stated that they regularly bought fish.

- 64.6% stated that they acquired sago exclusively through their own labour. For 78.9% own labour was the major form of acquisition. Only 15%, mainly "modern" and richer people who ate little sago, stated that they exclusively bought it.

2. The significance of sago

Sago as food

In the Central Moluccas, sago is prepared as food in two different forms. One is as wet sago, which is made into a pudding and is eaten together with fish, or a spicy sour sauce. The other one is in baked form, as sago bread, the *roti Maluku, sago lempeng (B.I.)* or *paputih (B.H.).*[18]

Most people in Hila eat sago pudding although it is not the preferred food for all. Many people prefer rice, and some people stated that they, or their children, found it physically impossible to eat it. Most people live on a mixed diet in which sago plays a larger or smaller role, the proportion between sago, rice and cassava (*kasbi*) varying with the preferences and the availability of money to buy imported food. Often, some members of a consumptive unit would not eat sago, but the others would.

Most villagers also eat sago bread, for breakfast, or as an additional food stuff at noon or at evening meals. However, rolls and sweets made from wheat flour, which are also baked and sold in the village, are preferred. At ceremonial meals accompanying marriages and burials rice is eaten but sago pudding is added to "fill the stomachs." Sweets and cakes which form a indispensable element in such ceremonial meals are made from wheat flour.

- for 73% of the concerned persons sago was one of the major food stuffs eaten;
- for 27% sago was the sole food;
- for 25% sago and cassava were the main food stuffs,
- for another 21% it was sago besides rice and cassava.
- only 27% stated that their main food was rice.

Sago as building material

Besides being an important foodstuff, materials from the sago palm, leafstalks of various length and thickness (*gabah2*), and leaves (*atap*) have traditionally been used for house construction on Ambon. It is possible to build a house largely from sago materials, and many people still do. It saves expenditures for wood, cement or stones, and for corrugated zinc plates for roofs.

Village house, built for permanent residence. The roof is thatched with sago leaves. The upper part of the walls are made by pieces of sago leafstalks.

In the meantime, stone houses with zinc roofs have become fashionable. During the 1970s a building boom began in Hila due to the rising income from clove sales. Now about a third of all residences are stone constructions. *Gabah2*-houses are looked upon as being old-fashioned and simple, but as very adequate temporary residences.

Kitchen building, made from sago leafstalks and thatched with sago leaves. Such buildings are often also used for sleeping.

Still, even in the 1980s sago plays an important role in house constructions. In Hila, out of the 355 houses which served as living quarters, 45% were thatched with *atap* (sago leaves). Adding to these houses the 71 kitchen buildings (which often are used as sleeping quarters, too), the percentage of all houses thatched with *atap* is 54%. 55 houses (16% of the living quarters) and the 71 kitchens were more or less exclusively built from sago palm material.[19]

Houses in Hila 1985

stone houses with zinc roofs	148
traditional/wooden houses with zinc roofs	46
stone with *atap* roof	67
traditional houses with *atap* roof	24
wooden houses with *atap* roof	15
gabah2 houses	55
	355
gabah2 kitchens	71
	426

3. The production of sago food

a. The processing of wet sago

Wet sago is usually produced by a team of three persons.[20] The work is usually done by younger married men, often brothers or more distant kinsmen or friends. The composition of teams varies frequently. Two of the workers are mainly concerned with the extraction of the sago pith dust from the tree, one with washing out the pith dust. After the palm has been felled and cleared of leaves and thorns, the trunk is divided into blocks of a length of 2 to 2,5 metres.[21] These blocks are split open with the help of wooden wedges. The sago fibres are beaten into pith dust[22] with the sago hammer (*naning*). The pith dust is washed and sieved in a tub,[23] and the starch in the muddy reddish water is caught in a reservoir (*lehit*), an old canoe or an empty sago trunk, where it settles and sediments.[24] When there is sufficient starch in the reservoir, the water is let out, and the muddy starch is dried a bit and then put into a basket woven from sago palm leaves, the *tumang*. One basket carries approximately 20 kgs of wet sago.[25]

The trunk pieces of the sago palm have been split open. The pith dust is hacked with the sago hammer (naning).

The pith dust is sieved in the tub (sahane Iunut).

The wet sago kept in the *tumang* used for making sago pudding is called *lapiah* (B.I. *pappeda*) or *lapiah tuma'i* (*sago tumang*). It can be stored for approximately 3 months. For shorter periods of time, it can be kept in the leaf baskets. If it is kept for a longer period, the wet sago is kept in *tumpayang*, large bowls. Every two to three days some water has to be added to keep it wet.

Besides for sago pudding, wet sago is used for making *sago tumbuh,* a very favourite sweet made from wet sago, red sugar and santen.

b. The processing of sago lempeng

If sago bread (*sago lempeng*) is to be baked from wet sago, the wet sago is ground fine by hand and then dried above a fire. The material then is sieved and filled into the forms of the baking stones (*porna sago,* B.H. *hatu paputih, paputih* stones). These forms have the size of a large brick. The forms are first heated above the fire. Then they are allowed to cool off a bit and are cleaned. The hollow spaces are filled with sago flour, and heated stones are put on top of the filled forms. The stones then are allowed to cool off, the sago being baked in the process. The result is a very hard and tasteless sago bread, which to be eaten has to be dipped into tea, coffee or a sauce. Sago bread can easily be stored for more than three months (reports speak of storage for approximately one year).

Besides sago bread, there are some other forms of processing baked sago. These are two refined versions of sago bread in which it, fresh from the oven, is filled with red sugar (*sago gula*) or chilis (*buburne*).

4. Access to sago: the normative framework for production and distribution

Sago palms, wet sago and sago bread can be acquired through various legal means, by sale, by gifts, by allocation out of a common property stock, by inheritance and by share-harvesting/processing. In my description I shall mainly focus upon access to palms since it is of greatest economic importance and access to wet sago to a large extent follows from it.

Access to and control and exploitation of land and economic trees is largely structured by the local adat system. This is fully recognized by the state administration and judiciary (see the Moluccan legal document: Pengadilan Tinggi Maluku 1981). The land laws introduced by the various governments have either been absorbed into adat, or are rejected by the majority of the population. The Basic Agrarian Law and its implementing regulations are known, but there have been no registrations of agricultural land under the law nor conversions of adat rights into the property categories of the law.[26]

Ambonese adat makes a distinction between rights to land and rights to trees or gardens, and the persons or groups entitled to land and gardens can be different.[27] There are different forms of legitimate access to sago palms. One is exclusively based upon individual or shared property rights, in which the "owner of the sago," the *tuan sago*, exploits his or her own palm. The other is based upon a *ma'anu* agreement, a form of share-harvesting.

a. Tuan sago-ship

Tuan sago-ship can be acquired by different mechanisms which represent the different legal statuses of sago palms.

1) Sago palms may be the property of a clan segment (*dati* property). This concerns wild growing sago (mainly sago tunih) growing in gardens (*dusun*) which for generations are considered to be the common or shared property of the clan (segment). Shared ownership in the case of *dusun dati* means that all patrinileal *dati* descendants have in principle a right to exploit such trees. Female *dati* members, however, lose this right once they have married out. The allotment of individual trees is subject to the approval of the *dati* elders, in particular of the *kepala dati* whose task it is to control and administer the *dati* lands and trees. Once a tree is allotted to an individual *dati* member, there is no obligation to share the sago with the other members or branches of the clan (segment).

2) Sago palms may be the individual property of the person who has planted it. The sago then is his enterprise (*perusah*),

which in most respects has the traits of private ownership, and which entitles the person to the exclusive use of the palm. After his/her death, the palm and its future off-shoots become *pusaka*, inherited property, for his/her heirs.

3) Sago trees can also be bought (*sago babalian*). In this case the buyer's right comes close to full ownership of the tree and its off-shoots. Should the bought trees not be harvested immediately — they may have been bought for future use — and the buyer/owner die, the trees become the *pusaka* of his descendants.

4) It is, however, rare that persons who have planted sago live to harvest it. It is more common that it is the generation of children or grandchildren of the original planter who want to harvest a palm planted by an ascendant, or an off-shoot of such a palm which follows the legal status of the "mother stool." Such palms after the planter's death become inherited property (*pusaka*) for his descendants in both lines.

In these cases, sharing is structured by inheritance rights. The *pusaka* property is controlled and administered by the elder men of the group of heirs, who in most cases belong to the generation of grandfathers. It is also on their generation level that the shares of the subgroups entitled to a part of the inheritance are determined. The general principle is that equal shares be given to the branches in the male line. Descendants of females (or females, sisters of the grandparent generation) are also seen as being entitled according to inheritance law. The actual shares given to them, however, vary. It is here that many people invoke the Islamic law principle according to which male heirs receive twice as large a part as female ones.

The *perusah* and *pusaka* rights to trees on *dati* land pertain to the crops; the land, however, remains under the control of the *dati*. Access to land and trees thus can be subject to different rules, and via inheritance members of different clans may have rights in gardens and/or trees on other clans' *dati* lands.

Should a *dati* become extinct, according to the standard version of Ambonese adat (also supported by the state courts as valid adat law) the *dati* land falls to the village and can be newly allotted or otherwise used by the village government. Similar principles pertain to previously unexploited land held by the village (*tanah negeri*). Once a cultivator has made a garden or planted trees, these become his or her individual property, and, after death, *pusaka*. According to classic adat (apparently already obsolete in the 1920s, see Holleman, 1923) also in these cases the village retained a residual right to the *dati* land. However, in more recent times, *perusah* and *pusaka* come close to full ownership rights on both trees and land.

The land and trees in a sago garden thus generally have an exceedingly complex property structure. The land may be *dati* land, and some palm stools be *dati* property. A great part of the sago stools will be *pusaka*. The *pusaka*, however, will belong to different, though overlapping, groups of heirs: some stools may have been planted by a great-grandfather, and all his descendants who belong to different clans, can claim a right to those palms. Other stools may have been planted by a grandfather or father of the present oldest generation of villagers, and be the *pusaka* of their descendants only. Between the sago stools, there may also be fruit trees, like durian, manggis or langsat trees, some of which may have been given to out-marrying daughters, in the present generation or a generation ago. And some *dati* members may also have planted some clove trees on the land.

Thus, upon a relatively small piece of land, say 70 by 70 metres, there may be, and usually is, a very complex set of rights to land and trees of various individuals and various groups, often partly overlapping but usually involving individuals and groups from several clans. It is not surprising that this legal system has been called "chaotic and precarious" (Holleman, 1923: 96, 97).

b. Share harvesting

The other form of legitimate access to sago palms is by taking over a tree in a share harvesting arrangement, *ma'anu*, "eating together." The general standard for the division of the produce is the relation of 40% for the owner(s) and 60% for the workers. If owners join the workers' team they receive their owner's share as well as their share as one of the workers. The workers divide their share equally. No distinction is made between rasping and washing. Village external share harvesters usually work on a

50:50 basis.

Share-Baking

Although most women bake sago bread themselves, for consumption and for sale, share-baking also occurs. The standard division in these cases is 20% for the woman who does the work, and 80% for the women who have provided the wet sago.

5. Access to sago: distribution

a. Access

Actual access to sago palms and wet sago is structured by this normative framework. It depends, however, on the actual accessibility of these resources. People must have control over sago palms or have to find someone who gives them access by way of *ma'anu*. As was mentioned above, most people acquire sago through their or their childrens' own labour, on the basis of their owner's or worker's share in *ma'anu* arrangements. Those who buy sago usually belong to those villagers who do not regularly eat sago.

Tuan sago-ship

Access to sago palms on the basis of individual or shared ownership rights is not evenly distributed in Hila. Most sago gardens are former *dati* areas with wild growing and regenerating palms. In these areas, people have also planted new sago palms which, and the "children" of which, become *pusaka* in the course of time. The current legal status of the *dati* areas is quite ambiguous. Some villagers maintain that most old sago gardens still have *dati* characteristics and that exploitation and cultivation rights should follow patrilineal descent and inheritance. A majority, however, declared their old sago gardens to be *pusaka*, and distinguished *pusaka* palms belonging to the whole clan (segment) and palms which had become *pusaka* through *perusah* efforts.

These old sago gardens largely belonged to the members of the clans which were regarded as the original settler clans of

Hila. Newcomer clans or individual newcomers in the past were incorporated into *dati* groups or were given sago gardens as their own *dati/pusaka* property. This practice has decreased during the past 100 years, so that the more recent newcomers have little or no sago areas of significance.

Sago palms, on clan-wide *dati* or *pusaka* land, is allocated for individual/family consumptive needs by the *dati* or *pusaka* head of that clan segment. This has to occur regularly, since the palms must be harvested before they die out. There is a preference that people should harvest their own (*pusaka*) palms before they lay a claim to the clan property. The *pusaka* palms of groups of heirs are allocated by the elder men in that group.

The extent of actual property rights proved difficult if not impossible to determine during the research. From our series of house interviews it appeared that in 37 houses (78%) people claimed to have access to sago palms on the basis of ownership rights. Eighteen, nearly half of them, stated that they had "many" sago palms or sago gardens. The reference in these cases, however, was always to *pusaka* complexes in which other persons in other houses had rights as well. In 11 cases (22%) people said that they had no sago of their own, or they evaded clear answers.

Ma'anu

Although sago palm ownership is not evenly distributed in Hila, most villagers willing to rasp sago will find an owner ready to give one or two palms for share-harvesting. Initiatives for *ma'anu* can come from both sides. Sago owners needing sago but not having the labour power, or the desire, to work sago themselves, ask their kin or acquaintances whether they would like to work one or more trees. On the other hand, persons having no, or no suitable trees at their disposal, may approach sago owners asking for a palm to be share-harvested. Most people who could exploit sago which is not yet fully ripe, will save their own trees for exploitation in future times, when the palm gives its optimal yield and/or when they may be in more need.[28]

For both owners and non-owners, access to labour power therefore is very important, and, given the availability of sufficient sago, sufficient in order to obtain sago. The availablity of labour to a large extent depends on the number of kinrelations. Poverty in Hila to some extent is "social" poverty, and persons lacking kin are considered to be poor even if they control significant material wealth (see K. v. Benda-Beckmann, 1988: 454, 455). If they find no one to rasp their sago trees, the palms will die before being harvested. This dependence of wealthier (in terms of sago palms) persons on labour also softens the exploitative potential inherent in palm ownership.

The sharing arrangements vary slightly. Much depends upon the circumstances of the individual arrangement (friendship, kinship etc.). However, there seems to be no clear correlation of, e.g., larger shares for owner or workers in the case of kinship or friendship. This is also not to be expected. Giving a larger share to the workers may be considered to be a token of kinship largesse of the owner (controller of the productive resource), but so is the provision of labour for the owner whose labour power may be limited. So they can help each other in both directions. I have never heard of instances where the manner of division led to a discussion, or unfriendly comment of one of the parties.

b. Unmonetized distribution

Primary distribution

Most wet sago is distributed in a non-monetized way on the basis of the *pusaka* and *ma'anu* distribution rules mentioned above. If workers, or workers and owners, belong to the same consumptive unit, "pooling" (householding, Polanyi, 1966) takes place. Each of them brings in his sago for the shared consumption. In such cases, the *lapiah/pappeda* will be cooked and eaten together, and the sago bread is baked for the consumptive needs of all members. But this usually does not involve all the sago harvested. Each person who acquires sago could sell a basket for his own needs (cigarettes). Also, if sago bread is baked for sale, the money obtained will be kept separately by the individual women and not automatically be put into a common fund, or come under the control of a senior male or female. Even if women work together, and the earnings are shared, it will be clear to all concerned *whose* sago was baked into sago bread.

Secondary distribution

Once the wet sago has been divided according to these rules, some part of it usually is further distributed to relatives, neighbours and friends on the basis of general reciprocity. One or two baskets, for instance, may be given to persons who have no right to share in the produce, although they may have stronger or weaker claims on the basis of the social relation they have with the possessor.

Such sago giving usually occurs when sago palms are harvested. But it is a particular feature of sago distribution occurring in the weeks before the fasting month. The fasting month is a period for which villagers require extra amounts of food, since more food than regularly is consumed and food production comes to a near stand still during this period. The weeks before the fasting month are used to generate a sufficient food supply, in sago and other foodstuffs like rice and flour. Thus relatively more sago is rasped during these weeks. Besides, the period before the fasting, and the holidays following the end of the fasting month (*hari raya, lebaran*) are ones in which good Moslims engage in gift giving. Of the sago rasped before fasting, gifts of sago to elderly and needy relatives and neighbours regularly occur. The obligatory alms, *zakat al fitrah*, which Moslims have to give in the night before *hari raya*, in Hila alone involves the redistribution of more than 2 tons of rice (see F. von Benda-Beckmann, 1988c). In the past, but also in more recent periods when rice was less available, these *zakat* food gifts were also given in the form of sago.[29]

Food spreading

This distribution has the effect that the produce of any single sago palm is spread over a considerable number of consumptive units. On the level of production workers, usually members of 2 or 3 different consumptive units are involved. On the level of owners, there are also usually 2 or more owners involved. It occurs, of course, that one of the owners and one of the workers are members of the same consumptive unit. But generally, the primary distribution of the wet sago will involve 4 to 6 consumptive units. In addition, one or two consumptive units will receive sago through the processes of secondary distribution.

The distribution of sago over consumptive units thus is rather complex. As an illustration, I shall give a (quite typical) example of the family of our neighbours already mentioned earlier.

The tree of Haji Abbas: Diagram of the relationships

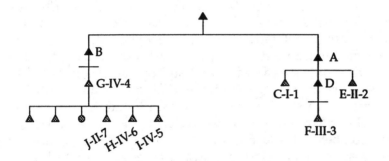

A - J = persons involved in production and sharing
(B = Hadi; A = Haji Abbas)
I - IV = houses (*e.g.* House I)
1 - 7 = kitchens/consumptive units involved (*e.g.* Kitchen 1)

The three brothers H, I, and J had worked a sago palm which had originally been owned by their grandfather, the father of A and B. He had divided the sago palms between his sons A and B. During the period of the study, C controlled the palms of their descent line. E was too old and weak to do so. The three brothers, C, E, G, harvested 15 baskets. Of these, 6 were for the owners, two each for the two sons of A and for D, their deceased brother's son F. H, I, and J received 9 baskets, three each. They each gave one to their father G. Thus the sago of a single palm was distributed among 7 consumptive units and over 4 houses.

c. Sago in monetized exchange

Not all sago is distributed in this way. Some wet sago is also bought and sold within Hila. The standard price during our stay was 2.000 rupiah per basket of about 20 kg.[30] Sago is not offered was 2.000 rupiah per basket of about 20 kg.[30] Sago is not offered publicly for sale. People ask you when you are busy processing sago or when you come home with sago, whether they can buy some. Or the fact that some surplus sago is for sale is made known among friends or neighbours. It is not brought to the market in Ambon.[31] There are different types of monetized transfer:

Accidental excess

It is quite normal that excess sago not needed for one's own consumptive needs is sold. Often when the number of baskets cannot be divided in a way that everyone gets an even share, the excess is sold for "uang rokok," to buy cigarettes. Excess baskets are also sold on a somewhat larger scale to obtain some extra money. However, in both such situations the sago has been primarily produced for one's own consumption.

Wet sago as petty commodity

This is different, however, in those cases in which sago is produced for obtaining a money income. In contemporary Hila, only a few men make the production and sale of sago one of their main sources of income. During our stay in 1985 and 1986, there were only two of such teams. One team consisted of three brothers, who regularly bought the trees. The other team consisted of two brothers and a friend or kinsman, who preferred share-harvesting. Both teams were rather permanent.

The degree to which villagers engage in sago production as one of their main income generating activities has varied historically, and also varies now. In contemporary Hila, it seems to flourish only in times of relative prosperity. When in 1986 clove prices decreased and people saw their actual or prospective money income from clove production dwindle, the sago producers were out of work. Nobody wanted to buy sago anymore. People went themselves to produce sago.

Sago bread

Not all sago harvested and distributed is used for sago pudding.

In nearly every consumptive unit, sago bread also is baked, for one's own consumption and for sale. Most village women bake their own sago bread. However, women of higher social and economic status often ask other women to bake sago bread for them.

Sago bread is sold in the village along the road. Sometimes, women bake more and bring it to the market in Ambon city. Here, the sago bread made from one basket (money value 2,000 rupiah) yields approximately 5,000 rupiah (in 1985 and 1986). Going to Ambon, however, involved 1,400 rupiah in bus fares, 500 rupiah for the bus transport, 100 rupiah in market dues and another 100 for the boy who would carry the sago bread to the market place.

IV. Analysis

1. Sago and food security

Let me now return to the characteristics of food security mentioned earlier and try to show how the Ambonese mode of producing and distributing sago relates to them.

The Ambonese food economy is a mixed economy. Within this encompassing system, the production and distribution of sago for the greatest part are still oriented toward livelihood and not to profit, and come close to what Sahlins calls the "domestic mode of production" (1974 :83), in which the producers' relation to the production process is one of use values, even though exchange may be involved (see also Krause-Katerla, 1986). While the scope of subsistence production is largely influenced by the "rest" of the economy — the availability and prices of other foodstuff, the money resources of villagers, the availability and value of labour — neither the production nor the exchange of sago or sago products is commoditized to a significant degree.

Sago still plays a significant role in the system of food provision and housing. Apart from the actual use in contemporary Hila, the flexibility of sago provides a safety-net for unmonetized access to food and house construction material should the provision of these requirements be threatened. Sago can be used to substitute for rice and wheat flour on a much larger scale than is done now. The same goes for house building materials. When people no longer can afford the ever rising expenditures for wood, cement, zinc, they can fall back on sago. *Gabah2* houses can serve as semi-permanent housing for young married couples and as cheap housing for the poorer section of the population.

The relative high degree of food security is maintained by a number of closely interrelated factors.

The absence of a commodity market for sago within and outside the Ambon-Seram region is, in more or less direct ways, important for the characteristics of food security mentioned by Barraclough. It gives the sago producers and consumers a high degree of autonomy and self-determination over these food resources by making access to the resources independent from external market fluctuations. This is also important for the reliability of the foodstuff. Sago is, by virtue of its botanical nature, available all year round and not subject to seasonal variations. Ambonese villagers are therefore less threatened by the *musin paceklik*, the pre-(rice)harvest period in which villagers in rice producing areas are faced with food shortage. Within the village contexts, there are cyclical deficit phases, but they can be overcome relatively easily by going to Seram, as long as the sago resources there remain accessible on a non-commoditized basis, and as long as no incentives channel them out of the region.

Since the demand for sago is determined by the flexible consumptive needs within the region, the dangers to the ecosystem are minimal, and the long term stability of the ecosystem used for sago production can be maintained. This also is relevant for the ecosystem surrounding the sago areas. As long as Ambonese eat much sago, the less new forest land has to be taken in shifting cultivation for other food crops like cassava which would lead to an increase of erosion and soil degradation.

Given the general accessibility of sago in the region, the relative dependable access to the sago resources and forms of rather equitable distribution are made possible through the legal regulations concerning property and labour relations. The provision of dependable access to sago, and the relatively high degree of equity in its distribution derive from the absence of large scale concentration of sago resources in the hands of a small number of small social units. This also enhances the relative autonomy and self-determination of the Central Moluccans over production and distribution of sago.

Saying that it is subsistence production and its legal regulation and/or the absence of a sago market which contributes to food security in the Central Moluccas comes dangerously close to a tautology. It therefore is important to see that it is not "subsistence production" or "legal regulation" as such which are relevant. Rather, it is the specific nature of the production process of a specific foodcrop and its specific regulation which exhibits those characterstics of food security. For our analysis of the present situation and for our consideration of its implications for future scenarios we must therefore take a closer look at the interrelatedness of the type of food, the technology employed and the legal regime under which production and distribution take place.

2. Subsistence and property law

It is specific for sago production that a) the produce of any single harvested sago palm supplies sufficient food for several consumptive units for about three months, the period in which wet sago can be stored rather unproblematically, and b) that the legal status of the resource and of the labour process ensures that the produce of any single palm is indeed distributed over a large number of consumptive units. It is this specific interrelation of property and labour in the process of production and economic transfers which gives sago subsistence production its distinctive character.

In this, we see a threefold distributive mechanism at work:

1) The employed simple technology and the hard physical work which sago production involves lead to the involvement of three labourers who, given the social organization of residence and consumption, tend to belong to different consumptive units.

2) Since sago property is controlled by older persons, and the labour is done by younger men, the production tends to lead regularly to a division between owners/controllers and workers.

3) Since most sago property is *pusaka*, there is usually also a division on the level of the owners/controllers.

Given the sporadic and ad hoc character of sago production, the configurations of owners and labourers also tend to be different, so no really permanent arrangements come into existence.

In case of clan-wide *dati* or *pusaka* property, the last distributory mechanism does not occur, yet the other two still would ensure that the harvested sago be spread over several consumptive units.

Besides this primary relation of production and distribution, secondary forms of distribution take place. Since the access to sago is relatively easy, there regularly is some excess sago, and since there is neither a market nor a commodity ideology for sago, people find it quite easy to give some part of their harvested sago to friends or kinsmen who would not be entitled to this purely on the basis of the distribution rules.

I emphasize these points since the specificity of sago subsistence elements cannot be adequately analysed in terms of the conventional categories which have been developed by economic anthropologists (see Polanyi, 1966; Sahlins, 1974; Elwert, 1980a, b). Nor do they fit the general image in which property law is related to economic activities.

Usually it is assumed that in subsistence, productive and consumptive unit coincide. However, sago subsistence production is not based upon units of production which are identical with units of consumption (or "households"). However such units — household, houses, or consumptive units — may be defined, the production of sago, whether seen as organized input of labour, or as the combination of owners and workers, always involves members of several of such units. The Ambonese case, thus, is another example showing that the analysis of subsistence economic activities should not proceed from such assumptions, a point which has been made cogently by Elwert (1980a, b); Evers et al. (1984), and Wong (1984).[32]

Sago production on Ambon can best be seen as an ad hoc co-operation which integrates members of different consumptive units in a joint productive effort, and in which sharing is prescriptive. This structure of co-operation and distribution cannot be fitted into the conventional categories of reciprocities or pooling. One cannot say that the sago share of owners or workers is "temporarily withdrawn from one's own sphere of consumption" (Elwert, 1980b: 683) because it has never been in that sphere. Elwert's conception of traditional solidarity[33] or reciprocity, like Sahlins before him, involves the stipulation of two sides, social duality and symmetry, two distinct economic interests (Sahlins, 1974: 189). Reciprocity, as Sahlins states, can establish solidarity in social relations, insofar as the material flow suggests assistance or mutual benefit, yet the social fact of sides is inescapable (1974: 189). Although some sago transfers based upon reciprocal social relations occur, the core of sago distribution according to *pusaka* rules is not found in such type of "between" relation (1974: 88).

Ambonese sago production can neither be accommodated in terms of the categories of "pooling," or of "householding" (Polanyi) as a specific type of pooling. Pooling and householding of sago occur in Ambonese villages, when owners and production workers bring in their sago share into their consumptive unit. But again this is secondary. The production process and the spreading of sago do not involve a centralized collection and redivision within a group" (Sahlins, 1974: 188-190).[34]

This requires a closer look at the legal dimension of labour relations and property, "this salient aspect in the organization of production and distribution" (Sahlins, 1974: 92). Sahlins assumed (and demonstrated with ethnography) that in a domestic mode of production, there is a certain autonomy in the realm of property which strengthens each household's devotion to its own interest. He asserted that this also holds in forms of property regimes which are generally called common, communal or family property/ownership, for under the level of clan/chiefly or family ownership, the individual households get usufruct rights. The communal level of property rights, Sahlins argues, is typically superimposed on the family rather than interposed between the family and its means of production. While a household in tribal society is usually not the exclusive owner of its resources, it retains the primary relation to productive resources (1974: 93). Therefore, relations of reciprocity or pooling can exist also between/in social groups which are considered to be "co-owners."

Sahlins' observation shall not be disputed here since it does fit many property regimes that go under the name of family or common ownership.[35] However, it does not fit the structure of sago *pusaka* production and sharing, where the rules about *pusaka* co-ownership and *ma'anu* co-operation do define the primary relations of production and distribution.

3. Analytical and practical implications for future scenarios

From the above analysis we can also see that food security could be undermined from a number of directions:

- The commercialization of sago in a market located outside the Ambon-Seram region.
- The introduction of a more effective technology.
- The individualization and simplification of rights to sago palms.

As in the case of the current system, these factors should be viewed as interrelated and mutually reinforcing. The process of change may start in any of these factors and would lead to changes also in the others.

Thus the individualization of rights to palms would lead to a decrease of the sharing/spreading mechanisms and also weaken one of the constraints on the alienation of palms, a precondition for palm property concentration. Though not a necessary condition for an increasing commercialization of sago exchange, it would most probably encourage such a development.

The introduction of a more effective technology (rasping machine, semi-automatic production) would reduce the number of workers required to harvest one or a few palms. Besides, it would be an important step in the commoditization of productive inputs, likely to result in restricting the numbers of producers. Such developments would reduce sharing. For there would be fewer occasions in which the sago produce would be distributed according to the rules described earlier. Commercialization and commoditization of sago would bring with them the demand of a money input for food. Consumptive units would buy their own food supply only for themselves. One would have to expect that also the current amount of secondary distribution would decrease as a consequence, and that also the ideological framework of helping and sharing would weaken since they would be less frequently maintained through actual social activity.

It thus can be expected that efforts to commercialize sago for export on a great scale would have consequences detrimental to food security. The accessibility of sago would decrease. One could expect a concentration of sago-ownership in the hands of fewer persons, and of the control over production and distribution in the hands of even fewer. In times of bad economic conditions, people would have less money to buy food. Switching to root crops would be harmful for the ecology.

The modernization of technology and the creation of an external market for sago would therefore constitute a grave danger to the food security based upon sago. This is not pure speculation, but would be a development similar to the one which has already occurred in the sago village in Riau described by Takaya (1986). He describes the far reaching changes brought about by the introduction of a new sago processing technology, a rotary rasper driven by engine (the piring) at first, and later of sago factories, and by the commercialization of sago production (1986: 92, 93). Since the factories required a large and constant supply of sago trees, the factories bought up sago from the villagers. Those who sold their trees naturally lost the chance to process sago themselves. Some of them became wage labourers in the sago factories" (1986: 93). Those who did not sell were also drawn into the new system of sago production. The hand driven rasper was slow and inefficient and could not compete with the machine, and people had to give up the hand driven rasper whether they liked it or not (1986: 93). When sago business boomed in the 1960s, the cultivation area expanded. A semi-automatic factory (pabrik) appeared in the village in 1975. In 1984, 12 such factories were operating. All of them were Chinese owned (1986: 94). This brought with it an even greater demand for sago palms, and even more sago land was bought up (1986: 97-98). As a consequence of these developments, ownership patterns changed drastically. More than half of all sago land (59%), which formerly was rather evenly distributed among the Malayan population, is virtually in Chinese hands (1986: 96), and only 3% of all sago procution is still controlled by Malayans. Many Malayans today buy sago for home consumption from Chinese shops (1986: 97).

Adat (law) and economic change

Since attempts to either encourage or prevent such processes of modernization as occurred in Riau would be faced with the local legal system, it is important to look at the relations between law and economic change in the Ambonese context.

We have seen that the Ambonese law relating to control, production and distribution of sago plays an important role in food security, and helps to keep at distance the commercialization of sago. These food spreading rules are further embedded in an exceedingly complex system in which different property rights are connected to a variety of social units (individuals and groups) with respect to a differentiated set of small property units, which inhibits the isolation of differentiated property relations between a small number of producers and large amounts of productive resources.

However, it is not these legal forms, or some "traditional" or communal character of the local law as such, which have this effect. It is the particular connection of rights to resources (property and labour), a particular form of local law tied to a particular form of production, which maintains the present system. If this connection were dissolved, a change of the local law would probably not be required in order to change the sago economy. Commercialization, individualization, and in its wake less dependable and equitable access to sago (and to productive resources in general) could occur under the present local law. Other sets of adat rules could structure also more commercially oriented forms of sago production. Sago trees *can* be bought in Ambonese villages. It is not obligatory to work in teams of three people. If modern technology would be employed, one person could do the work, and one of the spreading factors would fall away. There is nothing in Ambonese adat rules as rules, which would prevent the large scale ownership of huge sago reserves necessary for a large scale capitalist exploitation of the sago reserves. Adat would not prevent the emergence of the unity between individual sago palm owner and producer required for petty commodity production. It is therefore not the type of adat property rights which would inhibit such developments, but the complex structure in which different property rights to differentiated property objects are connected to a variety of social units.

It is thus not the law — in the sense of a body of abstract rules and principles — which would have to change, but the specific combination of certain rules to a certain mode of production. Attempts to replace the adat rule system with a more "modern" law therefore are likely to be frustrated as long as sago subsistence production is continued. In fact, such introduction would not be necessary, for it already exists in the form of Indonesian agrarian legislation. The fact that no agricultural land has been transformed yet to the individualistic property rights embedded in the state-made agrarian laws is good evidence for this.

Outlook

Such a future scenario is not very appealing. One should take care not to let such developments occur before there is a realistic means of safeguarding the present degree of food security for the rural population. And there are no really feasible alternatives in view. Given the fact that on the densely populated island of Ambon population pressure is already critical, a further expansion of food crop production would be a danger to the ecology. No other food would have the combination of an ideal relation between the production of energy per man-day or hectare (Flach and Luning, 1983: 13,14) and a high degree of labour absorption (see ESCAP, 1985). A reduction of unmonetized food supply in the villages would also stimulate migration into the city of Ambon, a development likely to cause (or increase) widespread urban poverty. Apart from the production of cash crops, the chances of earning money through other economic activities to enable rural people to buy imported food are dim. The high costs of transport of imported goods, "which hold the Ambonese in a firm grip of subsistence and self-sufficiency " (Flach and Luning, 1983: 12) is not likely to be broken. The development of industry as an alternative for earning money to buy food also is not very promising. So far, it has not had a visible employment effect, as the plywood factories on Ambon and Seram, show for the labour has been recruited largely from outside the province (LTA 72, 1983: 5.13).

These points should be particularly emphasized since the predominant attitude of local agricultural and extension officials is strongly commodity oriented (Flach and Luning, 1983: 9), and prospects for the development of sago are mainly seen in marketing prospects (NEI, 1982: 4.2). Also, the proposed regionalization of the province's economic organization, in which the island of Ambon is cut loose from the sago reservoirs in Western Seram (NEI, 1982: 60, 61) would negatively affect food security. As long as there are no alternatives for safeguarding food security in sight, development planners should think *preventively*, about protecting those elements of the contemporary food supply system which indeed seem to guarantee food security. They should also consider that any successful engagement of the rural population in commercial economic activities will have to be based upon food security. Instead of being a major step towards the modernization of the Ambonese economy, the commercialization of the subsistence food reservoir may turn out to destroy any prospect for such modernization.

NOTES

[1] Looking at subsistence food economies as a form of social security has recently been advocated as an important research perspective on food security in developing countries, (see Smits (ed.) 1986: 75). It is also a perspective underlying our research project on social security and law in rural areas in developing countries, (see F. and K. von Benda-Beckmann 1984).

[2] For a critique of the conventional anti-poverty strategies and an elaboration of an alternative strategy, see ESCAP 1985. The authors emphasize the need for a maximalization of labour absorption and the provision of land-based assets to ensure food security outside commercial food production.

[3] See generally Zacher 1979; for developing countries see Midgley 1984, Fuchs 1984, von Benda-Beckmann et al. (ed.) 1988: 19, Fuchs 1988: 46; for Indonesia, see Chhabra 1980, Department of Social Affairs 1984, Joenoes 1982, Stamboel 1986: 12, F. von Benda-Beckmann 1988b: 45.

[4] Like in Marris 1968-69: 317; Mouton 1975: 150; ILO 1984: 2; see F. von Benda-Beckmann 1986, Woodman 1988: 85.

[5] For a discussion of the question whether sago was original to the island of Ambon or has been imported from neighbouring Seram, see Taale 1988.

[6] For historical descriptions see Knaap 1981a,b, 1987, Chauvel 1981, Krause-Katerla 1986, Taale 1988.

[7] According to estimations based upon the available statistical material, the per capita intake of calories in the Central Moluccas is higher than the Indonesian average, 2,469 as compared to 2,300. The protein intake, on the other hand, is lower for the Cental Moluccas, 37.2 than the Indonesian average of 43.3. For the whole province of the Moluccas the average intake is 43.6 (NEI 1982: 18).

8 Dassen 1848:142; Deinum 1948:618, Knaap 1987: 173, Flach and Luning 1983:3. According to Ellen (1978: 73,167), 1979:49) the sago need per person/day is 0.55 kg, thus roughly 200 kg/year. The amount of wet sago won from individual palms varies, of course, with the lifetime etc. of the palm. In the literature, amounts ranging between 100 and 500 kg are reported, with an avarage of 200 kg . See also Ruinen 1921. It has been calculated that by working 80 hours, the sago need for one year could be fulfilled (Ellen 1979, Knaap 1987: 172, 173). This comes close to our own observations in Hila.

9 The situation as found in Hila is, of course, not identical in all respects with the one in other Central Moluccan villages (see for information about Tulehu, Van Paassen 1986). However, for the analysis of the food security elements in sago production and its legal regulation such differences may be negligible.

10 When I speak of subsistence production here I understood it as the production of food primarily as use value. Subsistence production does not exclude (and to some extent even presupposes) the production of a surplus; this surplus, however, is distributed by ways other than the market in which the food has a general exchange value (see Sahlins 1974:83, Evers et al. 1984, Krause-Katerla 1986:13). Neither does it necessarily presuppose the identity of units of production and consumption (see Elwert 1980a and 1980b, Evers et al. 1984, Wong 1984).

11 The research project on law and social security on Ambon is carried out by co-operation between the Department of Agrarian Law, Agricultural University Wageningen, and the Department of Social Science, Faculty of Law, Erasmus University Rotterdam. Field research in Ambon was carried out for 8 months in 1985 and 3 months in 1986. Besides, three student researchers, A. van Paassen, T. Taale and A. Brouwer, were involved in the project. The field research has been done under the auspices of LIPI and with the sponsorship of Universitas Pattimura, Ambon. For earlier publications see the list of references.

12 In this paper, I shall focus specifically on the functioning of Ambonese adat arrangements for the food security of the Ambonese population. For an analysis of the relationships between the Ambonese and the Butonese immigrants, see F. von Benda-Beckmann 1988a.

13 This series involved 48 houses with 353 inhabitants, approximately 15% of the total population of the Ambonese village of Hila, not including the residential areas of Butonese immigrants.

14 The composition of the 48 houses was as follows:

Number of inhabitants	Frequency
2 - 4	8
5 - 7	21
8 - 10	9
11 - 13	7
14 - 17	3

The average is 7.3 persons per house.

15 This discussion of consumptive units is limited to the normal daily life. Much food, however, is also consumed during the ceremonies, mainly at marriage and burial ceremonies.

16 I have described the activities of some of the family members in F. von Benda-Beckmann 1987.

17 Given the variable composition of houses, consumptive and productive units I have consciously avoided the use of the term "household" to denote any specific social unit here, since it could only lead to confusion.

18 Already in 1608, the first Dutch reports of the Ambonese mentioned sago as "the flour of the Ambonese from which they bake their bread. It is rather tasteful and nutritious, and so the Dutchmen used to prefer it to ship-biscuits" (Steven van de Haghen [1608] in Knaap (ed.) 1987: 9).

19 In the Butonese kampung of Hila (Tahoku, Waitomu, Mamua) there was a total of 305 residential dwellings. Out of those 165 (or 54 %) were fully made from *gabah2* and 224 (or 73 %) were thatched with *atap*.

20 The way in which sago is extracted has not significantly changed during the past three and a half centuries; see for one of the earliest descriptions Gijsels [1621] in Knaap (ed.) 1987: 34.

21 The trunk piece (*talal*) is divided from the leaf-crown piece (*uul*). If the palm is divided into more than one block, the middle block is called *etel*.

22 The rough fibres are called *me-l*, the pith dust *ela*.

23 The tub (*sahan-lunut*) is made from sago leafstalks. The sieve (*lulut*) is made from coconut leafstalk fibres.

24 The used *ela* is thrown away (*esi ela*). The starch sediments are called *sisi*.

25 In Hila, the sago palms harvested during our stay were between 6 and 38 tumang, thus roughly between 120 and 760 kg. The average was 16 tumang, approximately 320 kg.

Amount of sago harvested from 34 sago palms in Hila (1985) in tumang (1 tumang app. 20 kg wet sago)

5 - 10 tumang	5
10 - 15 tumang	16
16 - 20 tumang	7
21 - 25 tumang	4
26 - 30 tumang	1
35 - 40 tumang	1

26 More often than not, land and crop/tree transactions are concluded orally, or a written agreement is witnessed by the village chief. In rare cases, people go to the sub-district head, *Camat*, in order to make up a formal sales document (*akte jual beli*), as provided by the legislation. But this is not taken to the Office of Agrarian Affairs

(*Kantor Agraria*) in order to obtain a formal ownership title (*sertipikat*)(see F. von Benda-Beckmann 1986). The PRONA-registration program, a program of fast and cheap registrations by which the government wished to speed up the process of registration, has been a failure in Islamic Ambon. During our stay, the village government tried to find people who would at least have their house sites registered, but without much success.

27 However, interpretations of adat law of Ambon relating to land and trees vary, on village level as well as in the courts (see F. von Benda-Beckmann 1986, 1988a). For a classical account of Ambonese adat law concerning land and trees see Holleman 1923.

28 This "security" strategy was already noted in 1621 by Gijsels. He noted that the Ambonese would use as few of their own trees as possible and would rather go to Seram where sago was abundant. Gijsels speculated that such preventive action was rooted in the wish to store resources in expectation of future warfare (Gijsels [1621] in Knaap (ed.) 1987: 35).

29 Apart from sago, rice and other food also is distributed by the government to civil servants. The "dividends" of the government initiated social security projects are also distributed in the form of food (see K. von Benda-Beckmann 1988).

30 1 kg of rice at that time cost 350 to 400 rupiah.

31 During our stay in 1985 and 1986 there was only one stand at the Ambon market where sago tumang was sold (from Tulehu).

32 As a consequence of the assumed coincidence of productive and consumptive units, co-operation and sharing *between* consumptive units have rarely been considered systematically as an element in the relations of production. Elwert in particular has argued that non-monetized production and transfers of goods (and services) on the basis of reciprocal inter-household relations or "traditional solidarity" should be considered to be part of the production relations. He argues that "where subsistence production still determines the economy and where consequently traditional solidarity still exists, there are obligations to divide and transfer goods which systematically distribute a part of the produced goods beyond the productive units. In the conception of people's own need includes the need of those whom one is obliged to help (Elwert 1980a: 350, 352). In his research in Benin, he has shown the considerable redistributive effect of those transfers (1980a: 364, 1980b: 682). In his example, 25% of maize harvested by Beninese farmers was distributed within the inter-household relations of help/solidarity.

33 Under "traditional solidarity" Elwert understands a system of transfers of goods and services, serving the improvement of the chances of survival and standard of living of other persons. By such transfers, goods and services are temporarily and immediately withdrawn from one's own sphere of consumption; in the long term,

this also serves one's own interest (Elwert 1980b: 683, my translation).

[34] The Ambonese sago spreading is not characterized by "centricity" or by a "within-relation" (Sahlins 1974: 88, 188).

Pooling stipulates a social centre where the goods meet and thence flow outwards, and a social boundary, too, within which persons or subgroups are co-operatively related (Sahlins 1974: 188, 189).

[35] The system of property relations to inherited property in Minangkabau lineages which I have analysed in detail elsewhere (F. von Benda-Beckmann 1979) would be a good example.

REFERENCES

Barraclough, S. 1986. "National Food Policies in Developing Countries: Research Needs and Priorities," in Smits, A.P. (ed.), *Food Security in Developing Countries*. The Hague: RAWOO: 11-20.

Bartels, D. 1977. *Guarding the Invisible Mountain: Intervillage Alliance, Religious Syncretism and Ethnic Identity Among Ambonese Chratian and Moslems in the Molucca*. Ithaca: Cornell University.

Benda-Beckmann, F. von. 1979. *Property in Social Continuity*. The Hague: Nijhoff.

——1986. "Leegstaande luchtkastelen: Over de pathologie van grondenrechtshervormingen," in W. Brussaard et al. *Recht in ontwikkeling - Tien agrarisch rechtelijke opstellen*. Deventer: Kluwer.

——1987. "De ijsjes van de rechter: Een verkenning van complexe sociale zekerheidssystemen," *Recht der Werkelijkheid* 1987/I: 69-82.

——1988a. *Ambonese Adat as Jurisprudence of Insurgency and Oppression*. Paper presented at the Symposium of the Commission on Folk Law and Legal Pluralism, XIIth ICAES, Zagreb.

——1988b. "Sociale zekerheid en plattelandsontwikkeling in Indonesie." Wageningen: Studium generale.

——1988c. "Islamic Law and Social Security in an Ambonese Village," in F. von Benda-Beckmann et al. (eds.), *Between Kinship and the State: Social Security and Law in Developing Countries*. Dordrecht: Foris.

Benda-Beckmann, F. von, et al. 1988. "Introduction," pp. 7-20 in F. von Benda-Beckmann et al. (eds.) *Between Kinship and the State: Social Security and Law in Developing Countries.* Dordrecht: Foris.

Benda-Beckmann, K. von. 1987. "Overheidskoöperaties als particuliere ondernemingen," *Recht der Werkelijkheid* 1987/I: 54-68.

———1988. "Social Security and Small-Scale Enterprises in Islamic Ambon," in F. von Benda-Beckmann et al. (eds.) *Between Kinship and the State: Social Security and Law in Developing Countries.* Dordrecht: Foris.

Benda-Beckmann, F. and K. von. 1984. "Recht en sociale Zekerheid op Ambon," 5 *NNR* (2): 262-281.

Chhabra, H.R. 1980. "National strategies for the provision of rural social security in developing countries in Asia," in ISSA *Report of the Asian regional round table meeting on Social Security of the rural population in developing countries.* Kuala Lumpur: Social Security Documentation Series No. 5.

Chauvel, R. 1981. "Stagnatie, exodus en frustratie," *Intermediair.* 17 (8): 29, 31, 33, 35.

Dassen, M.H. 1848. *De Nederlanders in de Molukken.* Utrecht.

Deinum, H. 1948. "Sago," in C.J.J. van Hall and C. van de Koppel (eds.), *De landbouw in de Indische archipel,* deel 2, pp. 604-621, Den Haag.

Department of Social Affairs, Republic of Indonesia. 1984. *Basic Design for Social Welfare Development.* Jakarta.

Departement Pekerjaan Umum, Direktorat Cipta Karya, Direktorat Tata Kota dan Tata Daerah. 1983. *Proyek pemgembangan regional Maluku.* Jakarta.

Ellen, R. F. 1978. *Nuaulu Settlement and Ecology: An Approach to the Environmental Relations of an Eastern Indonesian Community.* Verhandelingen KITLV No. 83. The Hague: M. Nijhoff.

———1979. "Sago Subsistence and the Trade in Spices: A provisional model of ecological succession and imbalance in Moluccan history," in P.C. Burnham and R.F. Ellen (eds.), *Social and Ecological Systems.* London: 43-74.

Elwert, G. 1980a. "Die Elemente der traditionellen Solidarität,"

Kölner Zeitschrift für Soziologie und Sozialphilosophie. 32: 681-704.

——1980b. "Überleben in Krisen, Kapitalistische Entwicklung und Traditionelle Solidarität", *Zeitschrift für Soziologie.* 9: 343-365.

ESCAP. 1985. *Poverty, Productivity and Participation: Contours of an Alternative Strategy for Poverty Eradication.* Bangkok.

Evers, H.D., W. Clauss, and D. Wong. 1984. "Subsistence Reproduction: A Framework for Analysis," in J. Smith, I. Wallerstein and H.D. Evers (eds.) *Households and the World Economy.* Beverly Hills: Sage: 23-36.

Flach, M. 1983. *The Sago Palm: The Domestication of the Sago Palm, The Exploitation of Sago Forests, and Sago Palm Products Technology: A Development Paper.* Rome: FAO.

Flach, M. and H.A. Luning. 1983. *LTA-72: Maluku Development Project: Final Report of a Technical Mission on Agricultural Research and Extension Aspects.* Wageningen.

Fraassen, Ch. van. 1972 *Ambon-Rapport.* Leiden: Stichting WSO.

Fuchs, M. 1985 *Soziale Sicherheit in der dritten Welt — Zugleich eine Fallstudie Kenia.* Baden-Baden: Nomos.

——1988. "Social Security in Third World Countries," in F. von Benda-Beckmann et al. (eds.) *Between Kinship and the State: Social Security and Law in Developing Countries.* Dordrecht: Foris.

Holleman, F.D. 1923. *Het adat-grondenrecht van Ambon en de Oeliasers.* Delft: Molukken Instituut.

ILO. 1984. *Introduction to Social Security.* Geneva: ILO.

Joenoes, M. 1982. *Reading in Social Security: The Indonesian Case.* Jakarta.

Knaap, G.J. 1981a. "De komst van de kruidnagel," *Intermediair.* 17 (5): 23, 25, 27, 45.

——1981b. "Monopolie en monocultuur," *Intermediair.* 17 (6): 45, 49, 51.

——1987. *Kruidnagelen en Christenen: De Verenigde Oost-Indische Compagnie en de bevolking van Ambon 1656-1696.* Dordrecht: Foris.

Knaap, G.J. (ed.) 1987. *Memoires van overgave van gouverneurs van Ambon in de zeventiende an achttiende eeuw.* Bewerkt door G.J.

Knaap. Den Haag: M. Nijhoff.

Krause-Katerla, H.J. 1986. *Die Gewürznelkenproduktion auf den Molukken: oziale Auswirkungen langfristiger Weltmarktintegration*. Bielefeld, unpublished dissertation.

LTA 72. 1983. *Draft Development Framework for the Moluccan Province*. Ambon.

Macarov, D. (1980) *Work and Welfare — The Unholy Alliance*. London: Sage Publications.

MacPhearson, S. and J. Midgley. 1987. *Comparative Social Policy and the Third World*. New York: St. Martin's Press.

Marris, P. 1968-69. "The Social Barriers to African Entrepreneurship," *Journal of Development Studies* 5.

Midgley, J. 1984. *Social Security, Inequality, and the Third World*. London: J. Wiley.

Mouton, P. 1975. *Social Security in Africa: Trends, Problems and Prospects*. Geneva: ILO.

NEI (Nederlands Ekonomisch Instituut). 1982. *Maluku Regional Development Framework (provisional)*. Ambon-Rotterdam.

Paassen, A. van. 1987. *Sociale Zekerheid: Recht op Bestaan*. Doctoraalskriptie vakgroep Agrarisch recht, Wageningen.

Pearse, A. 1980. *Seeds of Plenty — Seeds of Want*. Oxford: Clarendon Press.

Polanyi, K. 1966. *Dahomey and the Slave Trade*. Seattle.

Ruddle, K. et al. 1978. *Palm Sago: A Tropical Starch From Marginal Lands*. Honolulu.

Ruinen, W. 1921. "Sagopalmen en hunne beteekenis voor de Molukken," in *Adatrechtbundel* 24: 235-243 (originally in *Indische Gids* 1921: 598-622).

Sahlins, M. 1974. *Stone Age Economics*. London: Tavistock.

Savy, R. 1972. *Social Security in Agriculture*. Geneva: ILO.

Schott, R. 1988. "Traditional Systems of Social Security and Their Present-Day Crisis in West Africa," in F. von Benda-Beckmann et al. (eds.) *Between Kinship and the State: Social Security and Law in Developing Countries*. Dordrecht: Foris.

Sen, A. 1981. *Poverty and Famines: An Essay in Entitlement and Deprivation*. Oxford: Clarendon Press.

Smits, A.P. 1986 (ed.). *Food Security in Developing Countries: Research Needs and Priorities.* The Hague: RAWOO.

Stamboel, I. 1986 *The National Experience of Indonesia in the Field of Social Security Protection for the Rural Population.* ISSA Paper.

Taale, T. 1988. *Ambon tussen kruidnagel en sago: een onderzoek naar de relatie tussen handelslandbouw en voedselzelfvoorziening.* Skriptie. Wageningen.

Takaya, Yoshikaru. 1984. "Two Sago Villages in South Sulawesi," in Narifumi Maeda and Mattulada (eds.), *Transformation of the Agricultural Landscape in Indonesia.* Kyoto University: Center for South East Asian Studies: 85-108.

———1986. "Sago Production at Desa Tanjung, Riau, Sumatra: Its Past and Future Prospects," in T. Kato, Muchtar Lutfi and Narifumi Maeda (eds.), *Environment, Agriculture and Society in the Malay World.* Kyoto University: Center for Southeast Asian Studies: 87-101.

Wong, D. 1984. "The Limits of Using the Household as a Unit of Analysis," in J. Smith, I. Wallerstein and H.D. Evers (eds.), *Households and the World Economy.* Beverly Hills: Sage: 56-63.

Woodman, G.R. 1988. "The Decline of Folk-Law Social Security in Common Law Africa," in F. von Benda-Beckmann et al. (eds.) *Between Kinship and the State: Social Security and Law in Developing Countries.* Dordrecht: Foris.

Zacher, H.F. 1979 (ed.). *Bedingungen für die Entstehung und Entwicklung von Sozialversicherung.* Berlin: Duncker und Humblot.

Chapter 5

HOUSEHOLD CREDIT STRATEGIES FOR FOOD SECURITY:
A CASE STUDY FROM SRI LANKA

Sarah Southwold - Llewellyn

The solution to the problem of food security for rural households has traditionally been perceived by policy makers as synonymous with increasing agricultural production. This is mirrored in the emphasis that has been given to supplying credit for agricultural inputs through formal credit institutions. More recently, however, emphasis also is being given to the problem of distributing food more equitably. Two assumptions on which these policies are based are: 1) that there is an intrinsic value in increasing agricultural production; and 2) that the role of traders in providing credit and in marketing crops is not advantageous to the producer, and that, therefore, the state should provide these services. In contrast, the members of rural households adopt a variety of strategies for coping with the problem of their food security. Credit is one of their major strategies. The case presented here is based on a Sri Lankan community where coconut is the major crop. Securing credit to increase agricultural production from formal credit institutions is not a major strategy for food security in this coconut growing community, while securing credit for consumption from traders is.

It will be shown that agricultural production and the sale of crops to traders are primarily means of securing credit for consumption. These facts have implications for food security from a national perspective. But, if we are to deal with the problem of food security from the wider perspective of national interests, we must also understand the problem from the perspective of the producer. His or her assumptions may be significantly different from ours. We must look more closely at informal credit facilities and at some of the social and economic factors which bind borrowers and lenders in the informal sector.

Institutional credit schemes do not meet the perceived credit needs of many rural households.[1] In the first place, securing credit for consumption takes precedence over credit for production. Rural households pursue multiple income generating activities. Agricultural production is one of them, but not necessarily the primary source of household income. Most households need to buy food and, therefore, often rely on credit for consumption to meet fluctuations in income and expenditure. Secondly, there may be no obvious financial advantages to increased inputs. There may be other intervening variables such as water, soil, and other labour commitments which do not make the risk of debt cost effective. Nor does increased production necessarily increase income, unless it is tied to a guaranteed price scheme. Thirdly, households need long-term credit relationships which will secure their comprehensive credit needs for both consumption and production.

Credit from the informal sector, that is traders, meets the perceived needs for food security of rural households better; but it tends not to encourage innovations which might have better pay offs for security in the long term. This is a strategy of risk aversion which has implications for individual households. This also has implications for national production which affects the national domestic market and export earnings for Sri Lanka.

Coconut affords a good illustration of the complex relationships among production, marketing and credit because most households are involved in credit transactions which involve marketing coconut. The Sri Lankan Government's policies on coconut production and distribution also illustrate the inadequacy of formal sector credit strategies to increase production and the bias against traders.

In view of the dominant position occupied by the smallholder, the future development of the coconut industry requires the smallholder plays [sic] a dynamic role in raising coconut output. Hitherto the smallholder had remained largely unresponsive to numerous policy measures introduced by the government. In short, government policies have failed to reach the small producer. The productivity of the smallholdings remains low; fertilizer use and cultural practices have not spread into small-holdings; replanting has not made much headway; and the small producer continues to receive low prices given his dependence on the middlemen traders (Tilakaratna and Perera, 1981: 182).[2]

CASE STUDY RESEARCH

Most of the following discussion will be in the context of an intensive, micro-level study I carried out for fourteen months during 1974-75, in Polgama, and a contiguous village, Gonnawa. (Both villages are pseudonyms.) These villages are located in Kurunegala District, where coconut occupies 70% of the total agricultural crop area (Tilakaratna and Perera, 1981: 2). Together all information is drawn from knowledge of another 8 villages in the vicinity. Polgama is located 6 miles from Kurunegala, an important provincial centre for administration and commerce.

COCONUT

Nationally, coconut is second only to paddy in land use among agricultural crops and in its contribution to the Gross Domestic Product of Sri Lanka (Tilakaratna and Perera, 1981: 4-5). It is an important source of food. On average, it makes up 22% of the total caloric intake in the average Sri Lankan diet (ibid.: 64). It is also the major source of collateral for credit for securing food.

"As a consequence of rising domestic consumption and declining production, the exportable surplus of coconut has declined from 59% in 1955 to 25% in 1982" (S.L.G., 1984a: i). It is unlike other export crops, such as tea and rubber, in a number of ways. In the first place, the majority of coconut has always been produced on smallholdings: 40% on holdings of five acres or less (Tilakaratna and Perera,1981 : 177), and only 21% from the estate sector (S.L.G. 1984a: 25). Secondly, only the surplus to national domestic requirements is exported (Tilakaratna and Perera 1981: 43-44). Moreover, it is an almost entirely indigenously controlled sector. And in the fourth place, most coconut products are processed in Sri Lanka.

Coconut production was below the historical average during most of the 1970s due to a combination of factors. A long term drought affected production. The threat of nationalization of estates over 50 acres led to neglect, which was exacerbated further after nationalization. The vast majority of trees were over 70 years old and needed to be replanted and respaced. Most important was the lack of investment — primarily in terms of the cultivator's time — in water retention techniques and fertilizers which could have doubled production.

CREDIT FOR AGRICULTURAL PRODUCTION: THE CASE OF COCONUT

Although most agricultural credit schemes have concentrated on paddy, since 1949 there have been a succession of schemes to encourage better coconut husbandry through subsidies and loans. Commitment to these programs has grown in recent years. "In the Kurunegala IRD [Integrated Rural Development] Project which commenced in 1979 coconut was identified as a major sector for investment and Rs. 62 million has been provided by the financing agency, the World Bank" (S.L.G., 1984b: 16). Large investment programs which include coconut development have been started and funded by various agencies in several other districts. In addition, a U.S. $30.4 million Coconut Development Project began in 1982 which is being substantially financed through loans from the Asian Development Bank and the International Fund for Agricultural Development (S.L.G. 1984b: 19).

In spite of these initiatives, the agricultural potential of coconut is not being met. Production could be doubled with the application of fertilizer and with adequate rainfall and water retention techniques (Wickramasekera, 1983: 47; Tilakaratna and Perera, 1981: 80). The acceptance of various schemes to encourage better cultivation practices has been very poor (S.L.G., 1984a: 9; Henegedara, 1984: 32, 34-35; Tilakaratna and Perera, 1981: 21-22). Relatively few people are aware that the schemes exist; and only a minority of those who do take advantage of these loans fulfill the conditions of renewal loans (Henegedara, 1984: 23). A study commissioned by the ILO showed that fertilizer was used on only 9.3% of holdings and the Kurunegala Rural Development Project study showed that only 5% of farmers used fertilizer (Wickramasekera, 1983: 46).

Part of the problem is delay in results. With regard to fertilizer, the full impact is not felt until after a lag of two or three years (S.L.G., 1984a: 18; and Tilakaratna and Perera, 1981: 80). Poor rainfall, however, may negate these advantages since, "... soil moisture is, perhaps, the most critical factor affecting coconut yields" (S.L.G., 1984a: 17). "Subsidies were paid to owners of holdings below 20 acres (but above 1 acre) for cutting contour drains for the purpose of soil and moisture conservation..." (Tilakaratna and Perera, 1981: 28). Ideally, the drains should be filled with husks. Landowners with more than 10 acres were the only ones who use this technique in Polgama. Yet, the only cost to adopting this technique is labour.

Increased productivity, however, does not necessarily produce a higher income. If other farmers also increase their production, over-production may depress market prices. Comparison of the incomes of two households with similar-sized holdings showed that coconut production increased in 1975; and yet their incomes were less than they were in 1974 (see TABLES 1 and 2). The difference in income was Rs. 34.32 (10%) less for Household X and Rs. 55.60 (12%) less for Household Y. "The operating surpluses in all productivity groups show a very low return to the capital invested [during the period 1973-82]" (S.L.G., 1984: 19).

Furthermore, production is insufficient as a primary source of income in most households. For the year 1974-75, the average yield of nuts per acre was 1,464 in Polgama. This figure corresponds with production averages from other studies carried out in Kurunegala District (e.g., Wickramasekera 1983, p.47; and Gunawardana, et al., 1981 :84). The average price for one coconut during the year was 21.5 cents; and the average income earned from the coconut produced on one acre was Rs. 315. A household with ten acres of land planted with coconut would earn Rs. 3,150, or the equivalent of Rs. 260 per month — an income which would provide subsistence to some of the poorest families. Yet, only four percent of households owned ten or more acres.

There is little demand for credit for agricultural inputs to increase coconut production nor to adopt other beneficial practices. Since increasing production does not increase income there is little advantage in doing so. To some extent this reflects international market prices; but it primarily reflects the government's main priority which is to protect the consumer and, hence, reduce prices for the producer (Southwold, 1987: 279-281). In effect, the policy to encourage production and the policy to protect the consumer conflict with each other. Another consequence of pricing policies is that few producers could live on their income from coconut alone. Therefore, for the producer the major function of coconut production is to secure credit for consumption.

Most households have access to some coconut which can be sold. In the Polgama area, virtually all high land (*goda idam*), i.e., land that is not cultivated with paddy (*mada idam*), is planted with coconut palms. In contrast to paddy land, 57% of the households in Polgama own some high land, while only 37% own some paddy land. The most significant difference in the distribution of these two types of land is that everyone, whether he owns land or not, has access to some high land. With one exception, every landowner who had a tenant living on his land — regardless of whether or not rent was paid or the tenant was a watchman on his estate — would permit the tenant to pluck coconuts for his household's own consumption, and to cultivate fruit and vegetables.

In contrast to paddy cultivation, the coconut crop is relatively reliable. There are fluctuations in income from coconut due to variations in productivity and market prices; but, the producer can be assured of some income. A coconut palm will continue to produce nuts for seventy years without any input costs, and in conditions of drought, although productivity will be adversely affected. In spite of dramatic fluctuations in output and in market prices, the producer can rely on a regular and relatively predictable, if fluctuating, income. Harvests are every two months rather than once or twice a year. Because it is the only substantial cash crop, it is the primary source of collateral for credit.

HOUSEHOLD DEMAND FOR CREDIT

Credit plays an important part in almost all households, particularly because of the fluctuating imbalance between income and expenditure. One aspect of why households are dependent on credit is the structure of incomes. Not only do different village households rely on different sources of income at one point in time; but there is also economic diversification within households and given individuals will pursue a multiplicity of income-generating activities. The multiplicity of income sources is an attempt to reduce risk and to even out the fluctuations between income and expenditure; but in itself it creates instability and fluctuation in income.

Most households in rural areas earn some income from agriculture, either in terms of cash from sales or in terms of subsistence. But rarely is agriculture sufficient. The example of coconut was cited above. With regard to overall agricultural production, cultivation was the primary, not the sole source of income, in only 14% of households; but it did make a substantial contribution to the incomes of 46% of the households. Nationally, ..."in 1971, only 59% of the rural work force was employed in agriculture or animal husbandry, including plantation production" (Moore, 1985: 124) .[3]

Secondly, income is seasonally variable. There are seasonal variations in the size of harvest, the market price, and in the expenditure for agricultural production. For example, coconuts are harvested every two months. The volume of the crop varies with an annual seasonal cycle. The high season is usually between April and July; the low season is between October and January. The two prominent features of the farm gate prices are, first, that there are wide price fluctuations between years and, second, that price fluctuations between months are much wider than yearly fluctuations (S.L.G. 1984 a: 19 and 56). Other types of income-earning activities, with the exception of salaried posts, also tend to have some seasonal variations.

Many occupations cannot be pursued without credit to enable the purchase of the prerequisites for carrying out the activity. Traders typically rely on credit to secure stock. Craftsmen and women in various cottage industries need credit to secure raw materials and farmers need credit for agricultural inputs.

A second aspect of why households are dependent on credit relates to the cycles of expenditure and consumption patterns. All households, even those having members in regular employment, use credit as a strategy for meeting long-term and short-term fluctuations in expenditure demands.

The life cycle of the family has a long-term influence on the pattern of consumption and expenditure. Households with younger children have fewer potential sources of income than households with older children. However, where there is youth unemployment, the older the family, the higher the level of consumption.

In contrast, the annual consumption cycle is a short-term fluctuation in the consumption pattern. For example, at New Year (mid-April) and *Wesak* (usually the end of May) there are more expenses for entertaining, food, clothes, and religious devotions than at any other time of the year. Another short-term fluctuation is a consequence of the agricultural production cycle. At some times of the year, households are more dependent on buying food than at others. Furthermore, the agricultural production cycle would make it necessary for most production expenses to occur at planting and harvesting.

Emergencies, such as deaths and illness, are additional burdens on consumption and they are unpredictable. These put the greatest stress on household resources. On the other hand, in such circumstances, households can expect assistance from their kinsmen. Wealthier kinsmen in particular have a moral obligation to help, as do other "big men" such as employers and copra merchants.

A third reason why households are dependent on credit is that the structure of the credit relationship within the informal sector continues the dependency relationship. Credit from friends and relatives carries with it obligations of reciprocity. Credit from coconut/copra merchants and paddy merchants is based on advances on a future crop — credit is given to ensure future supplies and thus in the hope that the debt will never be paid off in full.

In contrast, credit relations in the formal lending sector are structured to be short-term — geared to the production needs of the seasons and inflexible with regard to either social or economic circumstances. By definition, the relationship begins and ends with a single transaction over a particular period and for a particular purpose.

There are three major areas of expenditure: production, consumption, and emergencies. Although production is given most emphasis by planners, it is *consumption* expenditure which dominates expenditure in two ways. In the first place, it takes the largest slice of total income. In the second place, the proportion of consumption expenditure is inversely related to income: poorer households spend a larger proportion of their income on consumption than do better off households. Even in rural areas where agricultural production is high, poorer households have been reported in one study to spend an average of two-thirds of their total income on *buying* food (Ponnambalam, 1981: 59).[4] A larger proportion of income that was spent on food was concealed by government subsidies on most staple items.

The structure of income sources is such that income for households as a whole is not constant and, therefore, all households have strategies for coping with fluctuations in income and their expenditure needs. The reduction of expenditure by not investing in agriculture, buying less food, etc., is one way of coping with expenditure needs. A second way is to increase household income with additional income generating activities which may involve additional members of the family, such as children. Increasing agricultural production is a third avenue, but it usually entails increasing expenditure and, as we have seen, may not increase income. A fourth expedient involves the mortgaging or sale of assets. Charity for emergencies, especially deaths, can be expected from relatives and friends. Finally, two other ways of coping with expenditure needs are savings and credit.

Saving is not a long-term strategy that many households are able to pursue. Eighty-two percent of households in Polgama had no cash savings during the year of the study, which was a period of financial stringency and drought. Perhaps more significantly 71% had never had cash savings. This is particularly important with regard to the debate on the role of saving and capital formation for development (Firth and Yamey, 1964; Howell and Adams, 1980, Von Pischke, 1981).[5]

In contrast to savings, borrowing seems to be a strategy

employed by most households.[6] There were 56 out of 70 households (80%) who admitted to me that they had borrowed during the year before the interview. The 14 (20%) who said they did not borrow fall into two categories. Those nine (13%) who do not need to borrow, and those five (7%) who were too poor to get credit. Of the nine who do not need credit, five are traders who borrow for their businesses. Therefore, there are only nine households who do not borrow — five of whom are unable to get credit. This suggests that most households (87%) use credit as a household strategy. But in fact, every household uses credit as a strategy. The five who do not have a long-term formalized credit relationship still get credit through charity given to them because of destitution.

Eighty-eight percent (49 out of the 56) of all those who admit borrowing, borrow for domestic expenditures, primarily food (TABLE 3). In contrast, note that only five percent get credit for agricultural production. (This figure is for all types of agricultural production.)

CREDIT FROM TRADERS

In this chapter, the "informal sector" is taken primarily to mean traders and moneylenders, those who are not included in the status of "friend" or "relative." However, it should be remembered that traders and moneylenders are often *also* friends and relatives. In small communities the distinction is often a symbolic one used to denote the terms of the loan. For example, friends and relatives can be relied on for small loans; but these must be paid within a few days if future credit is to be given. They can also be relied on for help with household emergencies, such as illness or death. In Polgama, relatives were the major source of loans using mortgages as collateral: few were given by traders (shopkeepers and coconut/copra merchants). This is contrary to a common assumption that traders try to usurp land from peasants through their debts and mortgages.

It has been assumed by policy makers that state intervention to replace the private trader would lead to a more productive use of resources.[7] "...irrespective of the party in power, the government had looked to the elimination of the *mudalali* [trader] as the major goal of their rural economic policies" (Alexander, 1981: 122). Two major approaches to by-pass dependence on traders have been the establishment of institutional credit schemes and of marketing infra-structures. These schemes have mainly been aimed at paddy production, but there have been less comprehensive attempts aimed at dry grains, vegetables, and coconut.

The Changing Position of Traders. During the 1970s, a series of government measures had the effect of reducing household incomes and the circulation of cash in the local economy. The dramatic increase in the world market price for petroleum, and the increase in the price of raw materials and of intermediate goods (such as machines and their spare parts) led to the government's restriction on imports. This limited the goods and food sold in shops to essentials. It also limited the availability of raw materials for home industries such as weaving. The situation in Polgama was exacerbated further by drought. During the previous five years drought had virtually eliminated paddy crops.

The restriction on imports and other government measures transformed radically the role of shopkeepers and, hence, the prior patterns of credit extension. The restriction on imports meant that there was little in the shops to sell. A more profound effect was caused by more severe restrictions on paddy marketing, which made it illegal for shopkeepers to buy paddy. No doubt these restrictions could have been easily circumvented. There was a large black market in paddy elsewhere at that time; but it was more advantageous for traders in this locality not to become involved in the black market. It released them from obligations to give credit on a future crop which had a high probability of failing. The cumulative effect of the government's legislation and the failure of the paddy crop was that paddy was no longer used for collateral in extending credit. This altered the foundation on which credit in cash advances was given by shopkeepers and, hence, it reinforced the predominant role of coconut as collateral for credit and as a rural currency. The net result was that coconut merchants and those who process coconut into copra[8] took a central position in the distribution of credit in the informal sector at the village level.

At the national level, at the apex of cash credit are the

national brokers who lend cash to regionally-based coconut oil mills. Both the national brokers and the mill owners lend to the village-based copra merchants who, in turn, lend to individual households and to the many shopkeepers who also act as coconut merchants. This flow of cash down to the villagers ensures the reverse flow of coconut and coconut products into the national economy.

The pattern of credit tied to the distribution of goods in shops is the opposite to that for coconut distribution. The wholesalers in Kurunegala give credit, in the form of goods, to the village shopkeepers who in turn lend to the smaller shopkeepers and customers. They and their creditors are repaid in cash.

The major source of credit for domestic expenditure is traders. These are on-going regular transactions. The major credit role of traders is for on-going, daily consumption credit, in addition to providing credit for production and emergencies. In a 50% sample survey of households in Polgama, 79% of the households who admit borrowing, borrowed from traders for consumption, but only 18% said they borrowed from relatives and friends for consumption. The remainder borrowed from employers (TABLE 4).

Three of the most predominant characteristics of borrowing for domestic expenditure from both shopkeepers and copra merchants are: 1) the debt is spread over more than one creditor source; 2) the debts are for small amounts; and 3) the borrowing is frequent — perhaps several times a week. TABLES 1, 2, 4, and 5 give some indication of these characteristics. Individual variations are concealed in the averages presented in these tables. These characteristics may vary in scale, but the pattern is the same for landholding and landless households. The typical family spreads credit widely among traders. Most households shop at more than one shop. At each one, they will buy a few goods on credit. In addition, they get credit from coconut and copra traders.

Those with landholdings under two acres typically sell their coconut to shopkeepers who also deal in coconut. Those owning over two acres of high land typically have an account with a copra merchant. The pattern of borrowing is to borrow small amounts frequently. These are *advances* on future harvests.

TABLE 1 illustrates the borrowing pattern of one householder with two acres. During one year, he borrowed an average of Rs. 8.5 on 25 occasions. The following year, he borrowed an average advance of Rs. 10.88, 33 times. This pattern appears to be similar for all households, regardless of the size of their holdings.

Most households, even those with an account with a copra merchant, sell a few coconuts to shopkeepers on a barter basis. These shopkeeper coconut merchants are particularly important for the landless and for those with very small land-holdings who need to maximize their credit resources. In addition to these small subsistence farmers, landless tenants and employees also sell nuts to subsist. Landlords and employers have a moral obligation to give coconuts to their landless tenants or employees for their domestic subsistence. The landless, like marginal landowners, often sell these nuts to meet other, more pressing, consumption needs.

MUTUAL DEPENDENCE BETWEEN TRADERS AND HOUSEHOLDS

Credit, both receiving and giving credit, is central to understanding how traders operate their businesses. Traders need credit to secure an on-going supply of goods, to bridge gaps in income, and to finance expansion, as well as to meet the consumption needs of their own households. Traders also need to give credit to maintain their business, since indebtedness helps to maintain an on-going relationship with customers and suppliers of agricultural crops (e.g., Geertz, 1963: 36 Ward, 1960: 153; Yalman, 1967: 49). Traders operate within a hierarchy of interdependent credit relations as both borrowers and lenders.

A distinction between shopkeepers and copra merchants is useful for understanding how traders operate their businesses because the two types operate with different structural constraints. There are basic differences in the way they organize their businesses with regard to management and access to credit. On what terms advances are given is a central criterion for the distinction between shopkeepers and copra merchants. Shopkeepers give and are given advances in goods for repayment in cash; copra traders give and are given advances in cash for repayment in coconuts.

Most traders start with tea and vegetable shops. The initial strategy in these businesses is giving credit in order to build a clientele. Poorer households use this to their advantage. It is common for a poorer householder to visit several different shops each day, getting a few Rupees worth of goods on credit at each. But to some extent the "generosity" of the novice trader is exploited by everyone. Traders estimate that 10-20% of the advances they give are never repaid. Often, customers borrow to the limit the trader will give them and then no longer patronize the shop. Relatives expect, if not demand, goods for which they often do not pay. Repeatedly, traders complained, "How can we say 'no' to our relatives?" Furthermore, those that sell prepared food are most vulnerable to requests for charity from the destitute. In the cases of the destitute and of kinsmen and neighbours, most traders believe that they have a moral obligation to give goods on credit.[9] In all cases, however, the trader realizes that he is unlikely to be repaid for a substantial proportion of the goods he stocks and that this is a cost of running a business. Several traders told me that they ask for repayment once or twice, but no more than that for fear of losing customers. The trader hopes to build a "core" clientele.

To compensate for these losses, different traders have different strategies. Some charge debtors more. Some increase the prices of all goods to compensate their losses. However, if the prices are increased unreasonably high, few will go to the shop. To illustrate, only those who cannot get credit anywhere else buy from the shopkeeper, H.M. Banda.[10] It is an indication of their desperation that he holds, illegally, the ration books of some of his customers as collateral. These practices are generally held to be unscrupulous and I know of no other trader in Gonnawa-Polgama who uses them. Nor have these practices been beneficial to his business, as a whole.

More typically, the shopkeeper is most vulnerable to the charitable credit he must give to the destitute, kinsmen, and neighbours. Credit to marginal agricultural producers and wage earners who often barter the coconuts for their own subsistence typically is limited to Rs. 5 to Rs. 15. Those who produce an agricultural surplus can get more credit: usually from Rs. 5 to Rs. 50 and have an account. Wage earners with reliably good incomes (e.g., civil servants, teachers, etc.) have monthly accounts (see Table 5).

In contrast to advances in goods, *advances in cash* are made in the expectation that it will be repaid in agricultural produce, at least in part, at the next harvest. For paddy, it may be six months between planting and harvesting; for coconut, the harvest is every two months. For advances on a coconut harvest it may take several harvests or even over a year to pay off, although in effect the debt is continuous. More cash is advanced and the debt is never completely repaid. The lender, i.e. the trader, may or may not reduce the price paid for produce if the debt is not completely repaid. Amounts advanced depend largely on the size of the expected supply. In the coconut trade, it is necessary to make these advances to secure customers.

These advances do bind suppliers to particular traders. The trader can expect a proportion of the producers' harvest relative to the advance. This enables the producer-supplier to have the security of continuing their relationship. Yet the producer-supplier is free to sell to whomever he likes. Households spread their credit for consumption among several different sources. The competition among traders is such that they are anxious to continue the supply-credit relationship with suppliers. Producer-suppliers tend to have good knowledge about variations in prices given by local traders, as well as the national market prices. For these reasons, traders are careful to give a "reasonable" price for produce bought.

The strategies of the copra merchants for securing customers are similar to those of other traders. They give a good price, treat their suppliers well and give credit. While it is necessary to give advances to secure a clientele of suppliers, it is also a liability. In the first place, it ties up capital which increases the lender's dependence on his own creditor to secure funds necessary to supply credit. Secondly, there are obligations to borrowers to provide on-going credit for consumption and emergencies.

A number of points of comparison between shopkeepers and copra merchants emerge. As lenders, the structure of credit is least advantageous for shopkeepers. They are the most vulnerable to default because, unlike copra merchants, they are advancing goods without collateral, they often have little knowledge of their customers, and their relations with customers are less stable. They are also more vulnerable to the demands for credit from the least credit worthy. Nor can they deny food and the necessities of life to the destitute, while the copra merchants are less "available" and less "visible" to the destitute. Yet, the shopkeepers are under the least obligation to help kinsmen and clients for large amounts for emergencies or production inputs. In contrast to the shopkeepers, however, the copra merchants are under the greatest obligation to help in these types of circumstances and will borrow to fulfil these expectations.

Closer examination of the credit relationship between copra merchants and small-scale cultivator-suppliers highlights their interdependence in several ways. First, both are tied to a strategy of risk aversion. Second, this credit relationship is reinforced by shared normative expectations specific to that relationship. Third is the inequality in status between the copra merchant and the supplier which is founded on a relationship of asymmetrical reciprocity.

The structure of trading generates a structure of credit relations which acts to provide security for both the supplier and the trader. Both are mutually dependent on each other in order to avoid risk. The supplier needs the insurance of a long-term, stable relationship with a copra merchant for consumption and emergencies. And the copra merchant needs the assurance of a predictable supply of nuts.

Households are plagued by unreliable income sources. One way of coping with unreliable income is through credit networks. Hence, the importance of security in relationships with credit givers. Credit from family and friends cannot be an ongoing *debt* relationship since these credit relations are either reciprocal or one-off, large loans. Credit from shopkeepers is only advances of goods, has a relatively small ceiling, and must be repaid within the short-term (typically a month) in order to sustain the credit link. Credit from a copra/coconut merchant also rests on repayment (through coconuts) — but the repayment period is long-term. The account balances, roughly, over the year; but the debt is, typically, continuous (Southwold, 1987).

A major reason for the dependence on creditors is not because expenditure needs greatly exceed the credit given. Or perhaps, it would be more correct to say that the amount of credit given does not exceed the amount a person is able to repay. From the 42 accounts over a two year period that I have examined, credit and repayment more or less balance out (TABLES 1 and 2 are examples). At the arbitrary ending of the year, the short-term disbalance juxtaposed with the long-term balance of the account ensures an ongoing relationship. The reason for dependence on creditors lies in the fact that the pattern of credit does not reflect the two-month harvesting cycle for coconut. Rather suppliers borrow repeatedly between harvest sales. It also suggests that the nuts are sold to fit the strategies of the producer, for example by holding them until the price is higher, or selling them frequently when he needs more cash.

From the copra merchant's perspective, he is not tying up his capital or even taking any risks with it. By "investing" a small sum of money in the short term, and by continuing to be able to do this, he is ensuring his supply of coconuts for the long term. Furthermore, for copra merchants, the small-scale cultivator-suppliers of coconut are the backbone of their businesses. Locally, and nationally, these cultivators are cumulatively the largest source of coconut. Several of the large local estates do sell to local copra merchants; but these are not secure sources of coconut. Transactions tend to be one-off since these estate owners sell to whomever will give them the best price. This is largely because the trading relationship is not reinforced by credit.

The credit relationship between these small-scale suppliers and copra merchants is reinforced by shared expectations. If the supplier sells to a copra merchant, he can expect a reasonable price and credit for emergencies and consumption. In turn, the copra merchant can expect most of his harvest.

Implicit in the notion of shared values is the notion of *reasonableness*. For example, the charges made for a debt must be perceived as reasonable. They are not measured as reasonable by any absolute criterion, but rather by perception. "... what is exploitation and what is not are appeals to a normative tradition and not matters to be settled by empirical inquiry" (Scott, 1976: 159). Dewey's observations in Java are apt.

> In a society where the moneylenders must depend on informal sanction to enforce the repayment of debts, however, the consensus within the community will not support him against one of their number if they feel that his claims are exorbitant. Thus the community places a check on the interest

rate which can effectively be charged (Dewey, 1962: 93).

Thus, the shared expectation of *reasonableness* acts to constrain the potential exploitation by traders and to legitimize their business practices. Suppliers expect to be given a lower price if they are in debt. Yet, the charge made for debt on an advance must be seen as reasonable within the wider context of the community at large.

A copra merchant is not expected to give advances to someone who does not supply him with nuts. In this respect, the relationship is primarily an economic one. On the other hand, copra merchants are under some obligation to give additional credit in emergencies, regardless of rules of lending. When a widow needed to borrow Rs. 500 for her husband's funeral, "her" copra merchant did not have enough cash at the time. So he arranged an advance with another copra merchant. Further, the advance given to the widow was beyond that which would be recouped in several harvests. This illustrates the moral obligation that "her" copra merchant felt to supply funds to the widow for this emergency which surpassed the normal "rules" for advances. In part, this "uneconomic" transaction is motivated by a long-term economic strategy to maintain supplies. It also marks the transition from a purely economic relationship to one in which socio-economic obligations are acknowledged, and which represents a long-term investment strategy in both coconut supplies and in social status.

Not fulfilling these expectations is why another copra merchant in the vicinity has neither the respect nor the custom of smaller suppliers in the area. "A wealthy man who presses his tactical advantage does so at the cost of his reputation and moral standing in the community" (Scott, 1976: 42). Traders cannot be deviant from the norms because they could not stay in business if they were. Traders cannot be "outside" the community of shared values. They need to be able to legitimize their practices in order to stay in business.

The relationship between copra merchants and their small-scale suppliers is tied to the distribution of economic resources which is constrained and shaped by a framework of moral expectations and investment strategies aimed at life goals, e.g., income and status. Establishing a stable relationship where the supplier can rely on "his" copra merchant for help in emergencies and for ongoing consumption, has long-term economic pay-offs. On the other hand, part of the status of being a "big man" entails largesse for which there is no financial pay-off. This essentially economic relationship cannot be understood without an appreciation of shared moral expectations which protect the economic relationship and which is reinforced by motivation for social status.

......

Planning alternative marketing infra-structures for the distribution of agricultural produce should take household credit strategies into account. The example of coconut is instructive. In the first place, farmers reduce their risks by selling most of their crop to one particular copra merchant. This tends to be a long-term, stable relationship. Secondly, juxtaposed and often simultaneously, many households have a strategy of dispersing the sales of coconut to different types of buyers (shopkeepers and copra merchants, rather than to competing copra merchants) in order to increase their credit resources. Typically, sales to shopkeepers are for relatively small quantities. Third, credit motivates "sell-to-subsist sales."[11] Without credit many small suppliers would not sell their coconuts; hence, the coconut available for national distribution would decline further. And fourth, the assumption that increased direct market access implies higher prices for the cultivator holds true only for those who are able to by-pass dependence on credit. Higher prices, and indeed higher production, are not the most important considerations for the majority of coconut cultivators. Alternative marketing outlets are unlikely to be attractive to them unless they provide for most of their credit needs and provide the food security through credit that traders do.

NOTES

1   Only those reasons directly relevant to the argument of this chapter are mentioned.

2   One of the authors, U.V.H. Perera was the Director of Economic research for the Coconut Development Authority.

3   Moore is citing Dept. of Census and Statistics (1975), *Census of*

Population, 1971 vol. 2 Part 2: The Economically Active Population, Table 5. The proportion of the individual's time spent in these activities is not given.

4   Ponnambalam is reporting on the Socio-Economic Survey of Ceylon, 1969: 70.

5   The concept of savings is too problematic to discuss in this short chapter. It may include storage of crops and investment in various types of assets. In this discussion, I am referring only to savings of cash.

6   Based on research carried out in Sri Lanka in 1979, Piyasiri Wickramasekera notes that there was "...a certain degree of reluctance to disclose the extent of borrowing...." (1983 : 82). Several of my informants expressed shame that they were in debt. For example, one householder told me that they did not like to get credit: "We like to keep status. It's shaming if the shopkeeper says how much you owe in front of other people." In spite of the high rate of admitted indebtedness, I assume that my data under-represent the extent of indebtedness.

7   The development of an intellectual bias against traders in India has been carefully argued by London (1975). There seems to me to be a comparable development of this bias in Sri Lanka, which to some extent has been influenced by Indian intellectuals and the shared biases of the British Colonial Administration.

8   The dried kernel of the coconut from which coconut oil is pressed.

9   Harriss (1982: 259) and Scott (1976) argue that the idea of a "right of subsistence" is tied to the dependent class relations.

> The right to subsistence defines the reciprocal duty of the powerful, the minimal obligations that they owe to those from whom they claim labour (appropriate surplus value). The principle of reciprocity does not mean that equivalent goods and services have to be exchanged between the dominant and the subordinate classes, but that the legitimacy of the exchange depends upon the extent to which the expectations of the dependent class, rooted in their minimum needs for security, are satisfied. The argument suggests that people define "exploitation" in relation to their ideas about their minimum livelihood requirements. (Harriss, 1982: 259)

> In Polgama, these "dependent class relations" exist for those

few with patron-client relations, particularly between employers and employees. The relations between shopkeepers and kinsmen are based on social criteria. The obligation to give to the destitute, many of whom are strangers, is quite different. The moral obligation to give "subsistence" is, at least in part, intrinsic to Buddhist ideology.

[10] This is a pseudonym.

[11] This term was coined by T.S. Epstein, 1983.

TABLE 1
COCONUT SALES
AND ADVANCES FOR HH X (2 ACRES)

Period till	Nuts	Price cents	Sales Rupee	Advanced Rupees	No. of advances
			1973-4		
01/07/73					
04/08/73	190	18	32.40	10.00	1
08/09/73	124	17	21.08	15.00	3
20/10/73	119	35	41.65	30.00	4
11/04/74	380	35	133.40	32.00	5
08/06/74	318	38	120.84	55.00	9
29/06/74				70.84	3
Totals	1131		349.57	212.84	25
			Rs.136.53 in credit for 1973-74		
Averages		30.89		Rs. 8.48 per advance	

Period till	Nuts	Price	Sales cents	Advanced Rupees	No. of Rupees
			1974-5		
advances					
13/08/74	162	30	48.60	70.00	4
11/10/74	124	30	37.20	35.00	5
09/02/75	170	26	44.20	20.00	3
22/02/75	285	25	71.25	74.00	8
22/03/75	440	15	66.00	55.00	5
20/05/75	400	12	48.00	60.00	4
30/06/75				45.00	4
Totals	1581		315.25	359.00	33
			Rs. 43.75 in debt for 1974-75		
Averages		19.94		Rs. 10.88 per advance	

Difference in income between the two years: Rs. 34.12 decrease

TABLE 2
COCONUT SALES AND ADVANCES FOR HH Y
(2.25 ACRES)

1973-4

Period till	Nuts	Price cents	Sales Rupees	Advanced Rupees	No. of advances
01/07/73					
04/07/73	340	17	57.80	0.00	
03/12/73	110	25	27.50	106.40	10
31/01/74	200	35	70.00	10.00	1
06/04/74	400	40	160.00	171.50	4
04/06/74	360	40	144.00	60.00	4
30/06/74			109.00	2.00	
Totals	1410		459.30	456.90	21

Rs. 2.40 in credit fo 1973-74

Averages		32.57			

Rs. 21.76 in debt per advance

1974-5

Period till	Nuts	Price cents	Sales Rupees	Advanced Rupees	No. of advances
06/08/74	250	30	75.00	1.50	1
28/09/74	179	30	53.70	55.00	3
27/11/74	250	30	75.00	110.00	4
01/02/75	320	25	80.00	75.00	3
06/04/75	500	15	75.00	125.00	9
30/05/75	375	12	45.00	136.50	4
30/06/75				3.00	1
Totals	1874		403.70	506.00	25

Rs.102.30 for 1974-75

Averages		21.54			

Rs. 20.24 per advance

Difference in income between the two years: Rs.55.60 decrease.

TABLE 3:
REASONS FOR BORROWING (19 JULY 74 - 30 JUNE 75)

N = 56

Consumption

Food/domestic	49	(88%)
New Year	6	(11%)
(clothes and food)		
Clothes	5	(9%)

Emergencies

Medical expenses	12	(21%)
Funeral/mortuary ceremonies	6	(11%)

Miscellaneous

Wedding	4	(7%)
Start a business	5	(9%)
Agriculture[a]	3	(5%)
Education	2	(3%)
Repay debts	2	(3%)
Build a house	0	–
Consumer durables	0	–
Religious ceremonies[b]	0	–

Notes

[a] Reflects lack of cultivation during the year.
[b] Debts for funerals are common. Limiting the period to 1974-5
   distorts the pattern.

TABLE 4:
CREDIT FOR DOMESTIC EXPENDITURE: TYPE AND NUMBER OF SOURCES

N= 49

Number of sources	Shopkeepers[c]	Copra Merchants	Other (relatives and friends)	Employer	Total sources
1	23	12	9	3	47
2	8 (16)[b]		5 (10)	1 (2)	0 (28)
3	1 (3)	0	2 (6)	0	9
4	3 (12)	0	0	0	12
	54 (56%)	22 (23%)	17 (18%)	3 (3%)	96[a]

Notes

a) 96 sources for 49 households: 1.96 is the average number of sources per household.
b) The figures in brackets are numbers of sources; those without brackets are the numbers of households.
c) Many of these shopkeepers are coconut merchants.

TABLE 5: ACCOUNTS AT SHOPS

N=70

	With coconut holdings (N=40) Have accounts: 17 (43%)	Without coconut holdings (N=30) Have accounts: 12 (40%)
Mutubanda	5	5
Tilakasiri	8	3
Chandra	2	2
Punchibanda	1	1
Martin	1	1
Heenbanda	3	1
Gamani	1	1
Tangalle	1	0
Banda	0	2
Ratnayake	0	1
Outside P-G	1	0
	—	—
Total	23	17
Average per household with accounts:	1.35	1.42
Average per all households:	.58	.57

Note: More would get credit from shopkeepers than those who have formal accounts with shopkeepers.

REFERENCES

Alexander, Paul. 1981. "Shared Fantasies and Elite Politics: The Sri Lankan 'Insurrection' of 1971." *Mankind*. 13: 113-132.

Dewey, Alice G. 1962. *Peasant Marketing in Java*. Glencoe, Illinois: The Free Press.

Epstein, T.S. 1983. "Differential Access to Markets and its Implications on Agricultural Development." Paper for the International Workshop on Agricultural Markets in the Semi-Arid Tropics, Oct. 24-28 1983, ICRISAT, Hyderabad, India.

Firth, Raymond and B.S. Yamey. 1964. *Capital, Saving, and Credit in Peasant Societies*. London: George Allen and Unwin.

Geertz, Clifford. 1963. *Peddlers and Princes: Social Change and Economic Modernization in Two Indonesian Towns*. Chicago and London: University of Chicago Press.

Gunawardana, A.M.T., H.D. Sumanasekera, P.J. Gunawardena, and M. Wejetunga. 1981. *Kurunegala District Rural Development Project: An Analysis of the Pre-project Situation* (Research Study Series, 45). Colombo: ARTI.

Harriss, John. 1982. *Capitalism and Peasant Farming; Agrarian Structures and Ideology in Northern Tamil Nadu*. Bombay: Oxford University Press.

Henegedara, G.M. 1984. *A Process Evaluation of Coconut Cultivation in Kurunegala District: A Sub-Study of the Kurunegala Integrated Rural Development Project* (Research Study No. 62). Colombo: ARTI.

Howell, John and Dale W. Adams. 1980. "Introduction" in Howell, John (ed.), *Borrowers and Lenders*. London: ODI.

London, Paul A. 1975. *Merchants as Promoters of Rural Development: An Asian Case Study*. New York: Praeger.

Moore, M.P. 1985. *The State and Peasant Politics in Sri Lanka*. Cambridge: University Press.

Ponnambalam, Satchi. 1981. *Dependent Capitalism in Crisis: The Sri Lankan Economy, 1948-1980*. London: Zed Press.

Scott, James. 1976. *The Moral Economy of the Peasant: Rebellion and Subsistence in Southeast Asia*. New Haven: Yale Univ. Press.

Southwold, Sarah. 1987. "Sri Lankan Traders: A Case Study of Credit Relations and Coconut Marketing in a Rural

Economy." D. Phil. Thesis, University of Sussex.

Sri Lankan Government. 1984a. *Coconut Development Strategy.* Colombo: Ministry of Coconut Industries.

_____. 1984b. *Progress.* Colombo: Ministry of Coconut Industry.

Tilakaratna, S. and U.V.H. Perera. 1981. *An Economic Study of the Coconut Industry of Sri Lanka.* Colombo: People's Bank, Research Dept.

Von Pischke, J.D. 1981. In Consultation with Peter J. Heffernan and Dale W. Adams, *The Political Economy of Specialized Farm Credit Institutions in Low-Income Countries*, Staff Working Paper No. 446. Washington: World Bank.

Yalman, Nur. 1967. *Under the Bo Tree: Studies in Caste, Kinship and Marriage in the Interior of Ceylon.* Berkeley and Los Angeles: University of California Press.

Ward, Barbara E. 1960. "Cash or Credit Crops? An Examination of Some of the Implications of Peasant Commercial Production with Special Reference to the Multiplicity of Traders and Middlemen." *Economic Development and Cultural Change,.* 8 (2).

Wickramasekera, P. 1983. *Expansion of Employment and Income through Local Resource Mobilisation: A Study of Two Sri Lankan Villages* (Asian Development Programme). Geneva: I.L.O.

Chapter 6

HOUSEHOLD RESOURCES, WOMEN AND FOOD SECURITY:
AN ECOSYSTEM PERSPECTIVE
WITH CASE STUDIES FROM AFRICA

Lila E. Engberg

The Centre for Food Security at the University of Guelph (1988) has defined food security "...as ensuring that all members of every household in the nation have access throughout the year to a diet that is adequate for leading a healthy and active working life," but that kind of food security is an impossible dream for many people in Africa. According to CIDA's report "...African food production per capita has fallen at an average annual rate of one percent or more over the past 16 years" (CIDA, 1987: 6). The International Fund for International Development produces the same evidence, stating that "...smallholder farmers are the backbone of food output" and that "...women have emerged as the neglected key to Africa's food security" (Jazairy, 1987: 51). Dey's 1984 review of women's responsibilities in food production and food security in Africa identifies a number of issues, described also by Rwelamira (1987) with particular reference to problems in Lesotha. About 85% of women in Africa are reported to be involved in agriculture. They produce, process and store up to 80% of the food consumed by their families and provide other kinds of day to day provisioning. One of the consequences of this food production and consumption pattern is undernutrition and low productivity (Mureithi, 1987: 44).

Although the Priority Programme for Economic Recovery, 1986-1990, adopted by the OAU in 1985, states that the focus of attention in the food and agriculture sector is to be the peasant farmer with special reference to female farmers there are many constraints (Jazairy, 1987: 53-4). Noted are: unfavourable ecological, political and economic environments, population growth rates and inadequate support of small-farm agriculture (Lofchie and Commins, 1982; Eicher, 1986: Sands, 1986; Jazairy, 1987).

In this paper, another constraint is suggested; that is the lack of understanding of interdependent factors which influence the social organization and economy of the African household. Sands (1986: 2) reminds us that "...the small-scale farming system is embedded within the larger household economy and is organized to meet both the production and consumption goals of the farm family." Singh, Squire and Strauss (1986: 149) acknowledge that semi-commercial farm households do not separate producer and consumer behaviour.

African households, however, are not necessarily integrated systems, to be analysed as though they were unified in their decision-making about production and consumption. Male-female relationships, inside and outside the household, often make it difficult for women to gain access and control of resources (Beneria and Sen, 1981; Staudt, 1984, 1987; White, 1984; Safilios-Rothschild, 1985). Men and women may be members of the same households but aligned with different corporate kin networks. Also, women are generally not a part of the coalitions established by governments to foster food security.

Contributions of men to household functioning and food supply cannot be taken for granted even when there is an increase in cash income. In fact, men may appropriate the fruits of female labour for their own purposes (Staudt, 1987). A case study from Malawi, to be described later, shows that women shifted their labour into tobacco production and reduced the amount of time spent on food crops and domestic work in a tobacco producing village (Engberg, Sabry, and Beckerson, 1988).

In this paper a theoretical perspective and a production model are proposed in order to help us examine the ecology and micro economy of rural households and the influences on food security. First, the perspective and the model will be described, then case studies will be presented as illustrations of how labour is allocated in small-holder agriculture production. Influences on household food supply and nutritional status of household members will be described briefly. It is recognized that micro-level studies alone will not help us understand interdependent factors in a nation's food system, but they will contribute to our understanding.

ECOSYSTEMS PERSPECTIVE

An ecological systems perspective is proposed as a guide to our thinking and research about household food security. An ecosystem or ecological system is a system based on living things in interaction with each other and with their environments. Humans interact within and outside households, with other humans, with plants, animals and various forms of life, and with non-living materials in the environments where they live.

The environment is anything external to the household that impinges on it. One way to conceptualize environment is to consider three major types: 1) the natural environment (air, water, soil, forests, plant and animal life, fuel, etc.); 2) the social environment (kin, neighbours, community, public and private institutions); and 3) the constructed technological environment (agriculture, industry, transportation, housing, tools, facilities, food, clothing, etc.) (Paolucci, Hall and Axinn, 1977; Melson, 1980: 6-12).

The central task of households is to sustain life by obtaining, developing and utilizing resources from each of these environments and from their own system. But households operate within local communities and ecological zones which may have differing sets of resources. Longhurst (1985) provides evidence of difference in three West African countries. Linkages and interrelations between food production and consumption, and rural development are described. Farmers in selected areas are reported to have developed cropping patterns which suit their particular ecological and social situation. Traditional food crops, seasonality and women's activities are the major concerns noted. Average intercropped farms in the Sierra Leone study, for example, contained 20 food crop species in addition to rice (Longhurst, 1985: 13). Often a wide range of so-called "under-exploited" food plants were cultivated or gathered by women in order to meet seasonal shortages. Such activities are informal or non-monetized economic activities and are an essential component of the "whole" economy.

THE WHOLE ECONOMY

Study of the formal, monetized sectors of a national economy rather than the informal non-monetized economies of local communities and households is conventional in the field of economics. The macro-economic growth and modernization theories of development remain dominant and do not take into account the "whole" economy (Lisk, 1983; McFarland, 1988). Resource inputs required of industry and cash crop agriculture, and marketable commodity outputs are measurable and internationally recognized as contributing to national development but not the kinds of transactions which take place at household level.

Household resources are the tools and technology, the personal property, the human capabilities and environmental characteristics that have "use" value, as opposed to purely "market" value in a commercial sense. Household or family goals rather than national development goals are the ends towards which household production efforts and resources are directed. Livelihood goals are urgent but the role of the whole household system and of women in contributing to such goals continues to be underestimated and undersupported (Beneria, 1981; Gallin and Spring, 1985; Robertson, 1988).

A number of writers have urged us to question the dominant views of "economy" and economic development, and to find ways to integrate social and economic concerns. Folbre (1983) presents a helpful critique of the economic assumptions of the Laguna survey carried out by Evenson, Popkin, and Quizon (1979) in the Philippines. She presents a bargaining power perspective, and in a secondary analysis of the data from 576 households, shows how and why changes in access to wealth, income, legal rights, and political power change the nature of decision-making in the household. Huber (1988: 12-13) suggests that a theory of family, economy and gender must begin with "...what men and women do each day to secure food, clothing, and shelter, analyzing how they organize their work around the available tools," and "It must also consider ecological variables that affect human ability to sustain life such as climate, soil, and temperature."

The concept of *whole* economy, as described by Ross and Usher (1986: 55), is significant in its recognition of a continuum in scale, hierarchy and diversity of sectors of the national economy. See figure 1 for a presentation of the "whole." At the lower end of the hierarchy are the voluntary activities, barter and skills exchange, mutual aid, gift giving, household production and other non-market activities. The majority of women participate in this sector of the economy, rather than in the purely formal market sector, and are heavily dependent on resources available in local environments. In the informal sector a system of grants rather than exchanges prevail. According to Boulding (1973: 1-26) grants do not follow the rules of the market. They are one-way transfers of resources with no rules for reciprocity.

Figure 1
The World Economy

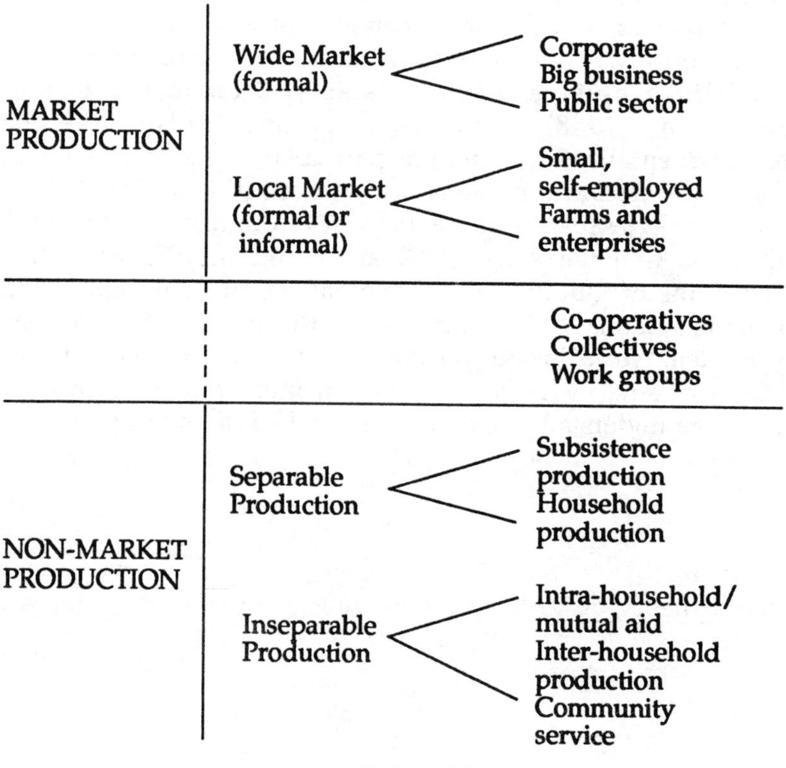

MARKET PRODUCTION	Wide Market (formal)	Corporate Big business Public sector
	Local Market (formal or informal)	Small, self-employed Farms and enterprises
		Co-operatives Collectives Work groups
NON-MARKET PRODUCTION	Separable Production	Subsistence production Household production
	Inseparable Production	Intra-household/ mutual aid Inter-household production Community service

(Adapted from Ross and Usher, 1986: 55)

At the top of the whole system hierarchy is the large scale market economy which includes the corporate sector of business and industry and the public or government sectors. Both have formalized national and international links and are politically powerful systems in comparison to the small sub-systems of community, family and household. In between the formal market and informal non-market economies, are the collectives, co-operatives and community enterprises. These are the non-profit or profit-sharing organizations which integrate social and economic goals. Co-operatives, for example, represent a form of collective which depends on social outreach. Management style differs from that of the corporate sector; is less hierarchical and more participatory in its organization.

The terms formal and informal economy are commonly used to designate differences in the structure of market transactions. The concept of informal economy is characteristic of the small self-employed, non-standardized and non-organized labour sector as contrasted to the modern regulated wage labour sector. Small business enterprises, street hawking, petty trading, transportation, recycling, and repair are examples found throughout the world (CUSO, 1987). But this interpretation of informal sector activities omits non-market work. The concept of formal/informal seems to imply a dualistic framework with mutually exclusive labour systems. Breman (1976) and Robertson (1988) state that labour cannot be so compartmentalized. Women, in particular, work in a range of economic sectors within the same day. According to Tiano (1981), it is difficult to separate household work from remunerated work carried out at home. Anker (1983) and Boulding (1983) argue that definitions of labour force participation and data collection methods systematically underestimate the amount of work done by women. Work "inside" the household is particularly invisible. Studies of such work by women and men cannot begin until there is an understanding of the household as a unit of analysis.

UNITS OF ANALYSIS:
FAMILIES OR HOUSEHOLDS

The definition of family and household for purposes of analysis is a conceptual problem. It is clear that the nuclear family or the conjugal family unit cannot be accepted as universal nor form the basis for studies of the household economy. The term "family" in Africa, for example, refers to the lineage and includes a large group of kin related by blood. *Household* is not necessarily co-terminous with family. White (1980: 13) suggests that we need not seek a universal definition to guide our research but seek out the household group "...which exercises the greatest autonomy (relative to other groupings in the society) with respect to responsibility for the well-being of its members."

Oppong (1982: 133) suggests examining family structure and women's familial rights and obligations within the kin network. Frequently different sets of kin are involved in various processes. Men are more involved with the social, ceremonial and political at community and national levels while women are involved with the more "private" day to day provisioning of food. In most African societies women are the centre of domestic functioning (Oppong, 1982; Safilios-Rothschild, 1985). Oppong, therefore, proposes a framework for analysis centred on women (1982: 145-147). In her analysis the household is defined in terms of the domestic group which has specific functions of production, reproduction, consumption, and of social, ceremonial and political interaction. In the analysis emphasis is placed on household function rather than on composition. Africa's rural households and farming systems are described more fully by Moock (1986).

The domestic domain is not necessarily a fixed and "natural" category of work for women. Feminists are quick to point out the danger of isolating the domestic sphere and of gender-typing activities and relationships within households (Harris, 1981). A woman's support system, however, revolves around the domestic and allows her to participate both inside and outside the boundaries of her household.

THE HOUSEHOLD ECONOMY

The concept of "whole" economy respects all categories of work or production carried out by humans, work with *exchange* value and work with *use* value. While Figure 1 gave us an expanded view of the national economy, Figure 2 presents possible overlapping domains of activity of a single household. Families or households organize the involvement of household members in each of these production sectors. Suggested categories of economic participation are:

a) commercial agriculture, or non-wage production of crops and livestock for the market

b) wage employment in the local or wider economy

c) self-employment in small scale enterprises such as trading or personal services

d) subsistence or household production of the goods and services to be used by household members

e) inseparable home production (child bearing, transmission of skills and knowledge, services to kin or community, maintenance of the labour force)

f) co-operative and voluntary community labour.

Household production and home production (d and e) are designated as separable and inseparable forms of production by Beutler and Owen (1980). These are important distinctions. Household production, first defined by Reid (1934: 11), is called *separable* because the activities involved may be delegated to others and separated from consumption. Home production, on the other hand, has "use" value and is not marketable. It has been called *inseparable* because of the human attributes and relationships involved in the activity. Also it is difficult to separate conceptually from consumption. The production categories described above subsume the production-reproduction concept common to social anthropology.

Three types of inseparable home production, described by Beutler and Owen (1980), have social dimensions. Activities contribute to sustaining the family and community, thus cannot be handed over to "outsiders" or paid workers. Note the descriptions below and the case study from Malawi as an illustration of the use of such categories.

1) *Intrahousehold* production takes place inside the household and includes such activities as teaching a son or daughter something in order to shape social behaviour or maintain a parental relationship. Cooking and serving a meal, in some family situations, might qualify as an inseparable obligatory activity. In fact, many goods and services, produced in households, contribute to social relationships rather than to economic efficiency.

2) *Interhousehold* production is the mutual aid or obligatory services carried out to help other households.

3) *Community Service* is the voluntary activity to which most households contribute in order to maintain their status or membership. Solidarity and self-help activities at community level could help generate and shape opportunities for families.

Figure 2
Categories of Work or Household Production

Market
Production

(logic of survival)

Non-Market
Production

(logic of survival)

237

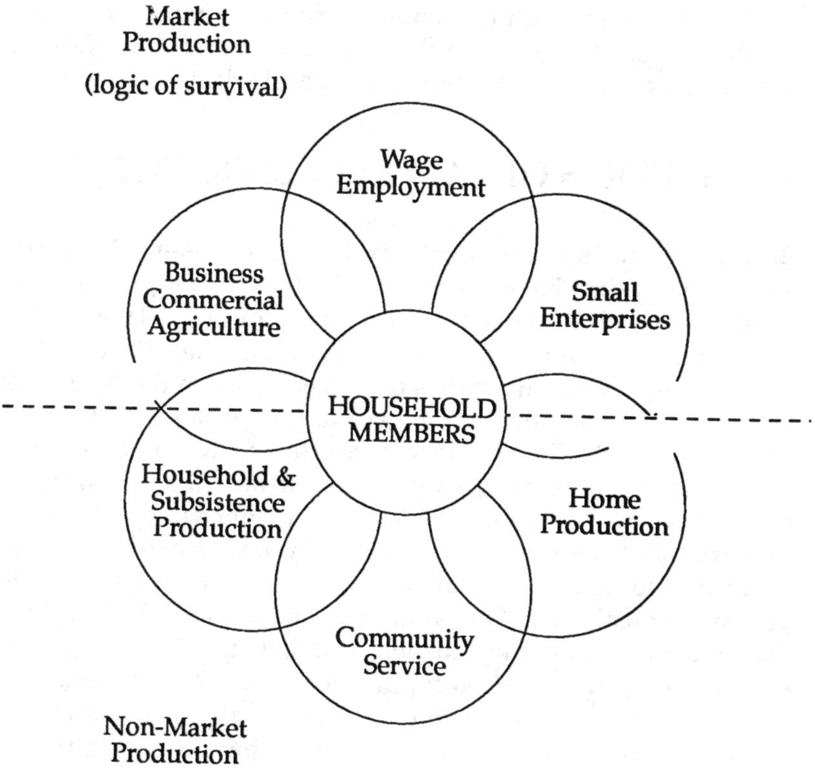

The expression "family status production" used by Papanek (1979) recognizes the importance to households of political status maintenance in a community, through formal and informal gift exchanges and participation in ceremonials. Time is allowed for such community activities and cannot be ignored.

Men and women do not develop their economic enterprises in isolation from each other. Neither do farming systems function in isolation from households (Sands, 1986). The Farming Systems Research and Development approach is said to be holistic in recognizing interaction of soils, water sources, crops, livestock, labour, and other resources within an environmental setting, but the tendency is to isolate farming from other income-earning household enterprises and community activities which consume resources and labour time (Garrett, 1983; Axinn, 1984). Household resources which are allocated to one enterprise are not available for another, hence the need to consider household as a whole system. The only way to find out who participates and who benefits from the allocation of resources is through community or village based household studies which disaggregate data by gender and age. National surveys cannot easily take into account ecological differences.

STUDIES OF LABOUR ALLOCATION

Because time is measurable and its use observable, time allocation studies have become a tool for learning more about human activity patterns (Minge-Klevena, 1980). The International Labour Organization (ILO) has funded two publications reviewing studies of unpaid work in the household and economic methods of evaluation (Goldschmidt-Clermont, 1982 and 1987). Time allocation studies were the central component of the studies of the non-market, subsistence economy of 872 men and 928 women in eight villages in Nepal (Acharya and Bennett, 1981). The study revealed that the time spent by women on formal economic activities was about 80 percent of men's time (an average of 4.62 versus 5.81 hours per day); with subsistence production added, women's average daily time input increased (6.80 for women and 6.72 for men); and with domestic activities included the over-all work burden for women increased to 10.81 hours average per day compared to 7.51 hours for the men (Acharya and Bennett, 1981: 306).

A number of other researchers have used time allocation or time-budget methods for intensive investigations of activity patterns or the sexual division of labour in small communities: Hanger and Morris in Kenya (1973); Clark in Malawi (1975); Gillespie in Nicaragua (1979); Evenson, Popkin, and Quizon in the Philippines (1979); Berio in Ivory Coast (1980); Tripp in Ghana (1982); Bloch in Senegal (Messer and Bloch, 1983); Grossman in Papua New Guinea (1984).

Basically three methods of collecting time-use data were used in the above studies: 1) the interview, asking respondents to recall time spent the day before on a limited number of pre-categorized activities; 2) day-long continuous observations providing a complete narrative record of all activities performed by one individual or as many as could be observed at one time; 3) random spot observations of activities. Usually a combination of recall and observation have been used. The self-study or time-diary method, where respondents record their own use of time, is a fourth method. It is not commonly used among illiterate populations but has been tried in India. The case study from Malawi, to be described next, is an example of random observations and interview data collection methods, and categorization of work based on the production activity model described earlier.

CASE STUDIES FROM AFRICA

Comparison of Time — Use in Two Villages in Malawi

A time-use study from Malawi demonstrates the use of a "whole" economy framework and the consequences of male and female labour allocation during two seasons (Beckerson, 1983). The purpose of the study was to compare work time of men and women in two farming villages and the influences on food supply and nutritional status of household members in one ecological zone. All of the participating households in the neighbouring study villages (32 registered tobacco growers in Mkwinda and 31 semi-subsistence food producers in Patsankhono) were members of the Chewa ethnic group. Apart from the attempts to implement government policy for tobacco production, the environmental conditions were similar. Data related to husbands' and wives' time use were categorized into four sub-sectors of production: market, subsistence, household, and inseparable home production.

The results of the time-use study are shown in Table 1. The mean time spent daily by the wives on all production activities combined, was about 12 hours regardless of season. In comparison the mean time spent by the husbands was 4.1 to 6.4 hours per day. The greatest time commitment for the men (average 6.4 hours per day) was in tobacco production during the growing season. The women in the tobacco producing village shifted their labour time away from home production to market production during the growing season. Time-allocation of men and women to subsistence production was more equitable in the semi-subsistence food producing village (Engberg, Sabry and Beckerson, 1988).

The consequences in terms of food stored and utilized are shown in Tables 2 and 3. In the food producing village, the food supply and the nutritional status of household members were sustained between seasons. Table 4 shows the proportion of children with normal weight for height in the two villages. Note that a greater proportion of children in the tobacco producing village lost weight between February and July.

Unfortunately the data collected about inseparable home production in the Malawi study is incomplete. The time spent in home-based learning, in helping kin and neighbours, in attendance at funerals or in community self-help was not recorded. It was noted, however, that interviews had to be rescheduled several times because the respondents were away at funerals.

Although the sample size was small, Beckerson (1983) was able to observe system dynamics and how the macro-level policies for tobacco production supported the work of male farmers. Decisions related to production were related to the power of males to appropriate the labour of women. It may not have been the women's choice to reduce time spent on subsistence and household production and suffer a seasonal food deficit. Such questions are speculative for the above study, but they are the kinds of questions that can be asked in micro-level studies of households.

The unit of analysis in the Malawi study was the household defined as "...a unit which could include family members and persons other than kin, who occupy a housing unit and act as a social unit in terms of division of labor, social interaction and sharing of benefits" (Beckerson, 1983: 7).

Household and Food Resources in Chilunga Village, Malawi

Let us turn now to the issue of resources and another case study from Malawi. The labour of men and women is the major resource discussed so far, but other resources need to be described and the systems of gaining access and control of these resources. Various means of access change. To be noted are means such as: marriage, inheritance, kin or group affiliation, gifts or income transfers, purchases with cash, leasing or rental arrangements, social relations and reciprocity.

A study of 66 households in Chilunga village, near Zomba in Malawi was undertaken in 1986 by Stephanie Ounpuu (1988). Female respondents were chosen for the study in order to assess the relationship of their resources to food availability and nutritional status of their 3-5-year-old children. A census of the village identified the women with eligible children (Ounpuu, 1988: 128). Thirty-two joint headed households (male and female heads present for at least three days a week), and 28 female headed households were randomly selected from the census data in order to make comparisons.

The study was divided into three parts: three consecutive day-long observations of activity patterns; concurrent three-day weighted dietary records for the child; and interviews of the women to find out about household and agricultural characteristics during three seasons; March/April (harvest and peak food season, July/August (post harvest, peak food) and October/November (planting and lean food period) (Ounpuu, 1988: 8).

Chilunga village is a semi-subsistence farming village in an ecological zone which is less productive than that of the villages described earlier. The people are predominantly Yao in ethnic origin and practise a matrilineal system of inheritance. This means that women are resident in the village of their birth and have rights to farm and inherit land which belongs to their lineage even though widowed or divorced. The women of Chilunga had access to land but the average size of the land

241

holdings in Zomba District is generally under one hectare (average .72 hectares). A study of rural women in the District by Hirschmann and Vaughan (1984) indicated that the number of divorced and separated women in that locality was higher than the national average, and in the absence of men, the women relied on the female sorority group or mbumba.

After harvest in July, 46.7 percent of the households in the sample were headed by women. This is above the average of 36.9 percent reported for Zomba District in the 1980/81 National Sample Survey of Agriculture. Men were absent from time to time participating in the wage economy; 21.7 percent of the households were involved in both farm and non-farm enterprises.

In Zomba District, where Chilunga village is located, 89.5 percent of the cultivated area is planted to maize, the traditional food crop (National Sample Survey of Agriculture, 1981). The Government of Malawi has been attempting to introduce high yielding varieties of hybrid maize in pure stands, for more than 20 years, but with little success on small-holder farms. During the time of the Chilunga study, only one household out of the 66 in the sample, cultivated an improved variety of maize. Most of the maize was interplanted with other crops: pumpkin, sweet potatoes, ground nuts, pigeon peas and other types of legumes needed for human survival. Out of 66, 38 households (61.3%) used fertilizer.

In regards to Chilunga women's access to agricultural tools, all women had the use of a hoe, 57.6% had an axe; 40.9%, a panga (large knife); 47.0%, a sickle; 15.2%%, a cutlass. For means of transport, 3.0% had the use of an ox and ox-cart for hauling produce; 45.2%, a bicycle used by the men of the household. The headload was the chief means of hauling used by the women. Women shared the use of buckets, clay pots, mortar and pestle and other household utensils. They had access to land, labour, tools and equipment by virtue of their kin relationships.

The major foods consumed by the sample households before and after harvest (based on a 3-day food recall in each season) are shown in Table 5. A larger number of households consumed a variety of staples (maize, sorghum, rice, cassava, sweet potatoes) after harvest. Very few processed foods were purchased. Food items purchased by two to sixteen households included tea, sugar, potashes, margarine, cooking oil and locally made fried cakes. The cakes were purchased as a snack food in the busy planting season in November.

Regarding women's labour time, Ounpuu examined six categories of time-use: food preparation, food processing, food gathering, water and fuel collection, farming activities and other income-generation activities (1988: 207). An average of 3.7 hours per day was spent on food preparation during the March/April season as compared to 2.8 hours during the planting season in November (Ounpuu, 1988: 207). Farming activities took an average of 12 minutes per day in March/April, 66 minutes per day in November (the planting season), an average of 6 minutes in July/August (after harvest). The average work time regardless of season was 6.4 hours per day, not a heavy work load compared to the women in Beckerson's study. However, the farm size was smaller and resources were limited. Also, Ounpuu did not collect data on the full range of men's and women's activities.

All the women in the study occasionally engaged in self-employed cash earning activities such as processing and sale of food crops and the brewing of beer, in the period after harvest and in the planting season, but they spent only an average of 10 to 30 minutes per day on such activity. (Ounpuu, 1988: 207). The most time consuming activity for the women was food preparation, taking an average of 2.8 to 3.7 hours per day, less time during the planting season than at other times.

Details of the nutritional status of the children in the sample will not be presented here. It was noted that the mean number of children per woman in the study was 5.4 (Ounpuu, 1988: 30), and that chronic child malnutrition showed up as stunting, rather than acute malnutrition. Seasonal differences observed in the prevalence of children classified as severely stunted and severely underweight suggest that seasonal differences in food availability are an important factor to consider (Ounpuu, 1988: 33-59).

Traditional Farming Systems in Nigeria

According to Okigbo (1986) and Okoro (1987), exploitation of traditional food plants in the context of the compound or homestead farming system has great potential for increasing food production. The compound farm system is reported to be the widespread permanent system which forms the centre of agricultural systems in many parts of Nigeria. Paths lead from the centre to other fields and other producing units which are a part of the household economy. The largest variety of crops found in mixtures are found in the compound or the piece of land near the dwelling. Plants are grown for food, oils, fats, condiments, spices, nuts, drugs, beverages, structural materials, bark, fibre, firewood, animal feed, boundary markers, masticants, stimulants, protection and shade, ornamentals, and for religious and social functions. Women have a vested interest in maintaining such a system because they want a reliable, year round source of vegetables, fruits and condiments. Report of a compound farm survey in Imo State, Nigeria, indicated that average yields from the compound farm were superior to those of other fields (Okoro, 1987). Many of these food items do not reach the market, and have the potential of being ignored.

CONCLUSION

The major objective of this paper was to present an ecological systems perspective and a more holistic view of the small-scale household economy. The "whole" economy perspective takes into account both market and non-market production within local ecological systems. In agricultural economies such as those in Malawi participation in the non-market economy is widespread. The two case studies presented from Malawi are illustrative. They are micro-level studies, presented as examples of studies which take a more integrated approach to the food problem. Relationships between activity patterns, household resources, food supply and nutritional status were examined. The case study from Nigeria, illustrates the wide variety of crops which are a part of the informal household economy. We suggest that many small-holder farm households in Africa, continue to produce, transform and process a large number of raw materials into the essentials needed for day to day survival. They are heavily dependent on the land and resources found in their own environments, and on the labour of women for obtaining their food supply.

The immediate environment is the context for households and their members. Men and women are not restricted to local environments, but work in small-farm production requires that more attention be paid to the whole ecological system and three environments: the natural, social and constructed. Within the social hierarchy women are somewhat more restricted than men. Men can transcend the boundaries of their household and family and participate more fully in the formal economy, but day to day provisioning continues to be assigned to women. Historically, women's income earning activities and responsibilities for food have tended to mesh with those of child rearing and home-based work. The compound farms of Nigeria, managed by women, are an example of indigenous knowledge systems, women's contribution to the household food supply and human survival.

In attempting to understand issues of household food security in Africa and elsewhere, it is important to link the many levels of concern. Female farmers cannot accomplish increased household food security on their own. They are part of a national cash-based system which places emphasis on exports. An ecological systems approach to the food problem would encourage interrelated macro and micro level studies and new program approaches which involve rural people. In developing programs for small-holder farmers, it is essential to involve the people themselves in examining the system of household organization, resource allocation, and the interdependence of various sectors of production. Production of food for local consumption and production of marketable commodities are interdependent activities. Both are essential to livelihood.

Time allocation studies at household level will help us understand activity patterns of men, women and children and labour constraints but may not help national level policy decisions about household food security. Among the factors which shape government policies and the allocation of resources are the alignments or linkages which form. Men are more likely than women to be able to form linkages inside the family and beyond the household, and to control resources for purposes other than household food security. Thus, it is important that men be involved, along with women, in identifying food problems as well as other livelihood issues. The ecological systems perspective assumes interdependence and participation in developing systems of action for small-farm households at village level. It is suggested that integration of research, training, and extension can take place at village level and facilitate action. The challenge at national and international levels is to allow such an approach.

Table 1

Time Spent by Husbands and Wives on Production Activities[1]
hours per day

Season & Farming Systems	Sex	Market Production	Home Production			
			a	b	c	Total
February						
Tobacco (Mkwinda)						
	M	4.1	0.4	0.6	1.3	6.4
	F	3.8	2.5	4.1	1.8	12.2
Semi-Subsistence (Patsankhondo)						
	M	0.3	2.4	0.6	1.3	4.6
	F	1.6	4.3	5.1	1.3	12.3
July Tobacco						
	M	0.2	2.4	0.9	0.6	4.1
	F	0.2	5.5	6.1	1.2	13.0
Semi-Subsistence						
	M	0.1	5.5	0.2	0.4	6.2
	F	0.4	4.9	5.4	1.3	12.0

14 husbands and 14 wives in each village.
a. subsistence
b. household
c. social

Source: [1]Beckerson, p. 117.

Table 2

Traditional Foods Stored by Type of Farming Household[1]

Season & Household Type	Maize (cu. metre)	Groundnuts (cu. metre)	Beans/Peas (kg)	Dried Leaves (cu. cm)
February Tobacco	0.71[a]	0	0	0
Semi-Subsistence	0.87[b]	0.12	0.8	0
July Tobacco	10.62	1.73	16.65	356.4
Semi-Subsistence	14.64	2.41	22.62	312.2

[a]Seven out of the 14 households had no maize when data were collected, having emptied their stores 5-9 weeks earlier.

[b]Four out of the 14 households had no maize, having emptied their stores 2-4 weeks earlier.

Table 3

Household Meals by Type of Farming and Season[2]

Season & Household Type	No. of meals (per day)	No. of cups of flour (per day)
February Tobacco	2.1	12.1
Semi-Subsistence	2.4	18.4
July Tobacco	2.4	16.3
Semi-Subsistence	2.7	21.2

Source: [1]Beckerson, p. 131 [2] Beckerson, p. 136

Table 4

Proportion of Children with
Normal Weight for Height in Two Seasons[1]

Season	Household Type	Per Cent
February	Tobacco	15.1
	Semi-Subsistence	28.8
July	Tobacco	6.9
	Semi-Subsistence	28.8

Source: [1]Beckerson, p. 162

Table 5

Seasonal Changes in Major Foods
Consumed by Households in Chilunga, Malawi
(One or more times per day)   n=60

Foods Consumed	March/ April	July (after harvest)
Nsima (from refined maize flour)	58	28
Ngaiwa (from unrefined maize flour)	27	14
Mapira (from sorghum)	0	30
Rice	5	37
Cassava	8	25
Sweet Potatoes	14	23
Groundnuts	42	11
Groundnut flour	22	38
Local fried cakes	3	9
Green leaves	43	45
Tomatoes	30	57
Fresh fish (small)	12	4
Dried fish	25	25
Smoked fish (large)	2	11
Chicken	2	3
Eggs	4	1

(Based on a 3-day food recall carried out by S. Ounpuu in 1986)

REFERENCES

Acharya, M. and Bennett, L. 1981. *The Rural Women of Nepal: An Aggregate Analysis and Summary of Eight Village Studies.* (Kathmandu, Nepal). Centre for Economic Development and Administration.

Anker, Richard. 1983. "Female Labour Force Participation in Developing Countries: A Critique of Current Definitions and Data Collection Methods," *International Labour Review.* 122: 709-724.

Axinn, N. 1984. "The Family and the Farm System: Some Thoughts on Collaborative Research," *The Rural Sociologist.* 4: 278-282.

Beckerson, Susan A. 1983. Seasonal Labour Allocation, Food Supply, and Nutrition in Subsistence and Semi-subsistence Farming Households in Malawi, Africa. Unpublished M.Sc. Thesis, Guelph, Ontario. University of Guelph.

Beneria, Lourdes. 1981. "Conceptualizing the Labour Force: The Underestimation of Women's Economic Activities," in Nelson, N. (ed.) *African Women in the Development Process.* London: Frank Cass & Co. Ltd. 1-28.

Beneria, Lourdes and Sen, Gita. 1981. "Accumulation, Reproduction, and Women's Role in Economic Development: Boserup Revisited," *Signs - Journal of Women in Culture and Society,* Special Issue: Development and the Sexual Division of Labor. Winter 7 (2): 279-298.

Beutler, Ivan and Owen, Alma. 1980. "A Home Production Activity Model," *Home Economics Research Journal.* 9: 16-26.

Berio, A. J. 1980. "The Analysis of Time Allocation and Activity Patterns in Nutrition and Rural Development Planning," FAO, Rome. *Food and Nutrition Bulletin.* 6:53-58.

Boulding, K. 1973. *Economy of Love and Fear.* Belmont, California: Wadsworth Publishers.

Boulding, Elise. 1983. "Measures of Women's Work in the Third World: Problems and Suggestions," in Buvinic, M., Lycette, M. A., and McGreevey, W. P. (eds.). Baltimore, MD: The John Hopkins University Press: 286-299.

Breman, Jan. 1976. "A Dualistic Labour System? A Critique of the Informal Sector Concept," *Economic and Political Weekly*: 1870-1876.

Centre for Food Security. 1988. Statement of Proposed Policy and Programme, University of Guelph.

CIDA. 1987. "Understanding Africa's Crisis," *Development - Special Issue: Africa*. Canadian International Development Agency: 6.

Clark, B. A. 1975. "The Work Done by Rural Women in Malawi," *Eastern Journal of Rural Development*. 8: 82-91.

CUSO. 1987. *The Informal Economy*. Ottawa, Canada: Canadian University Service Overseas. (December).

Dey, Jennie. 1984. *Women in Food Production and Food Security in Africa* #3, FAO Women in Agriculture Series No. 3. Rome: Food and Agriculture Organization of the UN.

Eicher, C. K. 1986. *Transforming African Agriculture*. San Francisco: The Hunger Project Papers, 4 (January).

Engberg, Lila E., Sabry, Jean H. and Beckerson, Susan A. 1988. "A Comparison of Rural Women's Time Use and Nutritional Consequences in Two Villages in Malawi," in Poats, S. V., Schmink, M. and Spring, A. (eds.) *Gender Issues in Farming Systems Research and Extension*: Boulder Colorado: Westview Press, Inc.: 100-110.

Evenson, R. E., Popkin, M. M. and Quizon, E. King. 1979. "Nutrition, Work and Demographic Behavior in Rural Philippine Households: A Synopsis of Several Laguna Household Studies," Discussion paper No. 308. New Haven, Conn.: Yale University Economic Growth Center.

Folbre, N. 1983. "Household Production in the Philippines: A Non-Neoclassical Approach" (Working Paper #26). *Women in International Development*. East Lansing: Michigan State University.

Gallin, R. S. and Spring, A. 1985. (eds.) *Women Creating Wealth: Transforming Economic Development*. Washington, D. C.: Selected papers and speeches from the Association for Women in Development Conference.

Garrett, P. 1983. "Farming Systems Research: An Introduction to the Literature," *The Rural Sociologist*. 3: 229-231.

Gillespie, V. H. 1979. "Rural Women's Time Use," in *Learning*

About Rural Women. New York: Studies in Family Planning. The Population Council. pp. 383-390.

Goldschmidt-Clermont, L. 1982. *Unpaid Work in the Household: A Review of Economic Evaluation Methods.* Geneva: International Labour Office.

Goldschmidt-Clermont, L. 1987. *Economic Evaluations of Unpaid Household Work: Africa, Asia, Latin America and Oceania.* Geneva: International Labour Office.

Grossman, L. S. 1984. "Collecting Time-Use Data in Third World Rural Communities," in *The Professional Geographer.* 36: 444-454.

Hanger, J. and Morris, J. 1973. "Women in the Household Economy," in Chambers, R. and Morris, J. (eds.) *Mwea - An Irrigated Rice Settlement in Kenya.* Verlag, Munich: Weltform: 209-244.

Harris, O. 1981. "Households as Natural Units," in K. Young, C. Wolkowitz and R. McCullagh (eds.). *Of Marriage and the Market.* Women's Subordination in International Perspective, London: CSE Books, pp. 46-68.

Hirschmann, D. and Vaughan M. 1984. *Women Farmers of Malawi: Food Production in Zomba District.* University of California, Berkley: Institute of International Studies.

Huber, J. 1988. "A Theory of Family, Economy, and Gender," *Journal of Family Issues,* 9(1): 9-26.

Jazairy, I. 1987. "How to Make Africa Self-Sufficient in Food," *Development: Seeds of Change* Special Double Issue 2/3. pp. 50-56.

Lisk, F. 1983. "Conventional Development Strategies and Basic Needs Fulfillment," in Todara, M. P. *The Struggle for Economic Development.* New York: Longman: 41-55.

Lofchie, M. F. and Commins, S. K. 1982. "Food Deficits and Agricultural Policies in Tropical Africa," in *The Journal of Modern African Studies.* 20: 1-25.

Longhurst, R. 1985. "Cropping Systems and Household Food Security: Evidence from Three West African Countries," FAO, United Nations, Rome: *Food and Nutrition* Vol. 11, No. 2: 10-16.

McFarland, J. 1988. "The Construction of Women and

Development Theory," *Canadian Review of Sociology and Anthropology*, 25(2): 299-308.

Melson, G. F. 1980. *Family and Environment: An Ecosystem Perspective*. Minneapolis: Burgess Publishing Co.

Messer, E. and Bloch, M. N. 1983. "Women's and Children's Activity Profiles in Senegal and Mexico: A Comparison of Time Allocation Methods," Working Paper #42 *Women in International Development*. East Lansing: University of Michigan.

Minge-Klevena, W. 1980. "Does Labor Time Decrease with Industrialization? A Survey of Time Allocation Studies," *Current Anthropology*. 21, 55-86.

Moock, J. L. 1986. *Understanding Africa's Rural Households and Farming Systems*. Boulder, Colorado: Westview Press.

Mureithi, L. P. 1987. "Crisis and Recovery in African Agriculture: Priorities for Dialogue and Action," *Development: Seeds of Change* Special Double Issue 2/3: 44-49.

National Sample Survey of Agriculture. 1981. *Household Characteristics, Labour Availability and Garden Details*. NSSA, Volume I. Zomba, Gov. of Malawi. National Statistical Office.

Okigbo, Bede N. 1986. "Broadening the Food Base: the Potential of Traditional Food Plants, *Food and Nutrition*." Rome: FAO. 12(1): 4-17.

Okoro, E. 1987. "Household Food Security - The Compound Farm," in Badir, D. (ed.) *Economic Security and Family Survival in Africa* (Conference Proceedings). Paris: International Federation for Home Economics: 105-110.

Olin, U. 1976. "A Case for Women as Co-Managers: The Family as a General Model of Human Social Organization," in I. Tinker and M. Bo Bramson (eds.). *Women and World Development*. Washington: Overseas Development Council. (pp. 105-128).

Oppong, C. 1982. "Family Structure and Women's Reproductive and Productive Roles: Some Conceptual and Methodological Issues," in Anker, R., Buvinic, M. and Yousseff, N. H. (eds.) *Women's Roles and Population Trends in the Third World*, London: Croom Helm: 133-150.

Ounpuu, S. 1988. "Seasonality, Child Nutrition and Women's

Activity Patterns: A Case Study from Chilungu Village, Malawi." Unpublished M.Sc. Thesis. University of Guelph.

Paolucci, B., Hall, O. and Axinn, N. 1977. *Family Decision-Making: An Ecosystems Approach*. New York: Wiley Publishers.

Papenek, H. 1979. "Family Status Production: The 'Work' and 'Non-work' of Women," *SIGNS: Journal of Women in Culture and Society*. 4, 775-781.

Reid, M. 1934. *Economics of Household Production*. New York: Wiley and Sons.

Robertson, C. 1988. "Invisible Workers: African Women and the Problem of the Self-Employed in Labour History," *Journal of African and Asian Studies*, 23 (1-2): 180-198.

Ross, D. P. and Usher, P. J. 1986. *From the Roots Up - Economic Development as if Community Mattered*. Toronto: James Lorimer and Co., Publishers.

Rwelamira, J. K. 1987. "Household Food Security and the Role of Women, with Special Reference to Lesotha." Paper presented at the Conference on Food Security Issues in Southern Africa. Maseru, Lesotho. 12-14 January.

Safilios-Rothschild, C. 1985. "The Persistence of Women's Invisibility in Agriculture: Theoretical and Policy Lessons from Lesotha and Sierra Leone," *Economic Development and Culture Change*. 33(2): 299-317.

Sands, D. M. 1986. *The Technology Applications Gap: Overcoming Constraints to Small-Farm Development*. FAO Research and Technology Paper No. 1. Rome, Italy: Food and Agriculture Organization, United Nations.

Singh, I., Squire, L. and Strauss, J. 1986. "A Survey of Agricultural Household Models: Recent Findings and Policy Implications," *The World Bank Economic Review.*. 1(1): 149-179.

Staudt, K. 1984. *Women's Politics and Capitalists Transformation in Subsaharan Africa*, Working Paper No. 54, Women in International Development. East Lansing: Michigan State University.

Staudt, K. 1987. "Uncaptured or Unmotivated? Women and the Food Crisis in Africa," *Rural Sociology*. 52(1): 37-55.

Tiano, S. 1981. "The Separation of Women's Remunerated and Household Work: Theoretical Perspectives on Women in

Development," *Women in International Development*. Working Paper No. 02. East Lansing: Michigan State University.

Tripp, R. B. 1982. "Time Allocation in Northern Ghana: An Example of the Random Visit Method," *Jr. of Developing Areas*. 16: 391-400.

White, B. N. F. 1980. "Rural Household Studies in Anthropological Perspective," in Binswanger, H. P., Evanson, R. E., Florencio, C. A., White, B. N. F. (eds.) *Rural Households in Asia*. Kent Ridge, Singapore: Singapore University Press.

White, M. A. 1984. *Breaking the Circular Hold: Taking on the Patriarchal and Ideological Biases in Traditional Economic Theory*. Occasional Paper No. 7 in Social Policy Analysis. Toronto, Ontario: Centre for Women's Studies in Education. Ontario Institute for Studies in Education.

Chapter 7

POLICY CHANGES AND NEW AGRICULTURAL TECHNOLOGY:
STRUCTURAL CHANGE IN NORTHERN CHINESE AGRICULTURE

Wayne C. Pfeiffer and Changqing Song

As China races to modernize its economy and struggles to control its population, the agricultural industry is weighing more heavily in the policy-making process than ever before. For thousands of years China has been an Agrarian society. Even today, at least fifty percent of the more than one billion Chinese live in rural areas and farm for a living. Today that farming is changing rapidly thanks to the introduction of new land holding policies and technology. Probably the most dramatic change in Chinese agriculture can be seen in the northern province of Heilongjiang. Since 1949, when the Chinese Communist Party under the leadership of Mao Zedong successfully took control of the country, continuous efforts have been made to develop the agriculture of the northern region. It is here that the famous State Farming System of China was born. There are many reasons behind the creation of the State Farming System ranging from re-deployment of revolutionary soldiers to reclaiming wetlands desperately needed to produce food. Hundreds of thousands of demobilized soldiers were available to work on agrarian projects. Heilongjiang province was a natural and obvious choice for re-deployment of this many skilled and unskilled workers. Today there are over one hundred State Farms in the State Farming System. They are all large, modern, mechanized farms.

They use farming practices that are comparable with those in Canada, the United States, or Western Europe.

During the 1960s and 1970s, prior to and during the cultural revolution in China, much of the large machinery needed for Chinese agriculture in the north was obtained from Eastern Bloc countries. Since 1978, North American agricultural equipment has found its way to Heilongjiang Province. Large state farms are the Chinese equivalent of Agri-business. Their output has been steadily increasing in the north. This decade will be the first time in history that China is able to feed its own population. With the successes of its agricultural reform, China is seeking places to export certain commodities. China's recent appearance as a net exporter on the world market for food has aroused great interest in the western countries, particularly in North America where net food export occurs consistently, year after year, to keep the agricultural industry running.

It is becoming apparent in China that while the State Farm System has been very successful in producing food, there is, in fact, underemployment in the system. A means by which to put labourers to work in more productive pursuits has been the focus of recent policy reforms. The allowance of private farming enterprises to take place along-side the State Farming enterprises or the Communal farms has been introduced. Private farming, of course, is not new to China. Farmers in China were private farmers for thousands of years. In fact, the "reformed" policy is seen by older Chinese as a return to traditional ways. However, this time, there is a completely new infrastructure which can support the endeavours of the new private farmers. As this process unfolds and as technology from the West enters Chinese agriculture, many adjustments will necessarily have to take place.

Because of the excess of agricultural labour in the north, the new policy reforms probably mean fundamental structural change is in store for Chinese agriculture. Not only in Heilongjiang province, but probably in many other places in China as well. It is very difficult to obtain statistics on the agricultural system in North, Central, or Southern China. However, what we do know allows us to construct several possible scenarios for the adjustments to rural communities which China most certainly faces. One such scenario is the subject of this chapter. The optimistic scenario of adjustment which is hypothesized is expected to affect the most people and seeks a Pareto optimal outcome.

Background

China, under the leadership of Deng Xioping, has embarked on a radical new course of economic modernization and social change. While urban China is seeing unprecedented rates of change, the rural areas are experiencing the greatest changes in Chinese history.

Over the past decade, economic and political reforms in the Chinese countryside have brought about fundamental changes in the operation of the rural economy. The central aim of these reforms has been the enhancement of agricultural productivity. A major assumption has been that productivity is directly related to individuals' attitude toward work. The early stages of reforms aimed primarily at creating work incentives by decentralizing farming activities into family units. In many parts of the country, this change was evidenced in a physical transformation of the landscape as large Collective fields were subdivided into small strips of various sizes for farming by individuals and households. During the late 1970s, Chinese agriculture embarked on a radically different path of development from that which characterized the twenty years between 1957 and 1978. Collective and state operated farms were no longer seen as the model for rural development, or even as the most appropriate form of organization for agriculture. The family type farm has re-emerged as the most important component of Chinese agriculture.

However, experts agree that re-emphasizing family farm organization can only partially achieve the goal of increased productivity. Once the gains resulting from raising individual work attitudes are realized, further productivity will necessarily rely on efficient management and the rate at which technology is adopted. As a result Chinese agricultural policy makers agree that a more essential aim of economic reform in the next stage will be to search for another mechanism which will push the Chinese economy to move toward steady development.

Characteristics of Chinese Agriculture in the North

The State Operated Farms of the northern Chinese farming industry were set up and run directly by the government. For the last thirty years, they have been operated as an independent system within the farming industry which has also continually encompassed Collective farms and family farms. State farms exist in almost all provinces in China, however, in the North they are by far the dominant form of farm organization.

Major features which distinguish a State Farm from a People's Commune Farm (PCF) are as follows:

(1) Land and major productive assets are owned by the state.
(2) Farm profits or losses are shared by both the farm units and the state in accordance with some detailed financial policies.[1]
(3) Farm workers earn salaries rather than share yearly profits as do members of a Communal farm. Thus, farm workers' incomes are secure and do not vary proportionately with farming performance.

These features made the State Farm sector economically similar to state operated urban industries in China, such as manufacturing and construction.

Even though the State Farm sector represents only a tiny fraction of national agriculture both in terms ⌐f land base and volume of output, the proportion in Heilongjiang province is much higher than the national average.[2] The Heilongjiang General Bureau of State Farms (HGBSF) operates 100 state farms which farm over two million hectares of land.[3] This represents nearly one quarter of the total farm land in this northernmost province. During the last 30 years, 23 percent of products and 40 percent of farm output shipped out from the province was produced by State Farms.[4] The state relies heavily on these farms to produce food for redistribution to the rest of China where serious food deficits occur particularly in the heavily populated areas along the Yellow and Yangtse rivers.

Most of the state farms in Heilongjiang are located in the central and northern parts of the province, in a region between 44.10 and 50.20 degrees north latitude and 123.40 and 134.40

degrees east longitude. It is one of the coldest regions in the Chinese territory. The lowest temperature normally reaches minus 44 degrees Celcius in winter. The frost-free season ranges only 112-149 days from north to south. Though short, it is ideal for growing wheat, barley and potatoes. Soybeans and corn can also be grown in most parts of the area except the far north corner. The rainfall in an average year ranges 45-60 centimeters from west to east. Also, 60-70 percent of the rainfall is concentrated during the summer months of June, July, and August. While this is good for the growth of corn and soybeans, it creates difficulties for the harvest of spring wheat and barley.

Historically the State Farm system in China played many important roles in the operation and development of the rural economy. It has reclaimed wet lands, increased agricultural productive capacity and speeded up interregional migration by creating jobs for both skilled and unskilled labourers. It has also served as a showplace for modern farming techniques, and has provided improved crop varieties and animal breeds specifically suited to the northern climate and soil types. In addition, State Farms have helped to solve such problems as the rehabilitation and resettlement of post war mobilized army personnel and returned overseas Chinese.

The first State Farm group in Heilongjiang province was created in the late 1940s.[5] During the period from 1955 to 1959, another larger group of State Farms was constructed mainly by demobilized military officers and young immigrants from other parts of the country. The most significant group was 80,000 army veterans in 1958 and 50,000 immigrants in 1959 from Shandong province, in the central part of China. Since then the population in the area has grown dramatically and steadily. Inflow of migrants has surpassed outflow for the last three decades. Another peak in the population boom was the period 1966 to 1969. A group of 450,000 city youths came into the State Farms under the call of "re-education in the countryside" by former Chairman Mao. The total number of people living on State Farms in the province reached almost 2 million by 1986, while the published figure for the total number of employees of HGBSF was slightly over 760,000 in 1986.[6]

The internal system of management organization on State Farms is very complex. The highest level of management is the

General State Farm Bureau. Subordinate to this are nine sub-bureaus in the area which directly manage many of the larger state farms. Basic management functions are carried out at the State Farm level such as decision-making directed toward the details of yearly production, marketing, and development. Each State Farm has up to twenty working teams; each team cultivates an average of 1000-1500 ha of land. The size of State Farms, as well as the number of working teams under each farm varies with the location and type of enterprise. [7]

Environmental Impact.

Contrasted with the long history and the high population density in other parts of China, the area in Heilongjiang was settled by Chinese only recently. Because of its remoteness and cold climate, individuals or small groups of farmers there were barely able to carry out large scale cultivation before the 1950s. During the last three decades, the development of State Farms has dramatically improved both the social and economic conditions for farming. With large scale government investment, this region has become much more physically developed. Some of the most important developments have been:

(1) Transportation and Communication

Transportation has been the most important single factor contributing to reducing the remoteness of Central Heilongjiang. Because it is surrounded by large areas of water logged marsh, many parts of the area could only be reached in winter when the land was frozen. Pioneers who were in the area before the 1950s were able to go to the closest town only in winter to purchase necessary supplies, in some cases only salt and kerosene for household purposes.

With construction of the State Farms, associated transportation facilities brought the area closer to outside society and greatly overcame the physical problems associated with seasonal remoteness. People became much more willing to settle in the area without worry about losing contact with the rest of Chinese society.

(2) Flood Control and Irrigation

Although the area is suitable for farming, there were several unfavourable climatic, soil and hydrological conditions that had to be overcome in order to obtain a higher and more stable yield of the principal crops. Besides the short growing season, summer flooding, water logged marshlands and spring droughts were major factors limiting farm production. To expand cultivation, agricultural development was accompanied by a comprehensive plan of flood control and irrigation along with massive earthmoving necessary to reclaim the wetlands.

(3) Electrification

Electrification was another critical factor in development. Rural electrification in the form of small scale generation facilities began in the 1950s. Since then the consumption of electricity has increased steadily. By the 1980s, yearly consumption reached 520 million Kilowatts on the State Farms. However, about 30% of the electricity consumed by the State Farms is still generated by power stations operated by these farms themselves. Their collective generating capacity was still 300 million Kilowatts annually in 1980. The electricity supplied by the regional network is not expected to be able to meet the demand of farms until after the turn of the century.

(4) Social Facilities

Alongside the growth of State farms, social service facilities in the area have gradually closed the gap in living standards compared with other rural regions in China. Banking, retail stores, a postal service and cultural facilities are all comparable with, or better than the Peoples Collective farms in the area.

With these improved conditions, small scale individual farming has become possible alongside the Collective and State Farms.[8] Therefore, when nation-wide rural reforms started, State Farms were not exempted from the decentralization policies for re-organization of farming into the smaller family units.

261

(5) Economic Reforms

Along with change to the physical environment, has come a relaxation of many policy rules. With nationwide economic reforms dating from 1979, political and institutional adjustment in the Chinese countryside has brought about fundamental change in the operation of the rural economy. One of the most important results of these reforms has been the encouragement of the State Farms to adopt more creative and autonomous methods of management to motivate individuals to work. After several years of experiments and preparation, and following the decentralization of PCFs, the Production Responsibility System (PRS), on State Farms all over the country began in 1984 to encourage the farm workers to run their own family farms on land previously under State Farm control.

As a consequence, the current situation in the State Farm System is that family farms and state-run farming businesses co-exist within one system. The major industries, input supply networks, and social service systems are still operated by State Farms. Land, forests, rivers and mines are still properties of the state by law. However, ownership versus use and management rights can be separated without changing the nature of socialism according to the official explanation.[9]

At present, farm workers can contract land from State Farms to run their own family farm businesses. The amount of land allotted initially to each family was based mainly on an equal per capita basis with proof of basic management ability. The duration of land contracts is usually a minimum of 15 years in order to stabilize family farm enterprises and encourage long term investment. In the beginning stages the supply farm equipment required to start family businesses came mainly from the old machinery used by the working teams. Its cost was estimated, and family farmers paid back these costs with their profits over a period of from 1 to 5 years, in accordance with their individual agreements.

Family farmers independently make their own production and marketing decisions so long as they fulfill their food production obligations specified by the government and do not violate the area's zoning. They bear full responsibility for their own decisions. The State Farm management network retains planning authority and sets food production obligations and taxes for each household, manages the remaining parts of State Farm businesses and some commonly used facilities. It also can be called upon to serve as a higher level of management for family farms. This arrangement resembles tenant or contract farming with State Farms acting as landlords.

Problems

With the dramatic changes under the new policies, rural individuals have gained a much higher degree of autonomy to make their own decisions. However, this has brought with it greater challenges to both households and State Farm managers. They experience more pressure today than at any previous time.

After living and working under the central command of State Farms for most of their working lives, rural householders are now suddenly required to make financial, technical and managerial decisions for their own family businesses. Frequently they are finding that they lack the ability and experience to do it. In the past most family farmers did not need to develop management abilities. In fact, it was discouraged. As farm workers on the State Farm, they were not required to understand the whole process of agricultural production. Therefore most workers did not have an overall knowledge of production management or marketing and lacked the ability to budget and do accounting. The skills they learned from being farm workers were either too specialized or insufficient to run a complete business. They now must learn many new skills to operate as independent farmers or seek alternative employment.

Rural households are still worried by institutional uncertainties. During most of the time since collectivization in the countryside, rural policies in China were characterized by an ever increasing process of tightening control over decision making. Even though today the Chinese government has repeatedly assured them that the liberal policies are stable, many farmers still predict that they will not last for very long. Thus, even with the relaxation of many policies, many rural householders still hesitate to start their own businesses. A common attitude among average families is that of "wait and see." Many farmers become only passively involved in family farming, often because their working teams no longer exist. This attitude has seriously impeded business expansion and investment in modern tools of production.

For what remains of the State Farms, the current management system was initially designed and developed to manage collective production. Management personnel directly made decisions on detailed farm activites which became the working orders to be followed by the labour units. Now this system is also challenged by the new environment of small family farms. Many family farmers seem to welcome the switch of functions but any suggestion for major change in State Farm operation usually faces strong objections from those in-position personnel. They are keenly aware of a loss in decision-making power. Some of them have been forced to start farming themselves, and they, too, are finding that they lack the type of knowledge and skill to function as independent farmers.

The decentralization of State Farms and Collective farms into smaller family units has indeed led to an increased supply of agricultural products. The tendency to raise agricultural productivity, however, is not expected to continue without further change in the farming industry. The major transition of organization will definitely cause corresponding changes in other elements in the economic and social system of rural society in the north. Predicting the exact nature of these further impacts has become the major question of concern for both theorists and the public.

Farm Enterprise Interrelationships in Heilongjiang

Farm planning models form a research thrust in Northern Chinese agricultural management science. Construction of models which faithfully explain relevant characteristics of the underlying structure of the farm sector, is being actively pursued to attempt prediction of the structural changes both likely and necessary in the future development of the agricultural sector.

Each farm is a large agribusiness organization. The average farm has 200,000 ha of farmland and over 2,000 employees. The most important productive and social activities on state farms as well as their interrelations can be illustrated by Figure 1.

FIGURE 1
State Farm Enterprise Relationships

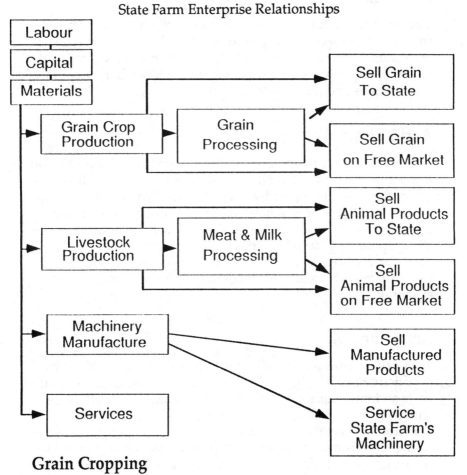

Grain Cropping

Grain crops are the most important enterprise in the north. During the last three decades, they accounted for more than 80 percent of production of State Farms. Most farm labour has been traditionally deployed working the grain fields.

Grain produced on State Farm and Collective farm lands can either be sold directly as grain or transferred into the livestock sector to produce animal products. Of all grain produced, only a small part will be processed by state farm factories for direct local consumption. The rest is sold either to the state food distribution network or on the free market depending on government procurement quotas and/or the free market demand in given localities.

Livestock

The livestock sector of the farm economy receives grain transfers from the crop sector and produces animal products for sale in both state run and local markets. Livestock products can be sold either fresh or processed depending on the physical nature of the commodities and distance to markets.

Agri-Industrial

The industry sector operated under the control of the General Bureau of State Farms is comprised of many sections. It ranges from manufacturing and repair of farm machinery to food processing. Machinery manufacture and repair serve to supply small farm equipment but provide machinery maintenance for all equipment on the State Farms. In recent years, however, more State Farm manufactured goods are shipped to outside markets to compete with counterparts originating in other sectors of the economy.

Input Supply

This sector purchases all inputs needed by the other farm productive sectors. It handles fuel, fertilizer, herbicides, spare parts and farm equipment. Owing to the nation-wide shortage of energy and an insufficient manufacturing capacity, farm inputs are often in short supply. To counteract these shortages, the state farms have typically built up their own stocks of productive materials. Farm inputs are usually purchased during the winter and stored for deployment in the next crop year. For fuel, fertilizer and spare parts for foreign-produced equipment, stocks are usually maintained at levels sufficient for 2-3 crop years.

Social Services

This sector functions to overcome the difficulties caused by remoteness and the underdevelopment of regional economic and social infrastructures. It includes schools, hospitals, and cultural facilities. Most of the service organizations in the State Farms are non-profit units. They provide necessary conveniences for local residents, mainly farm workers and their families.

During the past decade all these various units have been transferred to decentralized control. After the major parts of farm activities were alloted to family units, the service agencies were either leased to some households referred to as "Specialized Households" or have remained under State Farm control.

Predictions of Structural Change

Models used in research on the changing sectoral structure (Song and Pfeiffer) focussed mainly on the family farms in the crop and livestock sectors. The supply network, industrial and service sectors were included as adjuncts which determined business constraints facing the managers of the new crop and livestock sectors. The animal production sector competes for scarce resources with the grain sector on an equivalent level of priority (Figure 2).

FIGURE 2
Structure of General Industry Simulation

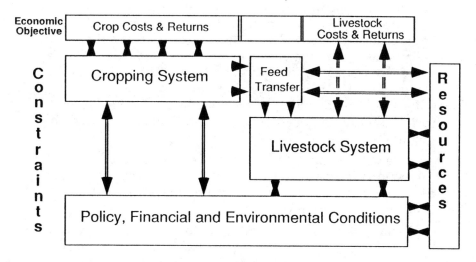

The grain production sector model contained only three major crops: soybean, corn and spring wheat. Other crops were excluded because they account for only 2-3 percent of total farm sales. The livestock section of the model contained only dairy cows and hogs. This was capable of determining a plan for the animal sector which indicated the livestock commodities which can be produced by using residual resources from farmers' field operations.

Thus the simulation which aimed at predicting the nature and extent of sectoral restructuring examined enterprises from both the crop and livestock sectors. The major emphasis of the modelling procedure was to choose a profit maximizing enterprise combination for family farms, both in terms of immediate farm planning and in terms of long-run restructuring of the industry. The results of research of this type is of concern to many state farm managers and specialists and is critical for today's family farmers.

Another critical decision facing farmers now is to determine a strategy for product marketing. Owing to the large population and shortage of farm resources, China has faced a vital problem of feeding its people throughout most of its modern history. Food products have often been in short supply. Productivity improvement in the last three decades only managed to match the minimum requirement of an increased population. This fact raised two results that directly affect the performance of the farm economy. On the one hand, food producers have fewer problems selling farm commodities; on the other hand, the short supply of basic foods caused governments to exert tight controls over food producers.

As a consequence of heavy controls, farmers face many extra restrictions imposed by the government. Product marketing decisions have become much more complicated under the liberalization of recent years.

Because of the serious shortage of food in modern China, the government has tried consistently since 1949 to fulfill a minimum national requirement for food commodities. Beginning in 1956, the Chinese government adopted a state procurement policy which required all grain, edible oil seeds and cotton as well as other relevant products to be traded through a government redistribution system. Producers of all types are given mandatory plans to devote a certain proportion of land to basic food production. Also specified are the amounts of grain that should be sold to the state at fixed prices.

Beginning in the 1980s, the state procurement was replaced by a new policy of combined quotas and contracts. Farms are levied a sales quota. Upon fulfilling the quota farmers are now free to decide what to produce and where to sell products. The state is always willing to purchase additional amounts of grain at a higher price than that under the quota. This part of farm sales is called a contract sale. Farmers can also benefit from increased allotments of short supply input commodities such as fertilizers by selling extra grain to the state.

When farmers decide not to sell over-quota grain to the state, they are gambling for an even higher price from delivery of products to the free market. As a result, there exist three prices for any single product in the crop sector. The restructuring research model was built to include marketing decisions in this respect.

The flow of products was simulated so that a comparison could be made across alternative avenues of selling products, given the restrictions levied by the quota. Price variations associated with the timing of product sales were also included in the simulation.

Results

The results for the simulation of agricultural enterprises in Heilongjiang indicate that some radical departures from traditional farming practices are likely to occur in future.

Without an immediate advance in technology and a large increase in inputs, the optimal plan for a newly established family farm operation suggests an annual income of 653.35 Yuan can be earned with 10 hectares of land and one full-time operator. This can be seen as the initial situation after decentralization of State Farms. Comparing this income with what was earned in centrally planned State Farms, shows a definite incentive placed on individuals. Nearly a doubling of personal income is expected on average. In fact recent surveys by the authors in the North have shown this to be the case.

Indeed, while the difference was large compared with the past, the profits from growing crops are also increasing on the

State Farms as well. For the future, private farmers may expect an equivalent of the salary earned by workers who choose to stay full-time with the State Farm. The questions are: what are the advantages of starting a family agri-business; can family farms consolidate; what are the implications of rural reforms on the regional economy in the long run?

Answers to these questions rely on a detailed examination of the labour balance on farms. The authors' crop sector research indicated that even though the immediate increase of profit from family farms was comparable to wage increases likely on the State Farms, the labour requirements show significant differences. For example, field operations consumed only a minor fraction of total fieldwork labour available in the province. There is excess labour even during planting and harvesting periods. Heretofore, State Farm managers believed that there was a shortage of hands during these periods. It is becoming apparent to many farmers that labour resources were not fully utilized in the past. Moreover, many economists readily assign zero opportunity cost to these excess labour resources. They can be left out of the farm planning process without affecting the operations of business and without other job opportunities these workers have bleak prospects for the future.

To investigate the reasons for the emerging phenomenon of excess labour, one must realize the constraints within which managers were forced to work before the liberalization of policies. With new incentives for self-managed family businesses, labour savings can largely be explained by better scheduling of field work, improved per hour working efficiency and a higher quality of work. As a matter of fact, the significant saving of labour during the organizational transition is best explained by comparing incentive-driven managerial orientation with the previous management system. On the State Farms, field activities were arranged by lower level management personnel. Each worker in a local labour force had to be hired and assigned jobs for every working day, no matter what the season. To ensure each worker carried a "full" load, as defined by policy, and prevent workers seeking the easy jobs, a complicated monitoring system was developed.

The monitoring system apparently did not work well in situations where there was in fact a serious surplus of human resources. With the high rate of population growth in the region, the rural labour force doubled in the last three decades. With urban development underway the area of farm land actually declined since the completion of reclamation projects in the 1970s. As a consequence, there was a conflict between the directive to maintain full employment and the actual volume of necessary and available work. The result was a large volume of labour implicitly under-unemployed inside the state farms but not recognized as such.

The reforms have uncovered this hidden labour idleness. With the relaxation of many work policies, family farms are searching out other income earning opportunities that might absorb surplus labour resources for productive purposes. New farm enterprises are growing rapidly, particularly those based on livestock, including dairying.

Time-saving advantages on family farms, however, will be partially offset by some labour consuming disadvantages. An obvious example is the fact that each family now operates a very small land area. Their small parcels of land are often subdivided further into smaller lots so as to ensure that each family controlled an equivalent productive capacity based on the varying quality of land. Field work efficiency on many family farms is significantly below its technical potential because of this arrangement.

The authors' research results indicate that significant numbers of dairy cows and hogs will be introduced on the private farms simply by using the resources left over from crop production. This could then be further enhanced to obtain higher profit merely by allowing resources to flow from the crop to the livestock sector. So long as government grain procurement quotas are fulfilled, it is likely that excess grain production will be mainly directed toward livestock enterprises by private operators.

Research indicates that the decentralization of farms will cause changes in the combination of farm enterprises for many years to come. The changes not only represent a higher income potential for family farms, they also reflect a dramatic switch in the operation of the farming economy. Thus, Northern Chinese agriculture is being steered away from a goal of feeding the population toward profitable enterprise. Many experts believe that a physical balance of food consistent with population trends and good nutrition will be achieved at the same time as profits are maximized. Farm planning will not serve purely as a means to fulfill government food production targets; it will function as a practical tool for achieving individual goals of private farmers subject to continuing conditions provided by state social development plans acting as constraints on managers decision-making latitude.

Feeding one quarter of the world's population will remain the priority task for Chinese agriculture. For various reasons, China will not willingly rely on world markets for food, and self-reliance in basic food production will be a basic policy for the long run. To maintain a sufficient level of food, production of basic commodities will continue to be encouraged by the government even though more liberal policies are developed with respect to the rights of individuals to control productive resources. The northern region is one of the major food producers in China. Besides local consumption, the government relies on farmers in the region to deliver grain for national redistribution purposes. If grain shipments dropped, the government would either restore stricter procurement policies or state prices would rise, or both. In either case, grain output will be maintained as first economic priority.

Grain outputs are also the most important intermediate input for the livestock industry. Any expansion of animal enterprises increases the demand for grains and will generally not drive overall grain production down. Assuming there is no significant volume of grain shipped into the region, the livestock industry is likely to push up local grain prices and hence foster increased crop production.

Livestock enterprises are in fact transferring grain outputs into animal products at an expanding rate. Although two sectors compete for scarce resources, livestock enterprises must rely on the crop sector. Even though the grain sector as a whole will not decline when livestock becomes equally comptetitive, the internal structure of crop production will be altered dramatically. Corn production for instance may consume a major proportion of crop resources since corn is the major livestock feed.

This all points to a reorganization of mechanical and manual work. As livestock enterprises become recognized with equal importance to crops, labour available in some periods of the year will become the key factor restricting farm profits. Because of this, the opportunity cost of labour will likely begin to rise within agriculture itself. It will thus become more profitable to substitute machines for labour so that more labour may be allocated to raising livestock. This process will likely oscillate through the rural economy as machinery becomes available and as production cycles unfold.

This is in itself an interesting result. Since the collectivization of Chinese agriculture, the state has constantly pushed collective farm units to increase the level of agricultural mechanization. Because there existed a large volume of under-employed rural labour, the use of machinery did not bring farmers an increased income. They often referred to the purchase of high cost machinery as "Buying an idle life," because the replaced labour resources were not employed elsewhere. Now, increased use of machines is expected to occur as part of the restructuring brought about by profit incentives. This indicates that the most practical promotion of agricultural mechanization is the development of wider opportunities so that displaced labour maintains income earning potential.

The authors' research suggests a major increase of livestock production. Livestock commodities already represent a higher share of total farm sales. The structure of the farm economy has become more diversified during the current decade. This diversification has been mainly the result of a greater level of autonomy in decision making by farmers. Farmers are free to switch resources from low income enterprises to more profitable enterprises. Nevertheless, farmers have maintained an expanding trend in grain output and diversified at the same time. This implies the extent of the prior under-utilization and/or mis-allocation of resources, particularly labour. Indeed, many northern Chinese farmers are quickly becoming better off by raising one or two milk cows, several pigs, or a few hundred chickens with previously underemployed resources.

Reform of the economic system will naturally cause changes in many other aspects of rural society. Many elements, such as banks, and social service industries will all experience fundamental change. Studies in these areas will be necessary to provide knowledge useful in guiding a comprehensive reform. Studies are needed to examine the future role of farm management organization. The current situation on State Farms is that although their organizations no longer make direct decisions over farm production and marketing, they still control capital and material distribution, land contracts, output delivery, farm services, etc. A critical fact to remember is that the offical definition for a family farm still refers to individual farms as the lower production units of the State Farm management network. This in many ways seems to be an attempt to fit changed practices into the old ideology. Farm planning models must be careful to investigate the actual roles played by the existing farm management network. Properly done, the results of research can lead to policy suggestions regarding regional management of farms.

Research must also be focussed on demand analysis for farm inputs and the impact of rural reforms on the farm input supply industry.

Researchers studying Chinese agriculture must remain cognizant that the society in which these changes are taking place is the contemporary legacy of the oldest human culture on earth. China has been closed off from the rest of the world for a little longer than a generation. During this time the population has doubled from 500,000,000 in the late 1940s to over a billion at the present time.

During the great Cultural Revolution between 1966 and 1976, the Chinese educational system was severly affected. The impact that this has had on the Chinese is profound. They must work closely together with the rest of the world and adopt technologies from wherever appropriate ones can be found to regain their strength as a vital and economically self-sufficient society.

Because the technologies needed are similar or identical to ours, drawing upon Canadian experience in the last hundred years is probably the best help in attempting to assemble the necessary concepts which will allow us to understand the process that is happening in China and enable us to interact with our Chinese peers.

It is incumbent upon Western nations to recognize both the needs of the Chinese and the vast potential that co-operation can mean for our own economies. Agriculture will likely be a major forum for Canadian interaction with China for several decades to come. The scenario for change presented here is intended to be thought-provoking, and stimulate discussion which can lead to better understanding and co-operation between agricultural professionals in China and Canada.

NOTES

1. These policies are subject to frequent changes. Currently, the state government requires farms to pay only taxes.

2. State farms take about 0.5% of the total land base in China. SOFs in this province own 50% of total land in all SOFs in the country. Zhang ed. [49].

3. State farms in the province also assess 1,100,000 ha of non-cultivated land, 870,000 ha of forestry, 50,700 ha of pasture and others, including lakes, town-sites, recreational land use, country roads, and industrial land.

4. Yang ed., "Economic Development of State Operated Farm in Heilongjiang Province." 1984 [47]

5. This part of the country has been controlled by the Communist Party since 1946.

6. *People's Daily*, June 1, 1988.

7. General Bureau of State Farms, Jamusi, 1984.

8. The term "Collective Farming" will be used as a general term referring to both PCF and SOF if not otherwise specified.

9. The Central Committee of the Chinese Communist Party, Document 75, 1980.

REFERENCES

Alekseev, A.M. 1975. *Multilevel System for Planning Industrial Production (in Russian)*. Vladivostok: Siberian Agricultural Department.

Anthony, Robert N. 1965. *Planning and Control System: A Framework for Analysis*. Boston: Harvard University Graduate School of Business Administration.

Association of Chinese Technological Economics, 1985. *Handbook of Economics for Technology (Volume for Agriculture)*. Liaoning, PRC.

Katesenelinboigen, A.I., and E. Iu. Faerman, 1985. "Centralism and Economic Independence in the Socialist Economy (in Russian)." *Ekonomika i Matematicheskie Metody*. 3(3): 331-346.

Kornai, J. 1971. *Anti-Equilibrium*. Amsterdam: North-Holland Co.

Lasdon, Leon S. 1970. *Optimization Theory for Large Systems*. Toronto: Collier-Macmillan Canada, Ltd.

Liang, Wenshen. 1982. "Balanced Development of Industry and Agriculture," in Xu Dixin (ed.), *China's Search for Economic Growth*. New York: New World Press.

Perkins, D.H. 1983. "Research on the Economy of the People's Republic of China: A Survey of the Field," The *Journal of Asian Studies*. 42(2): 659-685.

Riskin, Carl. 1987. *China's Political Economy*. London: Oxford University Press.

Schertz, Lyle P. 1975. "World Food: Prices and the Poor," in Bundy, William P. (ed.), *World Economic Crisis*. New York: Norton.

State Statistical Bureau. 1986. *Zhonggou Tongji Nianjian (Statistical Yearbook of China)*. Beijing: Statistical Publishing House.

United States Department of Agriculture, 1984. "Agricultural Statistics of the People's Republic of China. 1949-82," *Statistical Bulletin* No. 714: Washington, D.C.: USDA.

Watson, Andrew. 1984. "Agriculture Looks for `Shoes that Fit': The Production Responsibility System and Its Implications," in Maxwell, Neville and Bruce McFarlane (eds.), *China's Changed Road to Development*. Exeter: A. Wheaton & Co. Ltd.

Williams, P. 1985. *Model Building in Mathematical Programming*, Second Edition. New York: John Wiley & Sons Ltd.

Yang, Yuchun (ed.) 1984. *Heilongjiang Sheng Goying Nonchang Jingji Fazhanshi (Historical Development of State Operated Farm Economy in Heilongjiang Province)*. Heilongjiang, PRC: People's Publishing House.

Zhan, Wu. 1979. "Take a Chinese Path to Agricultural Modernization," *Jinji Guanli (Economic Management)*. No. 9,9.

Zhang, Linchi (ed.). 1986. *Dangdai Zhonggou De Nongken Shiye (State Farms in Modern China)*. Beijing: Chinese Publishing House of Social Science.

Zhao, Ziyang. 1985. "Loosen Control Over the Price of Farm Products to Promote the Readjustment of the Production Structure in Rural Areas," *Hong Qi.* January: 3.

Part III

CANADIAN NATIVE PEOPLE AND FOOD INSECURITY

"NATIVE ECOLOGY"
Native Canadians often used all parts of the animal and practised good conservation techniques. Faith Pegahagabow prepares a doe skin on Parry Island, Ontario.

Photograph by John Rive of Parry Island, 1980.

Chapter 8

THE ECONOMICS OF NORTHERN NATIVE FOOD PRODUCTION

Edward J. Hedican

Introduction

The Native peoples of northern Canada have hunted, fished and collected wild foods from time immemorial. Country food production continues to constitute a significant proportion of foods consumed even today, but their ability to utilize subsistence resources is now severely threatened. The source of this threat is a multi-faceted phenomenon involving a diminishing wild life habitat and environmental degradation. Pulp and paper companies have steadily moved northward and are now in the process of harvesting some of the last sizeable stands of boreal forest. Industrial pollution, mainly in the form of mercury contaminants and acid rain, have necessitated a reduction in the Native reliance on fishing. Dramatic fluctuations in water levels caused by hydro companies have virtually destroyed the wild rice harvest in some areas.

At this point in their history the news is certainly not good concerning northern Native country food production. To complicate matters there is also a wide range of other economic problems that have an impact on country food use, such as the decline in fur trapping sales, the rising cost of hunting and fishing equipment, and the integration of hunting communities into the wage labour economy. For policy makers and governmental planners, the problems associated with the modern northern Native economy must seem virtually insurmountable, leading to the realization that no easy solution is readily available.

The purpose of this paper is to examine the characteristics of the modern Indian and Metis subsistence economy and to offer some observations that could serve to ameliorate the pressing economic problems faced by the Native population. The focus is primarily on northwestern Ontario in the region between Lake Nipigon and the Albany river (Map 1), the area where I have concentrated field research since the 1970s (Hedican 1976, 1982, 1985, 1986, 1987). This research has led to the conclusion that only a long term familiarity with an area and its people can lead to the understanding necessary for the fuller appreciation of the problems faced by the Native peoples of the Canadian north. As such various aspects of the contemporary economic life of the Ojibwa Indians living in northern Ontario's bush communities are examined. In addition, some policy implications of these findings are discussed as they relate to impacts on the northern subsistence economy.

The Northern Native Economy:
Some Issues

A review of research publications over the last decade reveals that there has been a proliferation in basic research on food patterns, subsistence ecology and socio-economic change among northern Native peoples. In particular, this research indicates that a matter of considerable interest in the continuing process of modern economic change among northern peoples is the degree to which traditional hunting and fishing activities are being influenced by the impact of the outside industrial society. Studies have been conducted on the role that socially prescribed patterns of behaviour play in organizing the subsistence activities of the Clyde River Inuit of Baffin Island (Wenzel 1981), and on the alternative economic strategies utilized in the Inuit community of Rankin Inlet (Jansen 1979). In a study of commerical fur trappers and fishermen from a Chipewyan community on the Upper Churchill River in Saskatchewan, Jarvenpa (1980) employs geographical mobility as a variable in explaining the organization of economic-subsistence activities. Additional

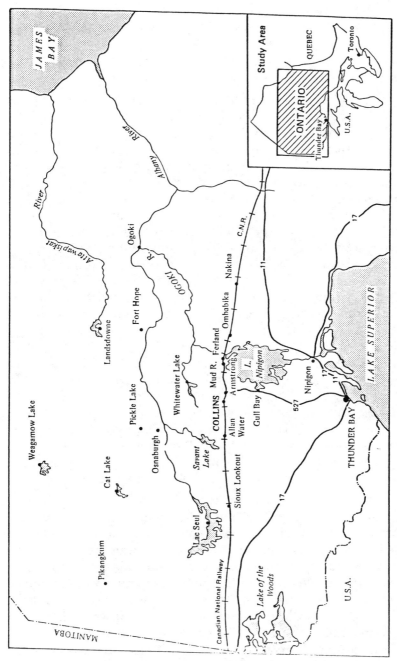

Map 1. Northern Ontario Settlements and River Systems

surveys of the changing economic life of northern Native people have focussed on the Mackenzie River Valley of the Yukon (Berger 1977, Usher 1976), the southwestern region of Alaska (Nowak 1977), and the eastern James Bay coastline of Quebec (Elberg 1975, Salisbury 1986).

The issues involved in much of the research have been put into perspective by the Hon. Thomas Berger who conducted the highly acclaimed study into the Mackenzie Valley pipeline debate, and who more recently was the author of *Fragile Freedoms*. The problem as Berger indicates is that "there had always been a traditional renewable resource sector in the North, but instead of trying to strengthen it, we had, for a decade or more, followed policies by which it could only be weakened or even destroyed" (Berger 1983: 366-367). In this sense much depends on the extent to which government agencies dealing with northern and Native issues are adequately informed on the current economic concerns of the Canadian north. The provision of statistical materials derived from first hand research is thus one of the pressing necessities for informed policy decision making, but much also hinges on how these materials are interpreted and acted on. In this regard researchers and Native people alike should find it disturbing that the Department Affairs survey of Indian economic conditions in Canada (DIAND 1980) has virtually ignored the non-wage sectors of fishing, hunting and trapping. However the survey does note that "a substantial proportion of income for many communities is derived from non-wage (traditional) pursuits — hunting, fishing, trapping... the value of the non-wage sector in three sample communities varied between 41 and 58 per cent of total community income" (DIAND 1980: 59).

One might conclude from such reports that these figures on hunting and trapping suggest that more attention could have been devoted to examining the role of non-wage activities in the northern Indian community. It is also possible that the hunting and trapping activities are far more significant to the economic well-being of the Indian community than is implied by the scant mention of them in government reports. However informed governmental decisions on the northern economy are also much dependent on informed research which has a certain degree of consistency with regard to the recommendations put forward, and on which government decision making can be reliably based. To give an example of this problem, despite the growing body of literature involved, it is still possible for a book on northern public policy to claim that "authorities on the subject agree that there does not exist at present adequate information on ... the renewable-resource economy" (Dacks 1974: 168). Lacking such adequate information one could be led to the conclusion, based on the reasoning behind the policies referred to by Berger, that the traditional economy is in rapid decline and would shortly disappear altogether.

There is much scientific research to contradict such a conclusion, yet a large part of the problem concerns how this research is to be interpreted. Diamond Jenness, for example, held the view that "the economic prosperity .... of an Eskimo community today is roughly proportional to the amount of wage employment it obtains, and not, as formerly, to the wildlife resources that exist in its neighbourhood" (Jenness 1978: 144). It is not my purpose in this paper to refute such statements, which would certainly be difficult to do in any event, the issue at point is that such statements nevertheless promote the view that there is little economic value to be gained by the increased utilization of local resources. From the perspective of the industrial economy we could also be persuaded by the view that wage work should reign supreme, and that it should, as the reasoning would go, take precedence over other forms of employment as part of the sort of natural evolution of the Canadian north.

The denigration of the non-wage economy (even the term "non-wage" tends to cast traditional hunting and fishing in a negative light) finds expression in various forms. Even the Indian Affairs survey mentioned above discusses traditional Indian pursuits under the category of "Unemployment" (DIAND 1980: 59). Given such a climate of interpretation Berger is certainly correct in noting that "people who tried to earn a living by hunting, trapping and fishing had often been regarded as unemployed" (1983: 367). For those involved in research into the contemporary economic life of the northern Native community, there are nonetheless alternative interpretations. With increasing regularity researchers have become critical of the "modernization" or "dual economy" perspective on the North which is seen to consist of one "backward" sector which exploits traditional resources, and a "modern" one which mainly exploits non-renewable resources.

The contrast of modern-backward, or modern-traditional, is

perhaps an inaccurate characterization of the issues involved in northern development. For one thing there are various perceptions of what constitutes "development" in the first place, and secondly on how this development, however it is defined, is to proceed. Nonetheless somewhat of a polarization has tended to characterize the debate over resource development in the Canadian north. Commenting on the Mackenzie Valley Pipeline debate, for example, Asch has taken exception in particular to the view that as time goes on "the inherent superiority of the rational industrial economy is such that it will inevitably replace the backward and irrational one" (1982: 4). In the North, part of the problem has to do with the disruption of fish and game populations associated with industrial development projects (Frideres 1984: 61), lending credence to the view that there exists an inherent competition between the wage economy on the one hand, and the non-wage sector of the economy on the other.

Rather than adopt the view of inherent competition, another approach would be to regard northern economic change as a complementary process such that a comprehensive view of northern Native economies would include a creative mesh of local production activity and cash transactions. Berger, for example, has referred to this combination or synthesis as "the mixed economy" such that "in the north today, the lives of many native families are based on an intricate economic mix. At certain times of the year, they hunt and fish; at other times they work for wages" (Berger 1977: 122). The implications of this perspective for government policy in the North are such that there is a need for a wider recognition of the benefits to be derived from a more extensive utilization of local resources. At present the pattern described for the George River Inuit is fairly widespread: "DIAND maintains the standard of living at an artificially buoyant level, and gives the illusion of economic viability" (Arbess 1967: 68).

As the George River case illustrates, as an alternative to the large scale dispensation of relief, more effort could go into the creation of programs aimed at developing viable and self-supporting local economies. One would think, however, that such goals are not possible until government agencies cease to ignore the economic value of traditional hunting and fishing activities. On the other hand, in order to live off the land, even if for part of the year, one needs good gear with which to hunt the game, so cash is a necessary prerequisite for the successful hunter. As an alternative to welfare dependency, more consideration by policy makers could also be given to a guaranteed annual income program for Native people engaged in wildlife harvesting, such as Quebec's Income Security Program for Cree hunters that was worked out in the James Bay Agreement (LaRusic 1979; Feit 1982).

Such programs encourage participation in hunting activities, and ensure the continuation of subsistence hunting and fishing as a viable option and means of livelihood in the face of disincentives to hunting created by external conditions. In addition, any means of ensuring the hunting way of life may serve to increase the self-determination and autonomy of contemporary hunting peoples. In all, the suggestion of this paper, in concert with previous research reported by other authors, is to extend this area of investigation of northern economic trends by adopting a more comprehensive approach, such that subsistence production is discussed in conjunction with the increasing participation of northern Native people in wage employment. The intent of this effort however, is not to suggest that this should be a sort of stop-gap method on the road to the eventual eradication of the hunting way of life, but to contribute to the working out of an advantageous mix of country food production and the cash economy. The contention here is that much of the very survival of northern Native communities depends on a more complete utilization of local renewable resources, in conjunction with outside income sources.

The first step is to begin to regard hunting, fishing and other forms of country food production as employment in its own right, rather than as a residual or peripheral activity. The use of local subsistence resources is also to be regarded as income-producing, at least to the extent that effort spent on securing country food reduces the necessity for cash to spend on food imported into the community, usually at considerable cost. As such an accent on wage work should be counterbalanced by a discussion centring on the contribution of country food production to modern Indian life in the North. One suggestion emanating from this discussion is that wage work can have a positive impact on the procurement of country food, at least to the extent that higher incomes allow for increased investment in better hunting equipment, maintenance, and transportation costs. While this idea concerning the interrelationship of wage work and an increased utilization of country resources awaits validation from additional studies, it does tend to stand in contradiction to an older view that would cast wage labour activities in direct opposition, rather than as a complement to, traditional hunting and fishing.

The research reported in this paper is mainly the result of fifteen months of fieldwork in one of the many log cabin Indian villages of Ontario's northland, called Collins. Most of the people continue to speak their native language (Ojibwa) in everyday conversation, heat their homes with firewood, and prefer a diet of moose meat, bannock, and fresh fish. As elsewhere in the world, these are a people concerned most of all with making a living, raising their children, and getting along with their neighbours. But in this case, "making a living" does not mean a nine-to-five job in the plant or factory. Instead, it means for the most part a complex pattern of hunting, fishing and working seasonally for the white man's wages as a tourist guide.

Northern Ontario: History and Economy

The economic history of northern Ontario over the last three hundred years has been interwoven with that of the fur trade, mainly initiated by the Hudson's Bay Company posts to the northeast, but also involving influences from various independent traders operating out of Montreal and Lake Superior locations. This is a rugged region consisting of some 800,000 km^2 of glacially scoured Precambrian shield covered with coniferous forest and numerous lakes and streams. North of the Canadian National Railway's (CNR) mainline through Ontario live about 30,000 people, almost exclusively Ojibwa and Cree, or *Anishenabek* as they call themselves.

Most of these northern Algonquians live in relatively isolated settlements of under 500 people, which are usually situated on the larger lakes and rivers. Since most of the roads from the south end at the CNR, the usual mode of transportation in the area is by boat, snowmobile, and bush plane. For the most part, northern Ojibwa have subsisted on fishing, trapping, and wild rice harvesting, but all of these activities do not have the income potential to adequately support the growing population. The tourist industry, government sponsored work projects, and commercial fishing provide the main sources of employment. While perhaps not readily evident to the outsider, almost every community in this region has a sizeable 'hidden' economy involving subsistence hunting and fishing, firewood collection, and the manufacture of local products such as snowshoes, sleds, leather products and so on. Some of these products are sold to outside visitors, but most are made for local use.

The area had little direct contact with the outside world until about 1850, with the signing of the Robinson-Superior Treaty. Afterwards an increasing wider array of outsiders aside from explorers and fur merchants could be found traversing the Indians' territory. Missionaries arrived to introduce new religious beliefs, government agents came to sign treaties and settle land claims, and surveyors plotted the future courses of railways, roads, and mineral development. The Ojibwa and Cree residing north of the Robinson-Superior treaty limits negotiated one of the largest land settlements ever when they signed the James Bay Treaty in 1905, and thereby extended Ontario's boundary to its present northern limits.

Completion of the CNR in 1911 signalled the start of new beginnings for the people of northern Ontario. A multitude of new trading posts emerged almost overnight along the rail line, offering the Hudson's Bay Company its first real competition in the area since the demise of the Nor'westers a hundred years earlier. Railroad construction, Innis (1970: 363) notes, "led to a marked increase in competition where former servants of the Company deserted to join the ranks of the competitors." Independent fur traders had the advantage of inexpensive transportation costs, which meant that they could offer high fur prices coupled with low-cost food and trade goods. To give an example, customers were charged $2.55 for twenty-four pounds of flour and six pounds of rolled oats at the Collins store in 1955, while the same goods at the HBC post in Fort Hope on the Albany River cost $6.12 (Baldwin 1957: 79-83). It was through economic incentives such as these that much of the Albany River trade was diverted to the rail line. In time, that is after WW II, the rail line post also became the centre of new Indian settlements such as Collins, Mud River, Ferland and Ombabika.

However, these continued to be somewhat transitory settlements until the establishment of schools after 1960, as most people remained out on the land for the greater part of the year until that time. Today the use of the land as a basis of the Native people's livelihood continues to be important, but the settlements are now much more sedentary than in the past.

In general, the genesis of settlements such as Collins can be attributed to increases in the population densities of northern reserve communities, and the resulting competition for trapping territories and other diminishing resources, such as fish, game, and firewood. Migrants to the rail line sought to extricate themselves from the restrictions and uncertainties of a limited resource base by moving to areas where there was a greater opportunity to supplement subsistence production with wage labour income. The local availability of country food was therefore an important factor influencing demographic shifts among the northern Native population.

Country Food Production

Included under the category of what is termed "subsistence-related activities" would be such things as trapping, hunting, fishing, berry picking, and firewood collection. These types of activities were prevalent forms of work for northern Native people until about 1950 when population growth and diminishing fur resources led to some displacement from their hunting economy. In later years an improvement in medical facilities, government financial aid, and the construction of schools contributed to more sedentary communities. The subsequent decreased mobility has tended to reduce the use of country resources and related activities.

The published reports for Native communities in northern Ontario provide a broader perspective on these trends. For the 1950s, for example, at Pekengekum (Dunning 1959: 24-35) and Round Lake (Rogers 1962: C53-C55) subsistence hunting and fishing made up at least three-quarters of the Native's diet. During this period all families maintained stocks of flour, lard, tea and sugar, but it is only the sick and destitute who rely to any degree on store foods, as indicated by the statement that "food from the hunt is relied upon as the staple diet" (Dunning 1959:

33). By the 1960s, at Osnaburgh House, only about one-quarter of food consumed came from the bush (Bishop 1974: 30). While the situation varies from community to community across the North, depending upon such factors as population size, fish and game stocks, and cost of store foods, one could still say with a fair degree of accuracy that today most Native communities secure anywhere from ten to fifty percent of their food from the surrounding country.

Does this trend then indicate that in the next few decades the use of country food will completely pass from the diet of northern peoples? The answer, I believe, is "no" because there are sound economic reasons even today for continuing to hunt and fish. One of the main reasons is that with the rising costs of store meat, and local incomes not rising at the same rate, there is added incentive to return to the bush for food and to invest in the capital equipment necessary for the hunt. As an additional factor, although there are probably fewer men engaged in hunting on a proportional basis than in previous years, nonetheless those that continue to hunt and trap are able to maintain high yields through labour-saving technology. They are also better able today to exploit the more inaccessible and distant parts of their territories where game and fish populations, because of underutilization, have remained relatively high. Such territories are therefore the most productive of economic effort, but travel to them requires additional costs compared to areas of closer proximity.

In historical terms, that is over the last three centuries, northern Indians have undergone a slow process of integration into, and dependence upon, the outside world. For the most part, especially people living in interior locations, northern Indians have remained on the margin of the Euro-Canadian social and economic system — what has been called "acculturation at a distance" (Dunning 1959: 208). Contacts with the outside are accelerating in today's world. This is especially true with regards to such areas as education, wage employment, and government subsidy. Yet complete incorporation into the wider society seems unlikely in view of the isolation of many communities and some basic conflicts between wage work and the demands of village life. One such conflict stems from the fact that full-time jobs are mostly absent in the small communities, and long periods away from home mean a difficult family life.

Another conflict is between country food production, a necessary activity to support life in many northern Native settlements, and the need for money to purchase other essentials. The trade-offs are not easily resolved, especially when cash and bush food are both scarce resources. What this means is that most Native families have some difficult decisions to make about how to allocate their time between living in the village trying to earn some cash, and making a living out on the land by hunting and fishing.

The food economy of the Indians of the eastern subarctic in terms of an approximate mapping of subsistence resources suggests three major patterns: (a) a "Waterfowl-Fish" area of the Hudson Bay lowland, (2) a "Moose-Fish" area in southern Quebec and central Ontario, and (3) "Caribou-Fish" for the Labrador peninsula (Rogers 1966: 87-118). In northern Ontario, for the Pegangekum population, it is noted that "during the winter season beaver and muskrat are relied on for the meat supply, in addition to hare when available. Larger game, at present mostly goose, are taken throughout the year except in mid-summer .... For a large part of the year, especially in warmer months, fish are relied upon almost entirely as the staple food" (Dunning 1959: 24). At Osnaburgh House, "Of the native foods, the moose is the most important and most sought after .... There is no question that the moose is king of beasts to the Osnaburgh people. The beaver, although of economic importance, is a distant second" (Bishop 1974: 24-25). It is further evident that the moose is "king of beasts" for most other areas as well, and for long periods into the distant past (Skinner 1911: 135; Rogers 1962: A14).

In fact the moose is so important to the Indian diet that with its 50-year disappearance from northern Ontario in the latter part of the last century, food shortages became critical and the Indians were forced to depend on rabbits and other small game to feed themselves (Rogers and Black 1976). Besides the delicious, low-fat quality of the meat, an important reason for the preference in moose is the opportunity to secure a large quantity of meat while expending a more minimal effort compared to the work required to secure other food sources. As indicated in a study of the Waswanipi Cree of Quebec, "Moose hunting is by far the most efficient harvesting technique ranging over 100,000 calories for human consumption per man-day of work" (Feit 1973: 121).

Moose, for the people of Collins, is by far the largest source of meat and accounts for about one-half of all country food production, while fish and waterfowl make up another third of the total. Each grown animal provides over 100 kg of edible meat, and therefore return on productive effort is relatively high. In the Collins area most moose are killed in the fall and winter months, usually by high-powered rifles. Occasionally people relate that moose are killed in the summer when they are found swimming across a lake and are thus easy prey. Besides meat, moose also provide an important source of hides for coats, mitts, and moccasins. Overall, if one were to provide a monetary value on bush food, subsistence production would contribute over $40,000 to the local Collins' economy, which is a conservative estimate. With a Collins population of 135 people, the value of country food therefore totals about $300 per person. Given a per capita income of $1650, one can begin to appreciate the economic contribution of country food, given the relatively high cost of replacement foods from the store.

Other Country Food Sources

Bears, next to the moose, provide the highest proportion of edible meat per animal, but bear meat is not greatly desired. Although they are fairly numerous in the area, bears are not usually hunted, but are shot when they become a nuisance to the village. While some people claim to eat bear meat on a regular basis, others say they avoid it because a skinned bear looks too much like a human being. While it is not readily admitted, the attribution of anthropomorphic characteristics to the bear could be taken as evidence of the widespread magico-religious mystique associated with the bear in the Northeast (i.e., Hallowell 1926). In a similar vein, I also occasionally saw large bear skins stretched out on frames outside of people's cabins which, since the skins are not sold or used as rugs, I took to be an attempt to ward off other bears.

Of the other large animals, wood caribou are shot when encountered, but since their virtual disappearance from the area some 30 or 40 years ago, they are seldom seen today. In terms of small game, rabbits are one of the most important animals in the northern diet. They are usually snared by women and teenagers close to the village. In former times they appeared to be caught in the thousands, especially since rabbit skins were used for blankets, coats, and mitt liners. Such uses, however, are seldom seen today.

Beaver is one of the most important animals as it yields the highest pelt value and the second highest source of edible meat which, like moose, is highly esteemed. Beaver are usually taken with steel traps during the winter and spring, although they are sometimes shot with small-calibre rifles. Games birds are a significant source of protein in the diet and yield several thousand kg of meat annually. Ducks and geese are mainly shot in the fall and the spring during their migration periods. In fact many families treat these migrations as a sort of vacation period when they set up special camps at a favourite site in early May when these birds, restricted to small areas of open water, are easily dispatched. Partridge or grouse, are shot in large numbers in the fall and early winter when the birds, or 'chickens' as they are called, tend to restrict their movements to small areas.

Numerous varieties of fish are a staple in the diet of northern peoples during the summer months, the most important of which are lake trout, pickerel (walleye), and sturgeon, although pike, speckled trout, and whitefish are also eaten. Gill nets are usually used for fishing, although angling has become somewhat of a novelty. Large fish such as lake trout and sturgeon are occasionally sold to other village members, or to Euro-Canadians, and as such provide an additional source of income.

The gathering of wild plants and berries provides seasonal variety to the northern diet. During August women and children can be found collecting large quantities of blueberries, but these are usually for immediate consumption. Up until a few decades ago blueberries were an important source of cash income for a family, but now there are fewer forest fires which rejuvenate berry patches. Also, berry picking is labour intensive and prices per basket have not risen substantially over the last decade. As such there is little incentive to invest one's labour in picking when more lucrative casual work can be found in the summer. Labrador Tea and other herbs are collected, but mainly by older people for medicinal purposes.

Hunting and Wage Work

What is the relationship between subsistence production and wage work in the northern Native economy? Conventional wisdom on the subject would have us believe that these are for the most part two largely incompatible spheres of activity in which wage work will eventually displace the subsistence realm. The field research on which this paper is based, however, tends to contradict this mode of reasoning. There is no inherent reason for concluding that a healthy subsistence economy cannot co-exist in the face of wage work opportunities. Much depends, however, on the interrelationships of these activities, such as the availability of each, and the emphasis placed on them by the local people. In fact, rather than regarding these two sectors as mutually exclusive, it is altogether possible that each economic area can make a positive contribution to the other, such that subsistence production is enhanced by wage work opportunities and, alternatively, a healthy subsistence sector creating additional opportunities for earning cash.

The evidence in support of this idea is presented in a far more extensive fashion in other published sources, namely (Hedican 1985, 1986), so that a brief summary of the pertinent ideas are presented for the purposes of this paper. In essence, comparative data was collected from a number of Ojibwa and Cree communities in northern Ontario and Quebec on per capita income levels, and quantities of bush meat consumed per day. The initial assumption was that rising incomes in a community would tend to lead to decreased utilization of country food. Only those with low incomes, the argument might go, would continue to hunt and fish. In fact, a different correlation was discovered — the higher the per capita income the greater the amount of country meat consumed by the northern Native people.

While it is evident that more research is needed in this area before any firm conclusion can be established, the evidence to this point is that some of the most prolific hunters in northern settlements are also those with some of the higher paying jobs. What this would suggest is that rising incomes increase efficiency in country food production to the extent that those with higher incomes can afford better hunting equipment and more frequent expeditions to the more remote, and less utilized, hunting and fishing areas. A high income also allows the part-time hunter to make more effective use of peak periods in game cycles, such as fish spawns or geese migrations. These sources of country food are widely dispersed throughout most of the year and, aside from times when large numbers can be found, the return on productive effort is low. As indicated for the Waswanipi Cree, "for each animal species the Waswanipi harvest, they attempt, like for the moose, to utilize it at times when chances of success are highest and the efficiency of capture is maximized" (Feit 1973: 120). This would also appear to be a fairly widespread pattern among northern Indian hunters, especially given the fact that most also allocate their labour to other ends besides hunting.

For the northern hunter, then, the most effective strategy is to exploit country food resources during high points in faunal cycles, and to work for cash when the highest paying jobs are available. Unfortunately for many northern Native communities, the best times for hunting and wage work often overlap. Such jobs as construction workers, guides, fire fighters are all occupations that absorb the most workers during peak hunting and fishing times. Thus, those who have difficulty securing wage employment are doomed to a double dilemma — they must hunt and fish when a return on their effort is uncertain, and yet they do not have the necessary cash for expenditures on capital equipment, maintenance, and transportation costs to increase subsistence production.

Clearly, then, hunting efficiency is dependent upon a number of important factors, many of which have little to do with hunting skill as such. For example, one of these is surely the time and energy necessary for the hunter to exploit his environment, both of which will tend to vary depending on the density of game available in a particular region, and the hunter's ability to reach it. These factors, consequently, will have a bearing on which game the hunter will seek.

At Mistassini in north-central Quebec, where game is dispersed and densities are low, several hundred square kilometres could be needed for a hunter to support his family (Rogers 1966: 93-97). This means that the Mistassini hunter, in relation to others in more favourable regions, will have to expend a great deal of energy travelling the area in search of game. In order to compensate for this loss of energy, the hunter in all probability will try to hunt big game in order to secure enough meat. However, in more favourable areas a hunter needs less territory to support himself and his dependants, and the energy expended in subsistence activity would as a result be less. With a greater concentration of game, the hunter could secure a greater yield in a shorter period of time, freeing the hunter from a reliance on large game, and an opportunity to secure a living from small game and fish, if that is his preference.

The lesson here is that this sort of variability, along with such factors as socio-spatial organization and settlement characteristics, should not be overlooked, or even treated as constants. It is clear, for example, that variability in the local biotic resource base, distribution of people vis á vis resources, distance to markets and distribution centres, prices of local goods, and related factors will intervene and complicate consumption rates of bush food versus store food. Although it is beyond the scope of the present paper to assess in any detail the importance such variable patterns have on Native subsistence systems, it is nonetheless important enough to bring them to the attention of the reader, and to suggest that they be made a focus of future research in the area of northern Native subsistence production.

Conclusion

Northern Native people run a perilous treadmill in their attempts to guard against the replacement of a high quality country meat diet by a diet of low quality store-bought carbohydrates, without seriously lowering health and nutrition standards. One of the reasons for this problem is that increasing expenditures on store food also tends to reduce the amount needed for capital investment and maintenance, and it is these sorts of expenses which involve the huge northern mark-up. What is to be avoided is the downward spiral of dependency that occurs when subsistence hunting is completely let go in favour of increased wage employment, with wages never catching up with the in-built inflation of prices in the North. It is only an extensive utilization of local resources that allows northern peoples a buffer against this inflation, and a means of keeping northern prices down. The implications, therefore, of government policy regarding northern areas is that the pattern of economic diversity in Native settlements should be encouraged because it tends to lessen dependence on the outside for food, fuel, and other renewable resources.

REFERENCES

Arbess, S. 1967. "Economic Realities and Political Development: The George River Case." *Anthropologica.* 9: 651-76.

Asch, M.I. 1982. "Capital and Economic Development: A Critical Appraisal of the Recommendations of the Mackenzie Valley Pipeline Commission." *Culture.* 2 (3): 3-9.

Baldwin, W.W. 1957. "Social Problems of the Ojibwa Indians in the Collins Area in Northwestern Ontario." *Anthropologica.* 5: 51-123.

Berger, T.R. 1977. *Northern Frontier, Northern Homeland.* Ottawa: Supply and Services Canada.

Berger, T.R. 1983. "Native Rights and Self-Determination." *The Canadian Journal of Native Studies.* 3 (2): 363-375.

Bishop, C.A. 1974. *The Northern Ojibwa and the Fur Trade.* Toronto: Holt, Rinehart, and Winston.

Dacks, G. 1974. *A Choice of Futures: Politics in the Canadian North.* Toronto: Methuen.

DIAND (Department of Indian Affairs and Northern Development) 1980. *Indian Conditions: A Survey.* Ottawa: DIAND.

Dunning, R.W. 1959. *Social and Economic Change Among the Northern Ojibwa.* Toronto: University of Toronto Press.

Elberg, N. 1975. *Not By Bread Alone: The Use of Subsistence Resources Among the James Bay Cree.* Monograph Series No. 5, Programme in the Anthropology of Development. Montreal: McGill University.

Feit, H.A. 1973. "The Ethno-Ecology of the Waswanipi Cree or How Hunters Can Manage Their Resources." In *Cultural*

Ecology, edited by B. Cox. Toronto: McClelland and Stewart.

Feit, H.A. 1982. "The Income Security Program for Cree Hunters in Quebec: An Experiment in Increasing the Autonomy of Hunters in a Developed Nation State." *Canadian Journal of Anthropology*. 3 (1): 57-70.

Frideres, J.S. 1984. "Government Policy and Indian Natural Resource Development." *The Canadian Journal of Native Studies*. 4 (1): 51-66.

Hallowell, A.I. 1926. "Bear Ceremonialism in the Northern Hemisphere." *American Anthropologist*. 28: 1-175.

Hedican, E.J. 1976. "Ecologic and Patron-Client Relationships: Algonkians of Eastern Subarctic Canada." *Man in the Northeast*. 12: 41-50.

Hedican, E.J. 1982. "Governmental Indian Policy, Administration, and Economic Planning in the Eastern Subarctic." *Culture*. 2 (3): 25-36.

Hedican, E. J. 1985. "Modern Economic Trends Among the Northern Ojibwa." *Man in the Northeast*. 30: 1-25.

Hedican, E.J. 1986. *The Ogoki River Guides: Emergent Leadership Among the Northern Ojibwa*. Waterloo: Wilfrid Laurier University Press.

Hedican, E.J. 1987. "The Land Base Problem Among Canadian Native People." *The Rural Sociologist*. 7 (5): 459-464.

Innis, H.A. 1970. *The Fur Trade in Canada*. Toronto: University of Toronto Press.

Jansen, W.H. 1979. *Eskimo Economics: Culture Change at Rankin Inlet*. Ottawa: National Museum of Man.

Jarvenpa, R. 1980. *The Trappers of Patuanak: Toward a Spatial Ecology of Modern Hunters*. Ottawa: National Museum of Man.

Jenness, D. 1978. "The Economic Situation of the Eskimo." In Valentine, V.F. and F.G. Vallee. (eds.) *Eskimo of the Canadian Arctic*. Toronto: Macmillan.

LaRusic, I.E. 1979. *The Income Security Program for Cree Hunters and Trappers*. Monograph Series, Programme in the Anthropology of Development. Montreal: McGill University.

Nowak, M. 1977. "The Economics of Native Subsistence Activities in a Village of Southwestern Alaska." *Arctic.* 30 (4): 225-233.

Rogers, E.S. 1962. *The Round Lake Ojibwa.* Toronto: Royal Ontario Museum.

Rogers, E.S. 1966. *Subsistence Areas of the Cree-Ojibwa of the Eastern Subarctic.* Ottawa: National Museum of Canada Bulletin 204.

Rogers, E.S. and M.J. Black 1976. "Subsistence Strategy in the Fish and Hare Period, Northern Ontario, The Weagamow Ojibwa, 1880-1920." *Journal of Anthropological Research.* 32 (1): 1-43.

Salisbury, R.F. 1986. *A Homeland for the Cree: Regional Development in James Bay 1971 -1981.* Montreal: McGill-Queen's University Press.

Skinner, A. 1911. *Notes on the Eastern Cree and Northern Salteaux.* New York: Anthropological Papers of the American Museum of Natural History.

Usher, P.J. 1976. "Evaluating Country Food in the Northern Native Economy." *Arctic.* 29 (2): 105-120.

Wenzel, G.W. 1981. *Clyde Inuit Adaptation and Ecology: The Organization of Subsistence.* Ottawa: National Museum of Man.

Chapter 9

UNWANTED CHANGE:
CANADA'S INTERFERENCE
WITH THE BALANCED FOOD CYCLE
OF THE WASAUKSIWUNINI*

Franz M. Koennecke

This chapter begins by looking at the traditional way one group of Canada's original inhabitants produced, processed and distributed its food resources. Their life, comfortably adapted to an environment of abundant freshwater, lush vegetation and a teaming wild life, was considerably changed by the arrival of British settlement with a cultural mentality directed towards economic usefulness for a growing world market. The willingness of the 'Indians' to adjust to a new system of food exchange was interfered with by a growing bureaucratic intervention of the Federal government and the destruction of, or restrictions to use, most of the original, natural food sources. In this small microcosm the interaction of other Indian groups with Canada is reflected. On a larger scale we see mirrored the experiences of other, colonized, Third World peoples.

The Wasauksiwunini are the Ojibwa, Potawatomi and Odawa of Parry Island in Georgian Bay, Ontario. To use their own terminology, the Anishinabek of Wasauksing. [1]

The original Wasauksiwunini were Ojibwa whose Potawatomi and Odawa cousins joined them in the 1870s. The latter two had originally fled their homelands in Wisconsin and Michigan not to be removed across the Mississippi in the 1830s. (Bigsby, 1969 : 96-98) [2]

The island of Wasauksing became a permanent home for the original Ojibwa population after the signing of the Robinson

Huron treaty at Penetanguishene in 1850. [3] One band had come from the North Shore and had moved into the area on its own. One band had lived in the area of today's town of Parry Sound and on Parry Island. The third band was to live around the southern Lake Rosseau area a few more years until in the 1860s Indian Affairs ordered their move to Parry Island. (Koennecke, 1984 : 15-17, 22-24) By 1846 most of these families recognized Chief Maitwaiosh as their leader and were considered part of the Wasauksing or Isle au Sable band. [4] Their territory was defined as reaching from the Parry Sound to the Severn river and back to the source of rivers running into Georgian Bay from the Haliburton Highlands. Added to this were the Georgian Bay islands fronting their coast. [5]

The territory of the Wasauksiwunini in what came to be known as the Muskokas is part of the Laurentian Shield. Lakes and rivers abound. The latter contain numerous rapids. Many of the hollows between high rocky ridges are swampland. Better drained areas contain fertile soil suitable for hardwood growth. (Schott, 1936 : 24; Hamilton, 1971 : introduction) [6]

The Laurentian forest of the Wasauksiwunini consisted of up to sixty percent white pine. This was mixed with red pine and stands of hemlock. In areas of thick fertile soil grew, besides, white pine, yellow birch and sugar maple. Also could be found red pine, beech, birch, oak, basswood, ironwood, poplar, white ash, jack pine, aspen, white and black spruce. In the swamps flourished cedar, tamarack, spruce and black ash. (Koennecke, 1984 : 7)

The Wasauksiwunini gained their livelihood from hunting, fishing, gathering and the produce of their gardens. It was a lifestyle in harmony with their environment and the seasons. They acknowledged that within this sacred hoop each new year was not a continuation but a return to the beginning of it. The Anishinabek celebrated six different seasons:

winter (bibon), the maple-sugar time (sigun), spring (minokamik), summer (nibin), autumn (tagwagig), and the trout-fishing season (nimegsikang), about the beginning of October. (Jenness, 1935 : 12)

The years were counted by winters. During the winter, generally lasting from December to March, the people separated and moved to their family hunting grounds. With them they carried dried stores of fish, vegetables and berries. Yet hunting and trapping were to provide the bulk of their food. (Jenness,

1935 : 13-15)

The animal life was very varied and the Anishinabek used up all they shot with their arrows or caught in their traps and snares. In their territory lived the black bear, bobcat, ground hog, hare, rabbit, lynx, marten, mink, fisher, muskrat, otter, porcupine, raccoon, red deer, fox, skunk, squirrel, weasel and wolf. At least around 1860, when the first surveyors gave detailed reports about the land, moose could not be found in the Muskokas. (Koennecke, 1984 : 7) Later on the moose became an important game animal. (Jenness, 1935 : 10)

Usually the men hunted. Every man had a hunting medicine made from a certain plant which helped him to draw game and fish. The more powerful the medicine was, the more successful the hunter or fisherman was also. Moose was also attracted by a birch bark trumpet. Deadfalls were used for bear, mink and porcupine. The women and children set snares for rabbits and grouse. (Jenness, 1935 : 13, 15, 83)

The men fished by cutting a hole into the ice of lakes and rivers. Over this a wigwam was erected. Sometimes the individual covered himself with a robe. The fish were lured by little carved decoys which were hung through the hole. The lakes and rivers teemed with bass, catfish, perch, pickerel, pike, smelt, speckled trout and sucker. In the deeper and colder waters of the Georgian Bay lived whitefish, sturgeon and salmon trout. (Report, 1858 : Sandy Island Census of 1857; Koennecke, 1984 : 7)

The hardest part of the winter came towards its end, when the snow started to melt and walking became tedious. Then the hunt was often at its lowest and the provisions from the summer and fall had been used up. Sometimes the hunters would find wild honey from a frozen bees' nest. The moss on white pines, roots of bulrushes or the brown lichens growing on rocks were integrated in these lean times. Some of the years had particular shortages of certain animals due to cyclical influences, as for example rabbits or muskrats. (Jenness, 1935 : 10, 12, 15) [7]

Around March the sun had become warm enough that the sap began to rise in trees. At that time the people began to move to their maple bushes to harvest the sweet liquid in bark containers. The sap was converted into grain sugar, cake sugar or gumlike wax sugar by boiling in large kettles or by letting it stand in the sun. (Jenness, 1935 : 13; Kohl, 1956 : 323, 324) The sugar was stored in birch or cedar bark baskets in earth pits, lined with birch bark. The people rejoiced again as they could season their fish soups with maple sugar. (Jenness, 1935 : 13, 17)

Most work in the maple bush was done by the women and children. The men went out onto the melting ice of rivers and lakes to spear muskrat and fish. On their return they might have helped their women and children in converting the maple syrup into sugar, as the fires had to be kept going all the time. If there was need, the sap from under the barks of the hemlock, black birch, basswood or black oak also could be used to enrich their diet. (Jenness, 1935 : 10, 13; Smith, 1975 : 112) [8] At least in this century a mixture of crushed gooseberries and cranberries was used for a spring tonic. [9] By now the lean times had passed.

When the maple sap had been harvested the Wasauksiwunini began to gather at their summer village, which was at the site of today's Parry Sound, north of the Seguin river. Actually, the people had also very extensive clearings on the island of Wasauksing. Napier reported in 1856 that he estimated those overgrown clearings at close to one hundred acres. As the Anishinabek practised slash and burn horticulture, their gardens were used on a rotational basis. A big circle was cleared and divided like a medicine wheel. For three years one section was planted, to be followed by the next, so that in 15 years the original section could be used again. Well into this century fences were not built as they disrupted the coexistence with other creatures. The rabbit or deer who ate from the garden would provide food for the people at a later date. [10]

Having settled in their summer camp the women put in their gardens. The most important agricultural tool was the digging stick. In the early days of the fur trade the small wooden spates and stone axes were soon replaced by iron hoes, spates and axes.

The corn was traditionally planted in small hillocks of soft earth, together with beans, squash and pumpkins. According to traditions corn and tobacco came to the people in dreams. (Johnson, 1929 : 195; Jenness, 1935 : 47; Trigger, 1969 : 27, 28; Report, 1858 : no page numbers)

Potatoes were first brought from 'Pinkaning,' potato island, in the Saginaw river, Michigan. [11]

The painter Paul Kane, who in 1845 travelled through the

Georgian Bay area, mentioned that the Anishinabek raised a lot of corn. When Lieutenant John Carthew visited a branch of the Wasauksiwunini on an island in Lake Rosseau in 1835, he was surprised to see that they had planted forty acres of corn and potatoes. (Johnson, 1929 : 6, 7; Murray, 1963 : L, 108)

During the spring and summer the people mainly feasted on fish. Pickerel and suckers ascended the rivers in May. According to one elder, in such abundance that "one could have walked on them." The men and boys built stone weirs from which the fish were picked. Whitefish, sturgeon and trout came to the shore waters for spawning. For trout and sturgeon the Wasauksiwunini used either spears or nets made of false nettle with floats of cedar wood and stone sinkers. Apparently the spears used for the large sturgeon were about ten metres long with two or three detachable points. For others, fish spears with only one point were employed. Often this type of fishing was done at night with a torchlight. (Jenness, 1935 : 11, 14 - 16) [12]

The fish were skinned and dried by the women and girls. The drying was done either in the sun or by smoke. Fish was boiled in stews. At other times, roasted over the fire on a stick or in the ashes. For stews, clay pots or birch bark kettles were utilized. The latter were heated with hot rocks put inside the water. Depending on the season, garden vegetables, the tubers of the 'wild' Jerusalem artichoke, the root of wild beans or other 'wild' vegetables like fiddleheads 'Odapiniig,' with a possible choice of three different types of mint, were added. Similar stews were common with meat. Along with their meals the Wasauksiwunini drank water or teas made, from among others, wintergreen, hemlock, labrador tea or creeping juniper. All of these being considered of medicinal value. (Jenness, 1935 : 10, 14, 16, 17) [13]

The men hunted for bear, deer and the smaller animals. Nesting ducks, geese or seagulls provided eggs. The migratory ducks and geese were also a welcome food source. With summer came the berries of which the blueberries were crushed raw and dried in the sun. Thimble berries were cooked into cakes and then dried. Strawberries, raspberries and blackberries grew in profusion and were also incorporated into the seasonal diet. (Jenness, 1935 : 14; Rogers & Tabobondung, 1975 : 305, 306)

Wild rice formed an important part of their livelihood. It is actually not a wild vegetable but is planted by the Anishinabek by wrapping a few grains in clay thrown into low, muddy water that remains at a fairly stable level. During September the men helped at the harvest by steering their canoes through the ripe rice fields. The women swept it into the canoes with a stick after which they did the drying and storing. The ripe rice attracted bull heads in great quantities. The same was the case with water fowl and passenger pigeons. These were caught whenever convenient. (Jenness, 1935 : 14) [14]

The fall brought the fruits of their gardens. Nature provided cranberries, wild plums, grapes, crab apples, whortle berries, hazelnuts, acorns and beechnuts. Dried meat was mixed with dried beechnuts, blueberries or rock cherries 'Pwaedjminan' and mint to be pounded into pemmican, the high nutritional value of which made it the favourite food of hunters. Acorns would be collected by women or their children to be boiled, then dried and pounded into a flour. In this century, and possibly earlier, this flour was added to cereal or used to bake cakes or cookies. Red and black currants and gooseberries were stored and used during the winter with maple sugar for desserts. (Jenness, 1935 : 10; Kohl, 1956 : 318 - 321) [15]

Corn and rice were stored in bark boxes after having been dried. The Anishinabek grew a summer squash with soft skin. It was sliced and dried in the sun. These pieces would be softened by cooking so that they tasted like pumpkin. Dried squash, the same as beans, was packed into basswood bags. Another variation, called winter squash had a very hard skin and was stored whole. Certain pumpkins were stored and soaked in water close to Christmas to make pies. Meat was pounded after drying and stored in boxes. Then a hole was dug, lined with bark and the food was kept from freezing by covering it with flags from a swamp. Earth was piled on top. (Jenness, 1935 : 10, 15, 16) [16]

While the women prepared for the winter the men went to the outer islands of Georgian Bay with their birch bark canoes and speared whitefish and salmon trout. These fish were used for the final fall festivities or dried for the winter. The yearly circle had been completed. (Jenness, 1935 : 15, 16, 108)

By the end of the eighteenth century the first fur trading post was built south of Wasauksing territory, at Matchedash Bay. Penetanguishene became a major fur trading centre in 1825. A few years before the Hudson's Bay Company had founded posts at Isle au Sable and near the mouth of the Shawanaga river. In times of need the Hudson's Bay factors assisted the Anishinabek with corn and potatoes. Also at the other places flour and other staple foods became available to be exchanged against furs and services. (Murray, 1963 : 18, 20, 108; Osborne, 1901 : 123 - 166; McCuaig, 1982 : 220, 222; Koennecke, 1984 : 55; Jenness, 1935 : 68)

In the early 1830s Christian missionaries began to reach the Georgian Bay region. In particular the Methodists, represented often by Native preachers, combined their proselytism with efforts to introduce European farming methods. As long as the traditional food chain had not been interrupted by white settlement, the Anishinabek were not ready to accept these changes. Characteristically in 1849 Reverend Dean considered them "outcasts," whose "living is abstracted from the deep and crystal waters of Huron and the wild beasts of the dismal forests which skirt the shores of these vast inland seas." (Koennecke, 1984 : 58, 60, 61) [17]

In 1850 the Anishinabek of the Lake Huron region surrendered their vast territory, with the exception of small reserves, to the British Crown. The treaty itself guaranteed "the full and free privilege to hunt over the territory now ceded by them, and to fish in the waters thereof, as they have heretofore been in the habit of doing, saving and excepting such portions of the said territory as may from time to time be sold or leased to individuals or companies of individuals and occupied by them with the consent of the Provincial Government." (Canada, 1971 : 149 - 152)

Commissioner Robinson assured the Chiefs and Headmen that their land was completely safe from being settled by white people. The agricultural potential was lacking. He predicted that the Anishinabek could continue their traditional lifestyle and if they desired to farm they would receive the Crown's support to learn it. Robinson made these promises to the Chiefs at Sault St. Marie. A few days later the Wasauksiwunini and those of Shawanaga signed the same treaty at Penetanguishene. At that time their land had been already chosen for extensive lumbering operations and agricultural settlements by the Province of Canada. (Morris, 1979 : 19; Boyer, 1979 : 7, 11, 12 -18) [18]

The actual white settlement of the Muskokas and the Georgian Bay region began in 1859. The large scale lumbering operations and the white settlers caused the decline of wildlife resources. Actually the game had been on the decline since the beginning of the nineteenth century. The newcomers soon became aware of more drastic depletions. According to the Member of Parliament for Algoma the game was dwindling by 1873. An 1878 publication complained of the wanton slaughter of deer by "Pot-Hunters" in the Muskoka and Georgian Bay region. In 1878 the Indian Superintendent responsible for the Parry Sound district reported that the Parry Island band cannot rely on fishing and hunting anymore. Following Indian Affairs guidelines he recommended their greater involvement in European type farming. (Murray, 1963 : LXXX, CV, 149; Hamilton, 1971 : 11, 12) [19]

At that time many people in Ontario believed that the decline of wildlife resources was caused by unrestricted Indian hunting and fishing practices. Led by this public sentiment the Upper Canada government considered Indian treaty rights no longer valid by 1860 and began to enforce on Indians the existing game and fish laws. In the years to follow the federal position wavered from a recognition of Indian treaty rights to an acceptance that the wildlife resources had to be protected. As a result those Anishinabek who continued to rely on their treaty rights and hunted or fished in the traditional manner experienced increasing intimidation and court actions. (Moore, 1978 : 112) [20]

The bulk of Wasauksiwunini food came from fishing. In 1874 very little of that was sold to white settlers. At that time the lumbering industry in Parry Sound and Parry Harbour had grown considerably and the sawdust dumped into the Seguin river and onto the spawning grounds along the shore line wiped out the fish. With the spawning grounds polluted, the Wasauksiwunini had to fish in the deep waters. Their small boats and nets allowed only for very limited catches. Yet they clashed with the commercial outfits. These were fishing the Georgian Bay at a rate of over two million pounds of fish per year. The protection of Wasauksing fishing grounds, requested by Chief Megis and promised in an Order-in-Council in 1853, was not forthcoming. (Brunton, 1969 : 41; Barry, 1978 : 110) [21]

Neither was there much protection when the Wasauksiwunini went out hunting. The Parry Sound Indian Superintendent Dr. Walton reported in 1884, that "Indians while hunting had been molested, their traps destroyed—and that had

Indians in such cases followed the usual course of white people in defending themselves many deaths would have occurred." [22]

In 1881 the annual fur sales at Penetanguishene were discontinued. The passenger pigeon became scarce by 1885, to be extinct soon. The collection of furs dropped considerably at the nearby Shawanaga band. Interestingly enough, individual reports of the fall deer hunt showed no such decrease. Only as late as 1902 were deer and waterfowl becoming depleted in the Parry Sound district. However, in less settled areas, as around Shawanaga and in Burpee township, the cutting of the mature forest helped to increase the deer population. (Barry, 1978 : 43, 66) [23]

The women and children continued to pick berries and the families harvested maple syrup at sugar bushes owned by them close to the four settlements on Wasauksing. Both cranberries and maple sugar were sold at Parry Sound or Penetanguishene. Wild rice remained a staple food until its destruction on and around the island by horses, cattle, pigs, gas and oil spills and the blasting of some channels to facilitate boat traffic. In the fall the pigs would be let out of their pens to feast on beechnuts and acorns. The more nuts they ate, the firmer their meat would become and enhance its taste. [24]

The traditional, cyclical life of the Anishinabek was not acceptable to the Department of Indian Affairs. Therefore it became the policy of the Department to promote European type farming. The officials hoped that the physical and mental labour involved would turn the Indians away from their own culture and make them 'civilized.' In other words British and Christian. [25]

The Wasauksiwunini were not prepared to accept the Department's concepts and changed only when traditional approaches had become obsolete. In 1870 the band purchased a yoke of oxen and some farming implements, including a plow. Four years later they had cultivated 80 acres of Indian corn and potatoes. Two years after that band members planted wheat and oats for the first time.

Spring harrows were purchased in 1884 and 1886, a thrashing machine in 1894 and a mowing machine before 1897. A few Potawatomies from Cape Croker had arrived who cleared and operated 25 to 50 acre farms. The lack of larger areas containing suitable soil restricted farming to these few families.

Besides, wage labour in the growing lumber trade as guides, and work in Parry Sound had become more promising by the 1880s. [26]

Life had changed for the Wasauksiwunini by 1908 when traditional food from hunting and fishing was no longer of primary importance. There were still a few individuals who obtained their sustenance in the old way but most people hunted and fished only to replenish the larder with some fresh meat or fish, predominantly in the fall. Apples which had been thrown as waste into the water near Owen Sound harbour had found their way to Wasauksing and by now had been nurtured into orchards around most homes. The harvests of their gardens and orchards played an important role and reflected in the annual Parry Island Agricultural Fall Fair where livestock, butter, cheese, buns, pies, tarts, cakes, pickles, preserved fruits and maple products were shown. Increasingly groceries were purchased in Parry Sound and Depot Harbour. [27]

The opening of the country by railroads brought a whole new town, Depot Harbour, onto an expropriated part of Parry Island by the turn of the century. Related to this was a decline of fish in the island's Three Mile Lake. Likewise the cranberries had to be controlled more closely by the band. With the railroad came an increase in the number of tourists, white pleasure hunters and fishermen. Pragmatically the Wasauksiwunini hired themselves out as guides with a good income. Indian Affairs did not accept that the people made a good living with wage labour and continued to stress the importance of agriculture. (McKean, 1965 : 180 -186) [28]

In their efforts to increase agricultural activity, in 1895 Indian Affairs legislated that personal loans to purchase machinery and livestock could be obtained from band funds. Moreover agricultural advisors were hired for the first time during the first world war. Among other things they taught the people that potatoes became scabby due to sandy soil conditions. The Anishinabek were advised to mix the soil with clay or with wet leaves brought in wheelbarrows from nearby creeks. Except for a few individuals, however, Parry Island never fulfilled the expectations of the Ottawa policy makers. (Moore, 1978 : 98) [29]

In 1915, Indian Affairs timber inspector Bury carefully

evaluated the island and pointed out that it was not suitable for agriculture. Only 2,500 acres were considered useful for agricultural purposes. The remaining 16,000 acres contained bush, rock, swamp and muskeg. Under actual cultivation were 80 acres, the same as in 1874. Fifty more acres had been cleared and 100 acres fenced, primarily for grassland. Instead, Bury considered the island's timber as a more promising source of income for the Anishinabek. (Koennecke, 1984 : 443) [30]

Provided with some clear facts by Bury, the Department did not alter its policy of encouraging agriculture. The Wasauksiwunini listened and did what was practical. They continued to earn money wherever and whenever they could, tended their gardens and doing some hunting, fishing and berry picking. More and more they began to rely on store bought staples of flour, sugar, lard, tea and salt. The island's valuable timber had been exploited largely by outside companies. Very little went to the Wasauksiwunini in the form of cutting fees and wages for lumber men. If Indian Affairs would have permitted the band to exploit this timber resource great economic gain could have resulted. "Ironically Indian Affairs, preaching self sufficiency, actually drove the Anishnabwe into dependency by bad economic counsel." (Koennecke, 1984 : 321) [31]

In contemporary times the Wasauksiwunini still cherish and prefer the traditional foods. At the frequent community feasts the boiled or roasted meats of moose, deer, beaver and muskrat can be eaten. Steamed or boiled whitefish, pickerel, pike and bass are also common. Wild rice has been planted again and under the nurturing care of some individuals will make a comeback. A few women and children still pick berries but no longer on a large scale. The same is the case with gardens which play a minor role and are no longer planted by every household. The fruit orchards have gone. Livestock is no longer kept. In general most of the food is bought at the modern supermarkets found in the nearby town of Parry Sound.

At present the Wasauksing First Nation, together with the other Anishinabek of the Province, is defining its view of self determination. The relationship with the game and fish wardens has improved and presently a lenient policy is in effect towards Native people. In return some of the First Nations have begun to introduce and supervise their own conservation policies. Wasauksing has to consider acid rain threatening to destroy

311

their substantial maple forests which still supply an annual crop of maple syrup. A further danger is the mercury found in the waters of Georgian Bay that allows only for a limited fish consumption. Yet the great determination of the Wasauksiwunini to again take responsibility for their own lives will increase their awareness to obtain more of their food from the environment in the healthy manner of their forefathers. [32]

ABBREVIATIONS

CM — Parry Island Council Minutes, *PAO*.

CSP — Canada, Sessional Papers, Annual Reports of the Department of Indian Affairs, University of Waterloo, Waterloo, Ontario.

MDD — Duncan Frazer Macdonald Diaries, *PAO*.

NAC — National Archives of Canada, Ottawa.

PAO — Public Archives of Ontario, Toronto.

Rep. I. A. — Annual Reports of the Department of Indian Affairs, University of Waterloo, Waterloo, Ontario.

NOTES

* I feel grateful to Wasauksing elder Fred Wheatley (Mahn Ki Ki) for his assistance in writing this article.

1 Today only Ojibwa and English are spoken. Wasauksing means 'White Stakes You See From Far.' The oldest living man on the island, Ted Wheatley (born 1901), showed us the place at which one part of the band, living at Sandy Island, saw white birches which gave their name to Wasauksing. Wasauksiwunini means inhabitants of Wasauksing. Anishinabek means People or Human Beings and is their name for all Ojibwa, Potawatomi and Odawa (Ottawa).

2 John Bigsby provided the earliest known description of an Ojibwa band close to Sandy Island in 1823. *National Archives of Canada, (NAC)*, RG 10, 2005, file 7752, in 1877 members of the Potawatomi King (Ogemawatch) family requested permission to live on Parry Island. Ibid., MG 29 D 53, Salt Papers, January 27, 1884, a note that this Methodist missionary had visited the settlement of the Odawa Nanibush family.

3 *NAC*, RG 1, E 8, vol. 46, Order-in-Council, January 31, 1853.

4 *NAC*, RG 10, 621, 1846 band list; for periods the neighbouring Shawanaga band was also considered to be part of the Isle au Sable band. This particular term was in use from the 1820s to the 1870s.

5 *Public Archives of Ontario (PAO)*, MU 1464, MSS Irving Papers, Box 26, Pkg. 31, Item 4, Anderson and Vidal report of December 5, 1849, appendix B of the typed version. The Commissioners added the Wasauksiwunini to the "Shawwaynagar" band and did not mention any ownership to islands. Those, however, have been always considered as belonging to Wasauksing. Other evidence showed that their southern boundary went only to the Moon river.

6 *PAO*, RG 1, B-IV, box 15, file 6, Surveyor O'Hanly to Crown Lands Department, Ottawa, January 19, 1866.

7 Personal discussion with Anishinabek elders about life cycles among animals.

8 Fred Wheatley, Parry Island elder, interview November 18, 1988.

9 Ibid.

10 Ted Wheatley, Fred's older brother, pointed out the site of Manitowabe's former camp, close to the CPR trestle, across the Seguin river. *NAC*, RG 10, 2050, file 9428, Napier's report of December 1, 1856. Fred Wheatley, interview Nov. 18, 1988.

11 Fred Wheatley, interview Nov. 18, 1988.

12 Fred Wheatley, about his youth on many occasions.

13 Ted Wheatley taught me about the medicinal value of teas & Fred Wheatley mentioned the mints.

14 Personal discussion with Peter Kelly, a Chief from the Treaty 3 area (Northwestern Ontario), who lobbied for the preservation of their wild rice fields in the late 1970s.

15 The German traveller Kohl provided a good list of plants collected around Garden River and a number of interesting recipes. Fred Wheatley, interviews November 18 & 20, 1988.

16 Fred Wheatley, interviews November 18 & 20, 1988.

17 *Annual Reports, Methodist Episcopal Church Missionary Society in Canada*, No. 25, June 1849 to June 1850. p. XX.

18 *Ontario Ministry of Natural Resources*, Toronto, J. C. Robinson Papers, typed transcript of 1850 diary, p. 4, September 5, 1850.

19 *NAC*, RG 10, Vol. 266, pp. 163,028 - 163,378, Vidal and Anderson report of 1849, p. 15. *PAO*, MU 1465, Irving Papers, Indian Claims, Robinson Treaties, box 27, package 31, item 5, Dawson to Secretary of Governor General, April 7, 1873. *Indian Affairs Annual Reports,*

(Rep. I.A.) 1879, pp. 25, 26, Skene's report of August 1, 1878.

20 *NAC*, RG 10, 2064, file 10099 1/2, Fisheries Branch, Ottawa to Indian Affairs, September 13, 1878. Ibid., Skene to Indian Affairs, October 22, 1878. Ibid., 2185, file 27328, Under Secretary of State to Indian Affairs, May 20, 1882. Ibid., Indian Affairs to Under Secretary of State, June 13, 1882. Ibid., 2936, file 196479, Indian Affairs to Stewart, December 28, 1897. Personal discussions with Parry Island elders about how they avoided the game and fish wardens.

21 *Rep. I.A.*, 1857, Commissioner Pennefather's report. *NAC*, RG 10, 1938, file 3778, Skene to Indian Affairs, September 7, 1874. Ibid., 2064, file 10099 1/2, Skene to Deputy Minister of the Interior, October 22, 1878. *PAO*, Parry Island Council Minutes (CM), Council to Skene, May 22, 1877. *NAC*, RG 1, E 8, Vol. 46, Order-in-Council, January 31, 1853.

22 *NAC*, RG 10, 1963, 5045-2, Walton to Superintendent General, September 4, 1884.

23 *NAC*, MG 29 D 53, Salt Papers, March 7, 1887. *PAO*, Duncan Frazer Macdonald Diaries (MDD), October 28, 1902, September 13, 1904, November 6, 1905.

24 *NAC*, MG 29 D 53, Salt Papers, April 6, 1884, March 30, 1885, April 20, 1887, April 15, 1888, September 20, 1890. *PAO*, MDD, September 12, 1878. Wellington Wheatley, Ted's older brother, September 4, 1977. The Wasauksiwunini do not remember when the wild rice disappeared. Fred Wheatley, interview Nov. 20, 1988.

25 *NAC*, RG 10, 615, p. 667, Spragge to DuPont, July 24, 1865. *Rep. I.A.*, 1865, Deputy Superintendent General Spragge's report for 1864.

26 *NAC*, RG 10, 723, Memo by Spragge, June 3, 1870. Ibid., 1938, file 3779, Skene's report of September 7, 1874. Ibid., 1995, file 6881, Skene to Indian Affairs, August 8, 1876. Ibid., 2339, file 68581, band to Indian Affairs, May 17, 1886 and Walton to Indian Affairs, June 2, 1886. Ibid., 2145, file 30301, Walton to Indian Affairs, April 28, 1897 & James Walker to Indian Affairs, January 21, 1897. *PAO*, CM, May 2, 1894. Ibid., MDD, December 16, 1874, July 10, 1876, November 14, 1884. *Canada*, Sessional Papers, Annual Reports of the Department of Indian Affairs (CSP), 1881, pp. 22, 23 Skene's report of September 30, 1880. *Rep. I.A.*, 1881, p. 10, Skene's report of September 17, 1881. *NAC*, MG 29 D 53, Salt Papers, August 27, 1883.

27 *Rep. I. A.*, 1908, p. 30, Macdonald's report of March 31, 1908. *CSP*, 1911, pp. 29, 30, Macdonald's report of March 31, 1910. Fred Wheatley, interview Nov. 18, 1988.

28 *NAC*, MG 29 D 53, Salt Papers, November 8, 1896. Ibid., RG 10, 1735, MacLean to Indian Affairs, September 5, 1900. *PAO*, CM, July

2, 1898, September 3, 1900, June 3, 1901, November 2, 1901. *Rep. I.A.*, 1898, p. XXI, Deputy Superintendent General Smart's report of December 31, 1898.

29 *CSP*, 1901, p. 33, MacLean's report of September 12, 1900. *Rep. I.A.*, 1908, p. 30, Macdonald's report of March 31, 1908. Fred Wheatley, interview Nov. 18, 1988.

30 *NAC*, RG 10, 3176, file 442626-2, reports of October 10,1915 and October 21, 1915.

31 *NAC*, RG 10, 7555, file 1022-5, Indian Affairs to Logan, September 25, 1917. Personal discussion with elders.

32 *Globe and Mail*, Toronto, Friday December 17, 1976, p. 3, "Don't eat the fish, Georgian Bay Indians warned." Personal conversations with the late Chief Goldwyn Tabobondung.

REFERENCES

Barry, James. 1978. *Georgian Bay The Sixth Great Lake*. Toronto: Clarke, Irwin and Company Limited.

Bigsby, John J. 1969. *The Shoe and Canoe or Pictures of Travel in the Canadas*. Vol. 2. New York: Paladin Press. Reprint of the 1850 edition, 1969.

Boyer, Robert J. 1979. *Early Exploration and Surveying of Muskoka District*. Bracebridge: Herald-Gazette Press.

Brunton, Sam. 1969. *Notes and Sketches on the History of Parry Sound*. Parry Sound: Parry Sound Public Library. Parry Sound Historical Society.

Canada. 1971. *Indian Treaties and Surrenders, from 1680 to 1890*. Ottawa: 1891. Coles Reprint, 1971.

Hamilton, E. E. 1971. *Muskoka and Parry Sound Districts*. Toronto: 1879. Reprint, 1971.

Jenness, Diamond. 1935. *The Ojibwa Indians of Parry Island, Their Social and Religious Life*. Ottawa: Canada Department of Mines, National Museum of Canada. Bulletin No. 78. Anthropological Series No. 17.

Johnson, Frederick. 1929. "Notes on the Ojibwa and Potawatomi of the Parry Island Reservation, Ontario." New York: *Indian Notes*. Museum of the American Indian, Heye Foundation.

VI, (3): 193-216 (July).

Koennecke, Franz M. 1984. *Wasoksing the History of Parry Island an Anishnabwe Community in the Georgian Bay 1850 - 1920.* Waterloo: University of Waterloo, Ontario. M.A. Thesis.

Kohl, Johannes G. 1956. *Kitchi-Gami, Wanderings Round Lake Superior.* London: 1860. Ross and Haines Reprint, 1956.

McCuaig, Ruth W. 1982. "Pointe au Baril." Parry Sound: *East Georgian Bay Historical Journal.* II: 220-254.

McKean, F. K. 1965. "Depot Harbour – The First Seaway Terminal." *Inland Seas.* Quarterly Journal of the Great Lakes Historical Society. 21, (3): 180-186 (Fall).

Moore, Robert G. 1978. *The Historical Development of the Indian Act.* Ottawa: Indian Affairs, Treaties and Historical Research Centre. August.

Morris, Alexander P.C. 1979. *The Treaties of Canada with the Indians.* Toronto: 1862. Coles Reprint, 1979.

Murray, Florence B. (ed.) 1963. *Muskoka and Haliburton 1615 to 1875.* Toronto: University of Toronto Press.

Osborne, A. C. 1901. "The Migration of Voyageurs from Drummond Island to Penetanguishene in 1828." Toronto: *Ontario Historical Society Papers and Records..* III: 123-166.

Report. 1858. *Report of the Special Commissioners appointed on the 8th of September 1856, to Investigate Indian Affairs in Canada.* Toronto: Stewart Derbishire & George Desbarats.

Rogers, Edward & Tabobondung, Flora. 1975. "A Period of Change in the Way of Life of the Algonkians of Southern Ontario: Parry Island Farmers." In David Brez Carlisle (ed.) *Contributions to Canadian Ethnology.* Ottawa: National Museum of Man Mercury Series, Canadian Ethnology Service Paper. (31): 247-359.

Schott, Carl. 1936. *Landnahme und Kolonisation in Canada am Beispiel S dontarios.* Kiel: Buchdruckerei Schmidt & Klaunig.

Smith, Donald B. 1975. *The Mississauga, Peter Jones, and the White Man: The Algonkians' Adjustment to the Europeans on the North Shore of Lake Ontario to 1860.* Toronto: University of Toronto. PhD Thesis.

Trigger, Bruce G. 1969. *The Huron Farmers of the North.* Toronto: Holt, Rinehart and Winston.

Part IV

TECHNICAL ISSUES AND ALTERNATIVES:
SOIL, WATER AND FISHERIES MANAGEMENT

"WOMAN AT THE WELL"
Many thanks to Nora Cebotarev and Linda Szato, 1989.

Photograph Coutesy of IDRC.

Chapter 10

SOIL CONSERVATION TECHNOLOGY AND WORLD FOOD SUPPLY:
OBSTACLES AND OPPORTUNITIES

Thomas J. Hoban

INTRODUCTION

Despite major technological advances in agricultural production, many people in the world do not have enough to eat. There are many reasons for this situation, but the most alarming is the rate at which the productive capability of our land and water resources have been and continue to be destroyed (Hauck 1985). Large areas of the world's agricultural land suffer from severe soil erosion. Each year huge areas are either entirely lost or have their productive capability reduced.

Soil erosion is a natural process caused by the action of wind and water. It is often accelerated by unwise land use brought about by economic and social conditions (Morgan 1986). In fact, the main causes of resource degradation are mismanagement of natural resources and attempts to farm the land beyond its capabilities. The most serious obstacles to successful soil conservation are social, economic, and political (Hauck 1985).

Soil erosion is one of the most serious natural resource problems many nations face. It threatens future food supplies, as well as pollutes valuable reservoirs, lakes, and rivers. Studies by the Worldwatch Institute document the severity of Third World soil erosion problems (Brown and Shaw 1982; Brown and Wolf 1984). They also report that most Third World nations have little information on the dimensions of their soil erosion problems, much less any successful programs for dealing with these problems.

There are a number of effective technologies for controlling excessive soil erosion. Many involve management practices that do not require large investments. However, many farmers are not willing or able to adopt the necessary technologies. There are various explanations for why soil conservation technologies have not been more widely adopted. This paper will examine some of these reasons and suggest strategies to promote more effective control of worldwide soil erosion problems.

The United States has over 50 years experience with encouraging voluntary adoption of soil conservation technologies. Various national, state, and local organizations provide technical, financial, and educational assistance to farmers. Concerns over continuing soil erosion problems have prompted a more focussed approach of targeting assistance to the most serious problem areas (USDA 1982).

Part of this targeting effort includes developing a variety of educational and assistance strategies for encouraging farmers to recognize and solve soil erosion problems (Hoban 1984). These strategies are based on several theoretical and applied areas, including: the diffusion of innovations, social network analysis, interorganizational co-ordination, farming systems research, marketing, and communication. This paper will outline these strategies to suggest how other nations can build on the United State experience to develop effective soil erosion control programs.

At the outset it is important to emphasize that Third World countries face many more difficult obstacles in attempting to transfer conservation technologies. On the international level, Morgan (1986) expressed the concern that "If American farmers with their history of soil conservation activity cannot be persuaded to protect their land, what hope is there for the rest of the world where the conservation message is less strong and less widely accepted?" This requires an initial overview of the nature of the soil erosion problems worldwide.

WORLD SOIL CONSERVATION PROBLEMS AND PROGRAMS

All countries experience soil erosion to varying degrees, depending on natural conditions, as well as social, economic, and political factors. Many governments around the world are responding to the challenges of controlling soil erosion. Their commitment and effectiveness vary. Many countries have patterned their programs after those in the United States and are attempting to transfer similar technologies (Troeh et al. 1980). There are, however, technical and social obstacles involved with efforts to transfer technology from one region to another.

This literature review will attempt to illustrate the nature and causes of soil erosion problems in Third World countries. Some general approaches selected countries are using to deal with these problems will also be highlighted. The focus will be on general trends and similarities between conditions in the various countries. In fact most of the points made for one country will apply to many other similar situations, as well.

According to Rapp (1986) tropical and subtropical semi-arid areas generally have great erosion hazard. This is due to a combination of sparse vegetation at the end of the dry season and very intense rainstorms or dust storms. Mountainous areas represent another potentially erosive environment. Many areas have been subjected to considerable exploitation by deforestation, burning, cultivation of steep slopes.

Soil erosion occurs extensively on rolling cropland in Thailand (Jantawat 1985). Recent studies have documented the magnitude and location of the most serious erosion problems. Erosion rates, especially where deforestation had occurred, were found to be much higher than the world average. Increasing land pressures have shortened the rotation cycle with the result that crop yields and soil stability have decreased (Marston et al. 1985). Better vegetative cover is needed in the mountains, especially where shifting cultivation is extensive (Ruangpanit 1985). Overall, lack of information is seen as an obstacle to effective management. One major project has relied on engineering and structural practices, with inadequate attention to agronomic and management systems (Marston et al. 1985). The project also includes an extension program for farmers.

Erosion control has not, however, been adequate because of various factors including lack of farmer awareness and administrative constraints.

Writing about conditions in Malaysia, Maene and Sulaiman (1986) explain that in the humid tropics, soil erosion is likely to increase as food production expands. They warn, however, that knowledge of the causes and magnitude of erosion is inadequate to design readily applicable systems. Information is especially lacking on the erodibility of various soils and climatic conditions. One basic principle is to maintain a vegetative or mulch cover over the soil at most times.

Soil erosion is a serious problem in Indonesia because few farmers follow proper management recommendations (Suwardjo and Abujamin, 1985). Soil erosion is worst when land is cleared by tillage. Most farmers prefer clean tilled land so they remove crop residue. Because land is limited, farmers often plant steep slopes with annual crops and deforestation is widespread. Terraces are needed but they are generally too expensive for most farmers. Farmers, therefore, need low cost farming systems that will reduce erosion and maintain productivity. Mulch and minimum tillage will be important components of such a system.

A combination of factors in Java cause rapid degradation of soil and water resources (Barrau and Djati 1985). Population densities are high, as is rainfall intensity. The land is intensively cultivated and conservation efforts are poor. Consequences from erosion include increased flooding, sedimentation in reservoirs, and damage to irrigation systems. The major sources of sediment are dryland farms on steep slopes which often have the following characteristics:

1. low productivity that causes farmers to expand their operations and neglect conservation
2. poor land use and farm planning
3. lack of technical advice and other assistance
4. lack of capital
5. lack of off-farm opportunities.

Erosion problems are also very serious in many parts of Africa. Rapp (1986) explains that the pressures of overcultivation, overgrazing, and wood collection have led to serious erosion damage, increased sedimentation and silting of reservoirs. He expressed great concern, however, that "we do not know how fast Africa's forests, grazing lands, and soils are being destroyed. Nor do we know to what extent the degradation is irreversible or where and how to concentrate reclamation efforts." It will be important that any reclamation and development efforts be adapted to social and ecological conditions.

Tropical soils in Nigeria show problems common to the tropical region (Lai, 1985). Soil nutrients are concentrated in a thin surface layer and the subsoils are infertile and unsuitable for cultivation. Serious gaps exist in our knowledge of the relationship between erosion and productivity on tropical soils. Increasing demographic pressures and rising demands for food in the tropics, however, require immediate decisions on land use policies and programs. During the last decade, the Nigerian government assembled experts to survey soil erosion throughout the country and recommend solutions (Aneke, 1986). This marked the beginning of concerted and systematic efforts to control erosion including reclamation, education, and policy changes.

Soil erosion is a serious problem in two regions of Ghana: the dry northern savannah and the rain forest where the fallow period of shifting cultivation has decreased considerably (Bonsu, 1985). Livestock manure is used extensively because of its nutrient value, water holding capacity, and soil building capability. Straw mulch is also used to reduce water loss and soil erosion.

Like some other African countries, Egypt faces serious problems with advancing deserts on the fringes of the Nile Valley and Delta (Kishk, 1985). Attempts to expand cropland areas to meet demands of its ever-growing population threatens existing limited cropland. Data are not sufficient for meeting the challenge of desertification. Kishk (1985) concludes that measures must be implemented to avoid further spread of the desert.

Overgrazing and trampling, especially near watering points, are major causes of soil degradation and desertification in Senegal (Valentin, 1985). Radical changes in pastoral practices have affected many aspects of the human and natural environment. Recommendations to control the problems that are being implemented include:

1. Assess the carrying capacity of a region before carrying out any projects.
2. Gain willing participation of the pastoral community.
3. Establish tree-planted shelterbelts around the waterholes.
4. Restore the land with the help of an experienced staff. Training is needed to transfer the simple and effective techniques beyond the limited groups of specialists.

China seems to have ambitious and relatively successful programs for dealing with its very serious soil and water resource problems (Howard 1981; Robinson 1981; Barrows, et al. 1982). Jiang et al. (1986) explain that since the founding of the People's Republic of China, governments at all levels have attached great importance to soil and water conservation. A large scale, comprehensive program has been continually implemented, with efforts targeted to the most critical areas. Some of the guiding principles include:

1. Technologies should be appropriate for local conditions.
2. Technologies implemented on slopes and gullies should be co-ordinated.
3. Engineering and vegetative means should be used at the same time.
4. Work should be aimed both at obtaining benefits and reducing costs. Conservation should be an integral part of agricultural development.

India also has a long history of intensive soil conservation efforts. They also face considerable challenges given the great diversity of natural areas (e.g., land and climate) and socio-economic conditions (Gumbs et al. 1985). As early as 1919, revenue concessions were granted to farmers who would reclaim ravines (Das 1986). More recently a number of pilot projects have developed and successfully implemented appropriate conservation technologies. Systematic inventories have been conducted and co-ordinated plans have been prepared. The effectiveness of various technologies is being continually evaluated and improved. Emphasis during implementation has been on involving local people to ensure follow-up and maintenance. Widespread use of demonstrations and technical assistance have been noted (Das 1986). India seems to be quite innovative in its efforts to develop and transfer conservation technologies (Narayana and Sastry 1985).

OBSTACLES TO SOIL CONSERVATION ADOPTION

The situation in the countries just discussed should indicate that Third World countries face serious problems in trying to adequately control their soil erosion obstacles. Those interested in promoting soil conservation need to understand and appreciate the voluntary decision-making process before developing promotional strategies. Given appropriate technology, information, and assistance most farmers will support and practise soil conservation as they come to recognize the importance of protecting their natural resources. However, they face a number of obstacles that prevent their good intentions from being translated into action.

This section briefly examines the conservation decision process, in terms of some of the obstacles farmers face that make them unable or unwilling to adopt the necessary technologies. Even though little is known about the technical details of conservation in many parts of the world, much less is known about the social, economic and institutional factors. This discussion will briefly outline some of the most serious technical, individual, social, economic, and institutional obstacles. In a later section practical strategies will be provided for overcoming these obstacles.

Technical Obstacles

Technical obstacles relate to the nature and availability of information and technologies for controlling soil erosion problems. Few countries have adequate information about the location and severity of their soil erosion problems. Such information will be vital, however, for targeting assistance to locations where the problems are most severe.

Information may not even be available on the nature and

325

effectiveness of alternative conservation technologies. Certain types of conservation technologies may not be appropriate for all types of farmers. Some may not be compatible with existing farming systems or local customs. This is a particular problem when technologies developed in the U.S. (where large farms prevail) are transferred to other countries where much smaller farms are the rule. Morgan (1986) emphasizes that successful soil conservation efforts must start with appropriate technology.

Natural conditions also pose obstacles to transfer of conservation technologies. Climate will influence the effectiveness and appropriateness of alternative conservation technologies. Topography will also limit the usefulness of certain technologies.

Individual Obstacles

One major obstacle many farmers face in the initial stages of the conservation decision-making process involves lack of awareness. Many farmers are not aware of the existence of soil erosion problems on their own farms. This is particularly true for the more subtle, often invisible forms of wind, sheet and rill erosion. Also, farmers may not be aware of the variety of effective technologies that are available for controlling their erosion problems. Further, studies have shown that farmers do not generally understand the types and sources of conservation assistance that are available (Bultena et al. 1984). Even if farmers are aware of erosion problems and solutions, they may lack the technical information, financial resources, and/or managerial skills to successfully adopt the conservation technologies.

Studies have found that certain characteristics of individuals influence their resistance to innovation (Rogers 1983). For the case of soil conservation innovations, these include: traditionalism or the belief that existing production methods are better than newer methods; independence or the attitude that individuals can handle their own problems without government involvement; or an inherent aversion to risk. As Hudson (1983) explains, a farmer is neither stupid nor lethargic when he sticks to his old ways of farming; but is simply accepting the realities of life. These personal characteristics and others serve as obstacles to the adoption of soil conservation technologies.

Economic Obstacles

Some conservation technologies may be hard for a farmer to justify because these practices may have few short-term benefits. Also, farmers may not even have adequate information to assess the benefits and costs of soil conservation systems. Brown and Shaw (1982) explain that economic realities influence the behaviour of Third World farmers who can muster little concern about the future when their very survival is at stake. Many farmers lack capital and often live at subsistence levels.

Unfavourable economic conditions present serious obstacles to even those farmers who are very interested in practising soil conservation. Many farmers may simply not make enough money for necessary conservation work or investments in new equipment. Even when cost-sharing is available farmers may not have the cash flow or access to credit for their share of the investment. Farmers with high debt loads may be unable or unwilling to obtain additional credit for conservation investments. Many Third World farmers face the dilemma that subsidized loans are difficult to obtain, while high interest loans are easier to obtain but difficult to repay (Barrau and Djati 1985).

Social Obstacles

Social obstacles involve a lack of support for soil conservation from the farmer's family and/or community. The family will have other important needs that may take priority over soil conservation. Also, older family members may be especially resistant to change and oppose any type of conservation that younger members may want to try.

Other social obstacles involve lack of support from the farmer's peer group and the community leaders. Even the most independent farmers look to their peer group for advice and support. If the local norms and customs don't encourage or may even oppose soil conservation technologies, then farmers will be unlikely to adopt conservation. Local political and religious leaders will play a vital role in shaping many farmers' soil conservation attitudes and behaviour.

Morgan (1986) explains that high population pressures on the land force people to migrate into marginal areas. Shifting cultivation is being replaced by permanent agriculture in areas where the land cannot sustain continuous production and is subject to serious crop failures. As Hudson (1983) points out some forms of land tenure will also present serious obstacles to soil conservation. "Communal ownership can lead to mismanagement... Other aspects of land tenure that can lead to topsoil depletion are short-term cultivation rights, sharecropping tenancies, and absentee landlords."(p. 448) Most landlords and tenants do not even discuss soil conservation. If they do they generally disagree about who is responsible for maintaining the land.

Political and Institutional Obstacles

Government policies and programs often present serious obstacles to the adoption of soil conservation. These involve governmental agriculture policies that encourage all-out food production. Hudson (1983) explains the conflict between the short-term objectives of increased food production and self-sufficiency and the long-term objective of maintaining the country's land resource base. Brown and Wolf (1984) explain that population pressures, competition for land, and settlement patterns often push farmers onto more fragile lands. Technological advances have made it possible for marginal land, with serious erosion problems, to be brought into production.

Many Third World countries lack the research and extension capabilities needed to develop and transfer conservation technology. Another institutional obstacle is the lack of an effective soil conservation delivery system. This may be closely related to a lack of commitment by government leaders, often resulting from conflicting needs for limited economic and other resources. Even where government conservation policies exist, they may not be translated into action programs unless there is the political will to make them work. Without widespread public concern and support for soil conservation, governmental leaders can be expected to focus their attention on more immediate and visible priorities.

Even where conservation programs are in place, there will be important obstacles to the effective diffusion of the necessary technologies. These obstacles include: lack of funding, lack of trained staff, inadequate local support for conservation programs, and conflicts among various agencies or bureaus with soil conservation related responsibilities. A later section of this paper presents some options for establishing an effective conservation delivery system.

CONSERVATION ADOPTION DECISIONS

The main reason for understanding these obstacles to soil conservation is so assistance programs can be designed and targeted to reach those farmers who most need assistance. This also requires a better understanding of the nature of conservation adoption decisions. Past innovation diffusion efforts often have reached only those farmers who were most ready, willing, and able to adopt the innovation. This results in problems of inequality and widening of existing gaps between social classes (Rogers 1983). Similar problems may result if ineffective strategies are used to transfer inappropriate conservation technologies.

Conservation programs will be most successful if programs are designed and implemented within the farmers' frames of reference (Shaxson, 1985). It is critical that we consider what farmers must do, want to do, and could be persuaded to do with the land they operate. Conservation recommendations have a better chance of being adopted if they assist, rather than hinder the farmers' overall goals.

Certain types of farmers will need special assistance to successfully adopt soil conservation technologies. This group includes small-scale farmers, who generally do not have the money, knowledge, equipment, land or other resources necessary for adoption of soil conservation technologies (Hildebrand 1980; Arledge 1980; Shaner, et al. 1982; Hudson 1983). Small farmers make up the bulk of the rural population in most Third World countries (Stocking, 1985). Small farmers' operations are subsistence, at best. They often fail to meet the family's food needs much less generate a surplus. They live in remote areas and receive little or no support in terms of research, credit, marketing, or extension. They tend to be traditional and prefer to stay with practices that have worked for generations.

Another important factor in promoting soil conservation in many Third World countries involves the need to work with groups of farmers and even communities in implementing soil conservation projects. Collective adoption may be particularly necessary for many poorer groups of farmers. West (1983) describes five factors influencing collective adoption of conservation projects in rural areas of developing nations:

1. The contrast among equity issues in optional and collective adoption.
2. The special importance of property rights considerations in collectively adopted natural resource development projects.
3. The problems that community factions present for collective adoption.
4. The role of community organizing and social learning in collective adoption.
5. The role of indigenous leadership in collective adoption.

West (1983) concludes that collective adoption is often desirable and even essential, given the economies of scale for many conservation projects and the advantages of collective implementation and maintenance of conservation systems.

There are a number of conditions that must be met before farmers will be able to practise conservation. These include development of the necessary technical, financial, and informational infrastructure. Other conditions involve changes in farmers' knowledge, managerial capabilities, beliefs, attitudes, as well as their behaviour. These conditions may be summed up, as follows:

1. Farmers need to recognize and accept responsibility for the causes and consequences of their own soil erosion problems.
2. They need to know about the variety of soil conservation technologies that are available and how they will fit into their own farming operations.
3. They need to understand the relative agronomic, economic and social consequences of conservation and erosion.
4. Technical, financial, and educational assistance must be

readily available to help with trial, adoption, and maintenance.

5. Farmers must be aware of the sources and types of assistance and information that are available.

6. They need to receive support from their families and communities for practising soil conservation.

If any of these conditions are not met, farmers may be unable or unwilling to practise conservation. Unmet conditions reflect the obstacles that farmers are forced to overcome. These conditions may also be seen as the types of information that farmers need in order to practise soil conservation. Effective strategies are available for providing farmers with information and assistance to overcome their obstacles.

INFRASTRUCTURE DEVELOPMENT

The first step in developing a national or local soil conservation program involves the establishment of infrastructure and a diffusion agency to develop and transfer the necessary technologies, as well as to provide assistance to farmers. A useful theoretical perspective, developed by Lawrence Brown (1981), examines innovation diffusion from a market and infrastructure perspective. This perspective recognizes two important steps that must be taken before individual adoption is possible:

1. The establishment of diffusion agencies through which an innovation can be distributed.

2. The implementation of strategies by each agency to induce adoption among the population in its service area.

This section addresses the first step in terms of how the necessary infrastructure and organizational framework can be developed. The next section focusses on educational strategies that can be used of motivate framers to adopt conservation practices.

The market and infrastructure approach shifts attention from the individual adopter to the system responsible for developing and diffusing the innovations. This perspective recognizes the supply side as having causal priority over the individual demand side. Individual adoption decisions have been the primary focus of the vast majority of adoption/diffusion research to date.

According to the market and infrastructure perspective, the first step in innovation diffusion must be the establishment of diffusion agencies responsible for promoting the innovation. Brown (1981) discusses several options for establishing a diffusion agency. Each involves a different organizational structure. He describes a continuum between diffusion under a centralized decision-making structure and diffusion under a decentralized decision-making structure. In between these two ideal types is a third situation termed, "diffusion under a decentralized decision-making structure with a coordinating propagator."

In this third case, some aspects of the situation, such as information flows, policies, and program guidelines are controlled by a centralized agency or agencies. These co-ordinating propagators may also furnish technical expertise and funding to the local diffusion agencies. These local agencies retain considerable discretion over the exact nature of the programs and priorities. In particular they have most of the responsibility for actively promoting innovations (e.g., soil conservation technologies). The U.S. system is primarily a decentralized decision-making structure with co-ordinating propagators. The overall goal is to retain the advantages of local programs, while also obtaining the advantages of centralized research, funding, administrative support, and technical consistency.

Successful soil conservation programs need to be decentralized and based upon unique local physical and social conditions. As Hudson (1983) explains, "Soil conservation programs can only be effective when they are 'moved from below, i.e. by full involvement of the rural population.' Programs that are 'imposed from above' will not succeed even if they are technically correct." Local efforts will be most likely to promote awareness of conservation and encourage co-operation by farmers (Hauck, 1985).

The U.S. soil conservation delivery system is based largely on the decentralization of leadership through locally elected soil conservation district representatives who set program priorities and policies for each county. The national level USDA agencies provide technical expertise through the Soil Conservation Service, educational leadership through the Cooperative Extension Service, and financial assistance through the Agricultural Stabilization and Conservation Service. These organizations all work through local, county level staff.

National governments must also pursue a number of actions that only they are in a position to accomplish (Hauck, 1985). They must develop and implement uniform and acceptable soil conservation policies. They can develop educational programs to build public awareness, as well as training programs for technical specialists. They should carry out inventory and monitoring programs to determine where the conservation needs are greatest, as well as research to develop and adapt appropriate technologies. National governments may be best able to make resources available to provide farmers with advice, incentives and technical assistance.

Some activities at the international level will also be important for promoting more widespread transfer of soil conservation technologies. Hudson (1985) explains that there is a great lack of awareness of what other countries are doing. Constraints to better communication and technology transfer include: distance, language barriers, lack of library facilities, inadequate funds to attend conferences, as well as ideological and cultural differences. Exchange of timely information can be especially important when planning a program.

The particular organizational structure could be developed around an existing framework or could involve a new organization. In any case, teamwork will be necessary to promote adoption of soil conservation technologies (Hildebrand 1980; Hoban 1984; USDA 1982). In particular, the nature of the problems requires interdisciplinary teamwork among social scientists, agronomists, engineers, development specialists, economists, politicians, and farm management specialists. Co-ordination among various government agencies, at the international, national, regional, and local levels will also be critical to the success of any soil conservation program.

The first step in promoting teamwork is to ensure co-ordination of all relevant government agencies who are involved with soil conservation, environmental quality, and agriculture (Mulford 1984; Rogers et al. 1982). Co-ordination must take place at all levels of government, but it is especially important at the local level. Interorganizational co-ordination will be necessary to ensure the most effective and efficient delivery of conservation programs, given the constraints of limited staff and financial resources that all countries face. It will also prevent duplication of programs and conflicting messages from the various agencies.

Once the local agencies are co-ordinated, it will be necessary to develop a broad base of support for soil conservation programs among the larger community. In particular, religious, social, political and economic leaders must play a critical role in successfully promoting soil conservation. They will add much-needed credibility and legitimation to the local soil conservation programs. Other groups can provide valuable time and talent for educational efforts. Such groups include schools, voluntary organizations, informal farmer groups, local businesses, and the mass media. The local conservation team will also provide valuable insights into the needs of local farmers. In this sense the team will provide a mechanism for public involvement in conservation program planning and implementation. This in turn should make the programs more effective and responsive to the needs of farmers and local social systems.

STRATEGIES FOR PROMOTING SOIL CONSERVATION

Once the soil conservation diffusion network is in place, the major job will be to promote the diffusion and adoption of the necessary technologies. This will involve helping farmers recognize their own erosion problems and providing assistance for selecting and implementing the necessary technologies. A variety of innovative strategies have been used successfully in the United States and elsewhere. These include educational efforts aimed at trying to:

1. Promote awareness of soil erosion and conservation.
2. Provide assistance to facilitate trial and adoption.
3. Promote informal interaction among farmers.
4. Build prestige of practising conservationist.
5. Use peer pressure to influence non-co-operators.

These strategies are based on social science theory, research, and application. They recognize that conservation systems have technical, economic, educational, social, and institutional dimensions. Farmers must balance economic and technical criteria against their personal, family, and social values. Promotional strategies therefore, need to see soil conservation as part of the total farming system, not as something tacked on, as an afterthought (Shaner et al. 1982).

Promote Awareness of Soil Erosion and Conservation

Before adoption can take place, farmers need to recognize the need for and potential utility of a given practice. In the case of soil conservation, the need is often hard to visualize. Conservation technologies represent preventive innovations, in the sense that their main purpose is to prevent some future problem (Rogers, 1983).

Farmers must understand the causes and consequences of their own soil erosion problems. One way to do this is to document and publicize the local costs of soil erosion and water pollution. Some of the off-farm costs include damage to water supplies and irrigation ditches. On-farm costs include yield reductions and production problems. It will be important to help farmers understand and visualize their soil losses. Farmers also need to become aware of the types of soil conservation systems available, as well as the types and sources of available assistance and information.

Some of the public information techniques that could be used are already familiar to many extension workers. It will be important to use a variety of media, such as the mass media (as available), posters, and public meetings. Localized demonstrations and tours should also be conducted to promote soil conservation awareness and interest.

It may also be necessary to pay personal visits to recruit some key opinion leaders. An important way to develop public informational messages will be to use case histories and testimonials of these local farmers. These will be seen as credible and useful to local situations. Another important point is to include soil conservation messages in other agricultural messages. In many countries, it will also be necessary to increase awareness among government officials, local leaders, businesses, and the general public (Hauck, 1985).

Provide Assistance to Facilitate Trial and Adoption

Public information is mainly useful for encouraging awareness of and interest in soil conservation. Trial and adoption will require one-on-one technical assistance. Soil conservation requires learning new management skills that may be unfamiliar to many farmers. Without proper instruction and support farmers' yields may fall.

Field trials and demonstrations are a vital part of any conservation assistance and educational program. These efforts must be supported by basic research (Morgan 1986). The existing knowledge of local farmers should not be neglected as many effective technologies may already be available.

The U.S. approach emphasizes the development of an overall conservation plan for the farm. This plan represents a custom-designed set of alternatives that works within the needs and goals of an individual farmer. This approach recognizes that soil conservation should be an overall way of farming that will be implemented over time.

Promote Informal Interaction Among farmers

Peer networks serve as important sources of encouragement and information for farmers (Rogers and Kincaid 1981, Rogers 1983). Family and friends are usually the most accessible and trusted sources of information. Local conservation farmers are generally the local "experts" on which types of conservation work best for local conditions. They often know how to modify systems to get optimum performance in terms of both crop production and soil conservation.

There are several ways to promote interaction among farmers. One way is to develop a farmer-to-farmer referral network (Hoban 1984). This is already done informally when an extension agent tells a farmer who is interested in a practice about another farmer who is successfully using that practice. The object is to link farmers who have questions about soil conservation with those who have the answers. It is important to develop and publicize a referral list with details on each farmer's operation and how he can be contacted. The farmers in this network could also be featured at tours, meetings, and demonstrations.

Another way to encourage informal interaction among farmers is to set up an informal organization. Peer groups provide opportunities for farmers to share experiences and ideas about conservation. Those with experience can support those who are new to conservation. Small group sessions for farmers in a particular community can be both informative and persuasive. These sessions should be held at a farm where conservation is already underway or at a community meeting place, as opposed to a government office.

Document and Publicize
the Benefits of Conservation

Along with pointing out the costs of erosion it will also be important to stress the benefits that result from using soil conservation both for the farmer and the larger society. Some forms of conservation have been shown to benefit farmers by: reducing production costs, allowing more precise crop management; allowing more flexibility in planting dates; and reducing off-site damages (Shaxson, 1985).

This strategy gives recognition to those farmers who are practising conservation. The point is to make soil conservation the sign of a good farmer who cares about his land, his community, and future generations. This also implies that a farmer who can maintain a productive enterprise, while also practising soil conservation, is a better farmer than one who simply has a productive farm. The conservation farmer should be seen as the "Farmer of the Future." This strategy not only helps support farmers' soil conservation decisions, but also helps build a conservation ethic for the local community.

One way to build recognition is to present symbolic awards to conservation farmers. These need not be elaborate and could include: names on display in public places; signs on the farmers' fields; patches for hats or clothing; or some sort of recognition at a special ceremony. It will also be important to provide mass media coverage of these farmers. It may even be possible to persuade business to give conservation farmers some type of preferred treatment, such as a small discount or special access to scarce supplies.

Use Social Pressure to Influence Non-co-operators

This final strategy represents the other side of the coin from building recognition. The object is to have the family and friends put pressure on those farmers who refuse to practise conservation. These non-co-operators should feel guilty and different for not practising soil conservation. This strategy should not be used until farmers have had the opportunity to voluntarily adopt the necessary technologies, with adequate assistance.

Competition can be one form of peer pressure where all those in a community have a stake in soil conservation. First, a contest must be set up between two or more areas (e.g., villages). This contest could be to see which group can instal the most conservation or sign up the most farmers for conservation assistance. There will need to be some type of "reward" for the group that wins. It will also be important to have adequate publicity for the contest.

Another approach to peer pressure would be to publicize pictures of dramatic erosion problems. These should probably not be from the local area, however. These could be in the local newspaper or as posters in community centres. Set this up as a challenge to identify whose farm it is. This activity should generate considerable discussion about who has the worst soil erosion problems in the area.

Another form of peer pressure would be to recruit farm wives and children to influence farmers' decisions. Work with schools to educate and motivate children. They need to feel that they have a stake in their parents' conservation decisions. Farm wives are very important to farm decisions and will be for successful conservation efforts, as well. Work with any existing women's groups if they are available.

CONCLUSIONS

These strategies should compliment one another, as well as existing activities. One strategy can accomplish a variety of purposes. For example a conservation tour is useful for providing information, encouraging interaction, and recognizing those farmers whose farms are featured on the tour.

Successful use of these strategies will be based on the team approach, discussed earlier. Team members will provide the necessary time, talent, and possibly financial support for implementing these strategies. It will be important to take a pro-active, as opposed to a reactive, approach to promoting soil conservation.

Any significant improvement in Third World soil erosion problems will only come through careful analysis and informed action at the local level. Local strategies must be designed that best fit farmers' concerns, needs, skills, and resources. This will also require the technical, informational, financial, and administrative support of regional and national leadership.

From a theoretical perspective, this paper has stressed the importance of taking a broader, supply-side approach to the diffusion of innovations. Brown's (1981) market and infrastructure perspective provides considerable insight into innovation diffusion. Individual behaviour (e.g., adoption) does not represent free will so much as a choice within a set of constraints established and controlled by government and private institutions. When combined with the more traditional focus on adoption of innovation (Rogers, 1983) a more complete picture emerges.

There is virtually no area of the world where soil erosion does not occur (Morgan 1986). Our challenge is to promote conservation by developing erosion control technologies and systems that are ecologically sound, economically feasible and socially acceptable. Our greatest need is for interdisciplinary research and extension programs with support from leaders at all government levels. As Morgan (1986) concludes, "The challenge is not simply better technology. Nor is it merely overcoming the nontechnical constraints. It is in devising strategies that are compatible with the farming system.... A much greater understanding of and sensitivity to the cultural environment is required."

World food supplies will need to increase to meet the needs of a growing population. Soil erosion and related natural resource problems could threaten our future ability to supply food. In fact, erosion is still a major constraint to eliminating world hunger despite decades of soil conservation research and application (Cook and Ellis 1987). Effective technologies are available to control most problems. Innovative strategies will be needed, however, to overcome the serious obstacles that limit transfer of these technologies.

REFERENCES

Aneke, D.O. 1986. "Coping with Accelerated Soil Erosion in Nigeria." *Journal of Soil and Water Conservation.* 41(3): 161-163.

Arledge, Jerome E. 1980. "Soil conservation at work: Guatemala's small farmer project." *Journal of Soil and Water Conservation.* 35(4): 187-189.

Ashby, Jacqueline A. 1982. "Technology and ecology: Implications for innovation research in peasant agriculture." *Rural Sociology.* 47(2): 234-250.

Barrau, E.M. and K. Djati. 1985. "The Chitanduy Project in Java: Toward a New Approach to Watershed Stabilization and Development." Pp. 729-739 in S.A. El-Swaify, W.C. Moldenhauer, and Andrew Lo (editors) *Soil Erosion and Conservation.* Ankeny, IA: Soil Conservation Society of America.

Barrows, Harold L., Ralph J. McCracken, Raymond J. Miller, William R. Oschwald, Thomas N. Shiflet, and Roland R. Willis. 1982. "Report on China: An American view of how that nation manages its soil resources." *Journal of Soil and Water Conservation*. 37(6): 315-318.

Blustain, Harvey. 1982. "Social issues in technology choice: Soil conservation in Jamaica." *Journal of Soil and Water Conservation*. 37(6): 323-325.

Bonsu, M. 1985. "Organic Residues for Less Erosion and More Grain in Ghana." Pp. 615-621 in S.A. El-Swaify, W.C. Moldenhauer, and Andrew Lo (editors) *Soil Erosion and Conservation*. Ankeny, IA: Soil Conservation Society of America.

Brown, Lawrence. 1981. *Innovation Diffusion: A New Perspective*. New York: Methuen.

Brown, Lester R. and Pamela Shaw. 1982. *Six Steps to a Sustainable Society*. Washington, DC: The Worldwatch Institute.

Brown, Lester R. and Edward C. Wolf. 1984. *Soil Erosion: Quiet Crisis in the World Economy*. Washington, DC: Worldwatch Institute.

Bultena, Gordon L., Eric O. Hoiberg, and Peter J. Nowak. 1984. *Sources of Conservation Information and Participation in Conservation Programs: An Interregional Analysis*. Ames, IA: Iowa State University, Sociology Report 156.

Cook, Ray L. and Boyd G. Ellis. 1987. *Soil Management: A World View of Conservation and Production*. New York, NY: John Wiley and Sons.

Das, D.C. 1986. "Soil Conservation Practices and Erosion Control in India: A Case Study." Pp. 118-150 in R.P.C. Morgan (editor) *Soil Erosion and Its Control*. New York, NY: Van Nostrand Reinhold Company.

Gumbs, F.A., J.I. Lindsay, M. Hasir, and A. Mohammed. 1985. "Soil Erosion Studies in the Northern Mountain Range, Trinidad, under Different Crop and Soil Managment." Pp. 90-98 in S.A. El-Swaify, W.C. Moldenhauer, and Andrew Lo (editors) *Soil Erosion and Conservation*. Ankeny, IA: Soil Conservation Society of America.

Hauck, F.W. 1985. "Soil Erosion and its control in developing countries." Pp. 718-728 in S.A. El-Swaify, W.C. Moldenhauer, and Andrew Lo (editors) *Soil Erosion and Conservation*.

Ankeny, IA: Soil Conservation Society of America.

Hildebrand, P.E. 1980. "Motivating small farmers, scientists, and technicians to accept change." *Agricultural Administration*. 8: 375-383.

Hoban, Thomas J. 1984. *Strategies for Promoting Soil and Water Conservation: A Team Approach to Action*. Report prepared for the USDA Soil Conservation Service. Ames, IA: Iowa State University.

Hoban, Thomas J. and Peter F. Korsching. 1984. "Information Transfer Strategies for Promoting Soil and Water Conservation." Paper presented at the Annual Meeting of the Rural Sociological Society, College Station, Texas, August 1984.

Howard, Paul M. 1981. "Impressions of soil and water conservation in China." *Journal of Soil and Water Conservation*. 36(3): 122-124.

Hudson, Norman W. 1983. "Soil conservation strategies in the Third World." *Journal of Soil and Water Conservation*. 38(6): 446-450.

Hudson, Norman W. 1985. "International Transfer of Soil Conservation Information." Pp. 740-746 in S.A. El-Swaify, W.C. Moldenhauer, and Andrew Lo (editors) *Soil Erosion and Conservation*. Ankeny, IA: Soil Conservation Society of America.

Hudson, Norman W. 1986. "Non Technical Constraints on Soil Conservation." Pp. 268-279 in R.P.C. Morgan (editor) *Soil Erosion and Its Control*. New York, NY: Van Nostrand Reinhold Company.

Hurni, Hans. 1985. "An Ecosystem Approach to Conservation." Pp. 759-771 in S.A. El-Swaify, W.C. Moldenhauer, and Andrew Lo (editors) *Soil Erosion and Conservation*. Ankeny, IA: Soil Conservation Society of America.

Jantawat, S. 1985. "An Overview of Soil Erosion and Sedimentation in Thailand." Pp. 10-14 in S.A. El-Swaify, W.C. Moldenhauer, and Andrew Lo (editors) *Soil Erosion and Conservation*. Ankeny, IA: Soil Conservation Society of America.

Jiang, D., L.Qi, and J.Tan. 1986. "Soil Erosion and Conservation in the Wuding River Valley, China." Pp. 99-117 in R.P.C. Morgan (editor) *Soil Erosion and Its Control.* New York, NY: Van Nostrand Reinhold Company.

Kishk, Mohammed Atif. 1985. "Desert Encroachment in Egypt's Nile Valley." Pp. 15-23 in S.A. El-Swaify, W.C. Moldenhauer, and Andrew Lo (editors) *Soil Erosion and Conservation.* Ankeny, IA: Soil Conservation Society of America.

Korsching, Peter F., Thomas J. Hoban, and Jane Maestro-Sherer. 1984. *The Selling of Soil Conservation: A Test of the Voluntary Approach.* Ames, IA: Iowa State University.

Lai, R. 1985. "Soil Erosion and its Relation to Tropical Soils." Pp. 237-247 in S.A. El-Swaify, W.C. Moldenhauer, and Andrew Lo (editors) *Soil Erosion and Conservation.* Ankeny, IA: Soil Conservation Society of America.

Lionberger, Herbert F. and Paul H. Gwin. 1982. *Communication Strategies: A Guide for Agricultural Change Agents.* Danville, IL: The Interstate Printers and Publishers, Inc.

Maene, L.M. and W. Sulaiman. 1986. "Status of Soil Conservation in Peninsular Malaysia and its Future Development." Pp. 202-221 in R.P.C. Morgan (editor) *Soil Erosion and Its Control.* New York, NY: Van Nostrand Reinhold Company.

Marston, D., C. Anecksamphant, and R. Chirasathaworn. 1985. "Soil Conservation and Land Development in Northern Thailand." Pp. 634-643 in S.A. El-Swaify, W.C. Moldenhauer, and Andrew Lo (editors) *Soil Erosion and Conservation.* Ankeny, IA: Soil Conservation Society of America.

Morgan, R.P.C. (editor). 1986. *Soil Erosion and Its Control.* New York, NY: Van Nostrand Reinhold Company.

Mulford, Charles L. 1984. *Interorganizational Relations: Implications for Community Development.* New York: Human Sciences Press.

Mulford, Charles L. and Gerald E. Klonglan. 1981. *Creating Coordination Among Organizations.* Ames, IA: North Central Regional Extension Publication 80.

Narayana, V.V. Dhruva and G. Sastry. 1985. "Soil Conservation in India." Pp. 3-9 in S.A. El-Swaify, W.C. Moldenhauer, and Andrew Lo (editors) *Soil Erosion and Conservation.* Ankeny,

IA: Soil Conservation Society of America.

Pathak, P, S.M. Miranda, and S.A. El-Swaify. 1985. "Improved Rainfed Farming for Semiarid Tropics: Implications for Soil and Water Conservation." Pp. 338-354 in S.A. El-Swaify, W.C. Moldenhauer, and Andrew Lo (editors) *Soil Erosion and Conservation*. Ankeny, IA: Soil Conservation Society of America.

Rapp, A. 1986. "Soil Erosion and Sedimentation in Tanzania and Lesotho." Pp. 76-87 in R.P.C. Morgan (editor) *Soil Erosion and Its Control*. New York, NY: Van Nostrand Reinhold Company.

Robinson, A.R. 1981. "Erosion and sediment control in China's Yellow River Basin." *Journal of Soil and Water Conservation*. 36(3): 125-127.

Rogers, David L., David Whetten, and Associates. 1982. *Interorganizational Coordination: Theory, Research, and Implementation*. Ames, IA: Iowa State University Press.

Rogers, Everett. 1983. *Diffusion of Innovations* (Third Edition). New York: The Free Press.

Rogers, Everett M. and D. Lawrence Kincaid. 1981. *Communication Networks: Toward a New Paradigm for Research*. New York: The Free Press.

Ruangpanit, Niwat. 1985. "Percent Crown Cover Related to Water and Soil Losses in Mountainous Forests in Thailand." Pp. 462-471 in S.A. El-Swaify, W.C. Moldenhauer, and Andrew Lo (editors) *Soil Erosion and Conservation*. Ankeny, IA: Soil Conservation Society of America.

Shaner, W.W., P.F. Philipp, and W.R. Schmehl. 1982. *Farming Systems Research and Development: Guidelines for Developing Countries*. Boulder, CO: Westview Press.

Shaxson, T.F. 1985. "Erosion, Economics, Subsistence, and Psychology." Pp. 667-673 in S.A. El-Swaify, W.C. Moldenhauer, and Andrew Lo (editors) *Soil Erosion and Conservation*. Ankeny, IA: Soil Conservation Society of America.

Singh, Gurmel, Ram Babu, and Subhash Chandra. 1985. "Research on the Universal Soil Loss Equation in India." Pp. 496-508 in S.A. El-Swaify, W.C. Moldenhauer, and Andrew Lo (editors) *Soil Erosion and Conservation*. Ankeny, IA: Soil

Conservation Society of America.

Stocking, M. 1985. "Development Projects for the Small Farmer: Lessons from Eastern and Central Africa in Adapting Conservation." Pp. 747-758 in S.A. El-Swaify, W.C. Moldenhauer, and Andrew Lo (editors) *Soil Erosion and Conservation*. Ankeny, IA: Soil Conservation Society of America.

Suwardjo and Sofijah Abujamin. 1985. "Crop Residue Mulch for Conserving Soil in Uplands of Indonesia." Pp. 607-614 in S.A. El-Swaify, W.C. Moldenhauer, and Andrew Lo (editors) *Soil Erosion and Conservation*. Ankeny, IA: Soil Conservation Society of America.

Temple, P.H. 1986. "Soil and Water Conservation Policies in the Uluguru Mountains, Tanzania." Pp. 280-292 in R.P.C. Morgan (editor) *Soil Erosion and Its Control*. New York, NY: Van Nostrand Reinhold Company.

Troeh, Frederick R., J. Arthur Hobbs, and Roy L. Donahue. 1980. *Soil and Water Conservation for Productivity and Environmental Protection*. Englewood Cliffs, NJ: Prentice Hall, Inc.

United States Department of Agriculture. 1982. *A National Program for Soil and Water Conservation: 1982 Final Program Report and Environmental Impact Statement*. Washington, DC: U.S. Government Printing Office.

Valentin, C. 1985. "Effects of Grazing and Trampling on Soil Deterioration around Recently Drilled Water Holes in the Sahelian Zone." Pp. 51-65 in S.A. El-Swaify, W.C. Moldenhauer, and Andrew Lo (editors) *Soil Erosion and Conservation*. Ankeny, IA: Soil Conservation Society of America.

West, Patrick C. 1983. "Collective adoption of natural resource practices in developing nations." *Rural Sociology*. 48(1): 44-59.

Chapter 11

SOIL-WATER MANAGEMENT AND FOOD SECURITY:
AN APPROACH FOR ASSESSING ECONOMIC VIABILITY OF AGRICULTURAL DRAINAGE IN DEVELOPING COUNTRIES

Hamid Jorjani

ABSTRACT

Agricultural growth and food self-sufficiency in developing countries are likely to be achieved by either increasing area under cultivation or raising the level of crop yield per unit of land. Due to extreme agroclimatic conditions in many developing countries, poor soil-water management, particularly in areas that depend upon irrigated agriculture, has been recognized as one of the most important obstacles in their quest for food security. Artificial drainage, because of its biophysical cause-effect structure and its impacts has become an increasingly important soil-water management technique to alleviate the harmful effect of waterlogging and salinity. However, artificial drainage systems are capital intensive and economic considerations necessitate a reliable pre-investment or feasibility study. Methods used previously have been considered deficient. Recognizing this, the chapter presented here will firstly, outline agricultural perspectives of drainage from farmers, and societal points of view under different agroclimatic and soil conditions. Secondly, it will examine a proposed interdisciplinary method to estimate potential incremental crop yields emanating from agricultural drainage. These incremental crop yields are an essential component for a more reliable economic analysis.

1. INTRODUCTION

Agriculture is an important sector of the economy in many industrialized and developing countries. While industrialized countries are trying to rectify problems associated with a surplus agricultural sector and an over-exploited environment, a number of developing countries are rapidly exploiting their limited natural endowments in the quest for self-sufficiency and food security.

Increasing agricultural production and self-sufficiency in food grains can be achieved through several ways, for example by: genetic means, increasing area under cultivation, and improving crop yields through better management techniques. However, these are not easy ways to increase agricultural production in most developing countries. In order to employ these methods a number of essential pre-conditions must be met. Firstly, the know-how and logistics to develop high-yielding varieties of food crops must be available. Secondly, it will be necessary to either reclaim additional land or to protect the existing crop lands for the purpose of increasing production capacity and maintaining a sustainable agricultural growth. Thirdly, there is a requirement for a threshold level of public awareness, motivation, and participation, starting from the village level all the way up to public decision makers.

Most developing countries by virtue of their population, limited skilled manpower and physical resources provide both the greatest opportunities and challenges in terms of their demand and supply of food products. There is a general belief among some experts on food security that many food deficit countries are markedly deficient in the scientific capacity for increasing basic food production (IFPRI, 1987). Urgencies and exigencies of measures to be taken to combat poor agricultural productivity due to inefficient soil-water management practices have been the central issue in most international dialogues on food security during the last decade.

With the emphasis on food self-sufficiency and the need for development of more arable land in a number of developing countries, soon we may witness various degrees of stress on natural habitats on a much larger geographic scale. To avoid these problems developing countries need to reassess their agricultural programs by developing a set of guidelines that would integrate expansion of agricultural output and environmental protection. This would entail conducting more and better basic and applied research on the interrelationships of technological changes, adoption of innovations, agricultural productivity, overall economic growth, and social welfare.

Due to the extreme nature of agroclimatic conditions (either too wet or very dry) in many developing countries, soil-water management is crucial to agricultural growth and productivity in those countries. Without adequate irrigation and/or drainage no significant increase in agricultural output can be expected in most of these countries. In some countries such as Bangladesh, India (eastern part of the country), Pakistan (mainly southern parts), and Cambodia, poor drainage and flooding constitute some of the main obstacles to agricultural production and growth (Rangeley, 1987). Furthermore, in some areas such as the Indus, Nile, and Tigris-Euphrates-Karoon river basins, drainage is required to minimize waterlogging and salinity in arable lands.

However, irrigation, drainage and almost every other soil-water management practice are costly technologies that only rich farmers and large scale private or state owned farm enterprises can afford to undertake in developing countries. Low income or limited resource farmers of developing countries would undoubtedly be willing to invest in such management practices provided adequate capital is made available to them. Whether an individual farmer or a large scale farm enterprise, economic optimization is the underlying principal in the decision-making process (Figure 1.). This principal requires that such projects be undertaken only if time streams of project benefits significantly exceed streams of cost over the economic life time of the project.

This concept is illustrated graphically in figure 1., where the vertical axis measures costs and benefits and the horizontal axis indicates time (that is, project duration). The benefit stream is shown by B_t and the cost stream by C_t. The net benefit NB_t is obtained by taking the difference between Bt and C_t. Because of the higher initial costs of a project NB_t is usually negative during those stages of investment. This is primarily due to construction costs in the first year of the project. Further, it might take one cropping season before benefits of a soil-water management project are realized.

Figure 1.
Project Costs and Benefits Over Time

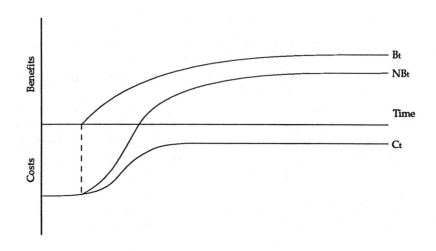

The issue here is that the large capital investment in drainage as a soil-water management technique must be considered within a broad framework of incremental crop yields over time. Measuring costs and returns of such investments not only are required from the strict investment planning point of view, but they are also needed to assess intersectoral impacts and multijurisdictional aspects involving agricultural and environmental management within geographic regions. This is particularly true where farm lands are in proximity of environmentally sensitive locations.

Regardless of the location and size of investment, farmers and the public at large must receive accurate signals about the true costs of such projects. Poor economic judgments for such capital intensive projects can easily cause overinvestment or underinvestment with serious environmental and economic ramifications. Inappropriate and badly conceived soil-water management projects that fail to recover their costs of investment, operations, and maintenance can cause serious setbacks in a developing country for several years. What is at issue is the economic efficiency of soil-water management techniques in developing countries, particularly in countries with a very limited resource base. Whether these projects are financed internally or externally, the point is that these investment projects must be self-sustaining and affordable to their beneficiaries. Less developed countries and their farmers would be unable to adopt these techniques for achieving agricultural growth and food self-sufficiency. Due to these complexities, a better understanding of agricultural perspectives of drainage is therefore, a key element in addressing some of these concerns. The general purpose of this chapter is to examine the agricultural perspectives of drainage from farmers' and societal points of view, and propose a method for estimating economic viability of drainage as an important soil-water management technique in developing countries.

1.1 Statement of the problem

Despite the importance of agricultural drainage in its role as an important soil-water management technique both in the past and at present, its biophysical cause-effect structure and economic linkages are not fully and correctly recognized. The biophysical cause-effect structure of artificial drainage (Figure 2) refers to a number of cause and effect relationships that include hydrological, biological, ecological, and economic linkages that are involved in agricultural drainage.

Removal of excess water from the soil profile is an important hydrological component in this process that enhances certain chemical and microbial reactions. Hence, biological, ecological, and economic linkages are set in motion after the removal of surface and gravitational water from the soil profile. These linkages indicate the different effects of various drainage projects on farmers and society at large. A better understanding of these linkages by donor agencies and local land use planners would enable them to satisfy the farmer's requirement for efficiency and society's requirement for minimizing off-site detrimental effects of drainage.

Choices concerning allocation of funds for drainage projects necessitate access to appropriate tools to quantify the stream of forthcoming benefits. The few studies that have evaluated drainage benefits for agriculture have not been well received because they are said to be too limited in scope (e.g., Brooks,

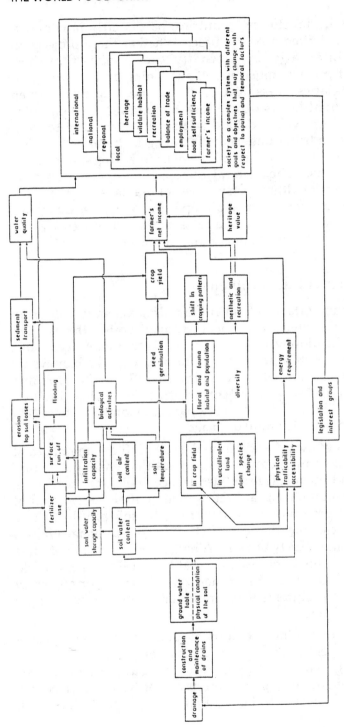

Figure 2.

Biophysical Cause-Effect Structure of Drainage and Its Impacts

Source: H. Jorjan, 1988

1971; Found, Hills and Spencer, 1976; Galloway and Johnston, 1982; Leitch and Kerestes, 1981). Benefits of an artificial drainage system are, commonly, measured in terms of annual differences in crop yields between drained and undrained farm lands. A reliable estimate of the average annual incremental crop yield over the lifetime of a drainage system is, therefore, essential to the economic evaluation of drainage investments. Annual differences in incremental crop yields emanating from agricultural drainage depend to a great extent on climatic changes during crop growing season, among other things. In arid zones crop yield will respond to variations in air temperature, precipitation level, soil water depth, soil salinity, and the amount and frequency of irrigation during crucial stages of the growth cycle of the crop. Since most of these factors can fluctuate over time, incremental crop yields (due to drainage), representing a particular year or an average over a few successive years, can create a bias in the feasibility analysis of a drainage project. Long-term time series data are needed to calculate a mean annual incremental crop yield over the life time of a particular drainage system. These data are often non-existent. However, using sophisticated statistical methods and simulation techniques, an agricultural economist, in collaboration with drainage experts can generate statistically more reliable estimates of long-term incremental crop yields.

Recognizing these shortcomings, it becomes extremely important to develop a broad and comprehensive framework that would provide accurate information for a precise economic judgment of such projects under different agroclimatic and soil conditions. To this end, the chapter presented here will first, evaluate the agricultural perspectives of drainage and then introduce a holistic approach for assessing economic viability of drainage investments in developing countries. A more complete understanding of these perspectives will improve chances of choosing an appropriate decision-making tool which is based on facts and not on subjective argumentation. This in turn will enable public planners, engineers, and farmers to make better choices among alternative schemes and technologies concerning drainage as a soil-water management technique. Immediate gains of better choices are reduced uncertainty, project success and longevity with a high economic and political reward for all the parties involved, particularly farmers.

2. AGRICULTURAL PERSPECTIVES ON DRAINAGE

2.1 Background

Agricultural drainage consists of removal and disposal of excess moisture from farmlands. Excess moisture in soil can be attributed to (a) precipitation, (b) irrigation water, (c) overland flow or underground seepage from adjacent fields, artesian flow from deep aquifers, flood water from rivers/canals, or (d) water applied for special purposes other than irrigation, such as for leaching salt (or pollutant material) from soil or for temperature control.

In nature the drainage process involves ground water flow to natural outlets, vertical seepage to lower aquifers, and lateral seepage to adjacent areas. Under certain agroclimatic and soil conditions this natural process is adequate enough to allow a normal plant growth and agricultural production. However, if soil is naturally poorly drained, crop production will not be possible unless artificial drainage systems are installed. Restrictive conditions are usually due to one or a combination of factors that are related to the inherent soil, landscape, and climatic characteristics of a region. Sometimes these restrictive conditions might even occur in regions where: (a) Fertile and irrigated lands have been cultivated for a long time. Continuous irrigation and inadequate outlets are responsible for waterlogging and its ramifications in such areas. (b) Areas where interflow resulting from seepage causes poor drainage in the adjacent farm lands which are otherwise well drained. Hence, most soils require drainage for efficient crop growth. However, drainage requirements and the design of an appropriate artificial system will depend mainly on soil factors, topography, crop type, tillage practices, and the prevailing climatic patterns of the specific location.

The importance of agricultural drainage should be examined from two sets of perspectives: those of farmers and those of society at large.

2.2 Farmers' Perspectives

In market-oriented economic systems farmers are assumed to be rational decision makers who normally allocate scarce resources to alternative uses in such a way that their revenue exceeds their production cost by the largest amount possible. Farmers invest in agricultural drainage systems to increase their net benefits through one or a number of economic linkages (or benefits) of agricultural drainage. Mathematically, this can be expressed as:

$$NB = [(Y = f (L, K, l, m, X_i....X_n) * PY) - C] \quad 1$$

where:

NB = net benefit,

Y = production,

f = functional relationship

L = land,

K = capital,

l = labour,

m = management,

X = variable inputs,

PY = price of output, and

C = costs of production.

Agricultural drainage is an input that can help increase farmers' benefits through its biophysical cause-effect structure (Figure 2.). Some of the most important benefits of agricultural drainage are as follows.

2.2.1 Increased Productivity

Agricultural drainage will improve the yield of existing crops, particularly moisture-sensitive crops such as corn which reacts negatively, in terms of yield, to excess soil moisture during crucial stages of its growth (Jorjani, 1982). The removal of groundwater improves soil aeration and increases soil temperature. The increased soil aeration and temperature has a direct influence on biological activities in the soil. One of the most important benefits of the improved biological activities in crop production is that it enhances the process of nitrogen mineralization. This means a better crop yield with smaller amounts of nitrogen fertilizer. Crop production under waterlogged conditions requires additional doses of nitrogen fertilizers to offset the harmful effect of poor drainage (Van Hoorn, 1958). Van Vuuren and Jorjani (1984) estimated the increased value of corn yields resulting from subsurface drainage on test plots at the Elora Research Station in Ontario, Canada, to be CDN $70.46/ha annually. The average yield difference between drained and undrained lands was 770 Kg/ha annually.

El-Guindy (1983) has reported that introduction of drainage in the northwest and northeast of the Nile Delta contributed to 36 and 18 percent increases in dry matter production of Berseem (Trifulum alexandrium) on heavy clay soils of the region. In another study by Mashali (1983) it is reported that with the introduction of surface drainage and other management practices in Kalioubia (Egypt) in 1968, cotton yield increased 58 percent.

2.2.2 Diversity and Flexibility

Agricultural drainage, because of its impact on the soil's water table, oxygen content, and temperature, facilitates a greater diversity in cropping and flexibility in tillage (e.g., a shift from lower value crops such as pasture to higher value crops like corn or soybeans), and/or a better crop-rotation pattern (Briggs and Courtney, 1985).

2.2.3 Trafficability and Timeliness of Farming Operations

Improved timeliness of planting and harvesting is one of the most important benefits of agricultural drainage, particularly in areas which are characterized by high rainfall during planting and harvesting time, and a shorter growing season. Under these conditions, drainage usually helps farmers get into the field earlier, and harvest their crops on time (Smith, 1972; Reeve and Fausey, 1974). Based on considerations of soil-water regimes and water-table levels at several sites in the U.K., Armstrong (1986) estimated drainage benefits, in terms of increased working days during the growing season, to be 84 days. This indicates why workability constraints on wet, undrained lands may result in no crop at all if access to fields, particularly during sowing or harvesting periods, is prevented due to a high water table.

2.2.4 Input Costs

Flooding and erosion during seedbed preparation are responsible for seed, pesticide, fertilizer, and topsoil loss and soil degradation. Drainage lowers the water table which in turn alters the physical conditions of soil. By lowering the water table, more pore space becomes available and consequently the soil-water storage capacity in the profile increases. Increased water storage capacity in the soil profile enhances the infiltration of water into the soil and as a result surface runoff is reduced. Reductions in surface runoff decrease the chances of flooding and erosion. In an experiment on hilly silty-clay soils in Italy, Chisci and Zianchi (1981) found that the amount of over-land flow and the resulting soil losses were much lower on drained plots.

Thus, by reducing surface runoff from agricultural land, drainage can minimize or alleviate costs of reseeding and application of additional chemicals.

2.2.5 Salinity Control

Drainage becomes a crucial factor particularly in irrigated farmlands (mostly in arid zones) where poor natural drainage systems might fail to remove accumulating salts. Moreover, in these areas drainage can also bring the water table into a dynamic equilibrium with the irrigation system.

It is documented that continuous irrigation and inefficient drainage in the once fertile Tigris-Euphrates-Karoon river basins of ancient Persia and Babylon caused salt to accumulate in the soil surface and subsequently, the appearance of soil salinity problems (Luthin, 1957; Adams, 1962). Today, millions of hectares of fertile land in the arid regions of the Middle East, Indian subcontinent, North Africa, and South America are affected by salinity (El Gabaly, 1977; Abrol, 1987; Aceves-Navarro, 1987; Rangeley, 1987). Much of this problem is attributed to deficient irrigation water management and poor drainage in irrigation districts of these regions.

As an example, consider Egypt where the Nile river is the life line of her agricultural industry. Its natural rise and fall nourishes farm lands with rich alluvial silt that fertilizes soil in the surrounding areas. For many years Egyptian farmers have cut narrow channels along the Nile river to irrigate their farm lands during dry periods. Today Egyptian farmers have more access to irrigation water because of modern technology and massive irrigation systems (Aswan Dam). However, intensive farming and continuous irrigation and seepage from irrigation channels has raised the ground water table to an alarmingly high level. Consequently, crop yields are depressed and arable lands are turned into saline marsh or salt poisoned lands. Since there are no natural outlets for the irrigation water, excess salt is not flushed from the soil and vast tracts of farm lands have become uncultivable. Because agriculture is one of the important sectors of the Egyptian economy, one can fully appreciate the staggering cost of this loss of productivity due to the twin effect of water logging and salinity.

2.2.6 Efficient Machinery and Farm Equipment Use

Farming in wet zones, characterized mostly by heavier soils, necessitates the use of powerful and consequently expensive farm machinery. Under these circumstances, drainage can reduce specific machinery costs by providing a better trafficability and/or traction on farmland. With improved trafficability, smaller tractors can accomplish the same job at a lower cost. In the wet regions of developing countries (e.g., Asian, and south east Asian countries), this aspect becomes an important economic consideration. Artificial drainage in these countries would allow farmers to use their animal powered farming equipment more efficiently.

2.2.7 Indirect Economic Benefits

Indirect economic benefits are those additional benefits that are not directly related to the biophysical cause-effect structure of drainage and its impacts. Instead, these are different types of incentives that are provided by a government in order to increase agricultural productivity. Examples of these incentives are tax credits, export subsidies and the like. However, most developing countries lack a well defined taxation system that would allow them to introduce drainage tax credit incentives.

Nevertheless, the successful experience of a few other developing countries with similar incentives (e.g., Saudi Arabia), indicates the effectiveness of such programs in increasing agricultural productivity. Van Vuuren and Jorjani (1986) have reported that tax regulations have a profound effect on the profitability of drainage investment in Canada and the U.S. where modern taxation systems prevail.

The tax benefits of drainage investments in these countries include mainly investment tax credits and various forms of depreciation write-offs and expense deductions. However, these benefits may vary among income brackets. Furthermore, there are also some other economic and policy factors such as export subsidies and drainage subsidies that influence the indirect economic benefits of agricultural drainage.

2.3 Societal Perspectives

2.3.1 Background

There is no doubt that today's prosperous industrialized societies evolved out of an agricultural environment. The quest for agricultural productivity in developing countries is indeed a reflection of their desire for achieving a relatively comparable agro-economic evolution. Hence, in dealing with societal perspectives of agricultural drainage it is important to recognize these aspirations of developing countries.

With this in mind, perhaps it is not a crass or erroneous generalization to state that the general objectives of drainage programs or projects, particularly in developing countries, are either (a) to maximize economic efficiency in terms of higher productivity, or (b) to strive for self-sufficiency in food and other agricultural products. Albeit, sometimes a society may have objectives that are other than an immediate agricultural development and economic efficiency. For example, correction of adverse income distribution effect through more employment opportunities may be the most important socio-economic priority in a society, at the time. In this case the criterion for optimality is generating jobs that will likely affect the unemployed and lower income members of society. Consequently, this objective receives a greater weight than generating benefits that might only affect large farmers or other members of society who already have a job and an income.

These aspects of project planning and optimal socio-political efficiency of welfare economics have already been discussed in detail elsewhere.

No matter what societal goals at the time may be, these objectives can influence the general state of the economy through a chain effect that is sometimes referred to as the multiplier effect (Eichner, 1985). In other words benefits generated through these projects can spill over to other sectors of society either directly or indirectly. An example of such economic chain effects can be noted in Punjab region (India), where increased agricultural productivity due to green revolution increased farmers, income and subsequently their demand for more farm inputs and other goods and services. In response to this gradual regional prosperity the local services sector and industry had to be expanded and diversified in order to offset the increasing demand. Nevertheless, it must be mentioned that the most important force in this dynamic agro-economic chain effect was the aspiration and motivation of local farmers in that region.

Hence, from a broad macro-economic point of view, drainage programs (and the resulting increased agricultural productivity) can influence levels of national output, agricultural commodity prices, employment, international accounts surpluses or deficits, and government budget surpluses or deficits (through changes in tax revenue). There are several forces that produce intertemporal variations in regional and national economic states during and after implementation of regional drainage programs and that have significant impacts on the time-stream of macro-economic benefits:

1. changes in employment and the number of workers choosing to relocate their families to communities near drainage projects;

2. changes in the rate of purchase of goods and services; and

3. variations in the rate at which the service sector adjusts to changes in basic human activities.

There are a number of frameworks, simple to more complex, that may be used for appraising the effects of regional development policies such as drainage programs at the macro-economic level (e.g., Hoffman and Jorgenson, 1978; Fitoussi, 1983; and Shoven and Whally, 1984). The following discussions of the economic performance of the agricultural sector delineate the importance of agriculture (with drainage as an endogenous factor) in the economy.

2.3.1 Productivity and Economic Efficiency

Higher economic efficiency and economic growth imply sustained increases in societal welfare derived from conventional goods and services, or from new inputs, the production of which often requires natural resources such as prime agricultural land. As the world's population and standard of living increase, demands for agricultural products increase. These increases in demand necessitate the expansion of farming. This is particularly true in the case of many developing countries where the twin effect of increased demand for food and lack of foreign exchange to import food can push prices high and beyond the means of their population. Expansions are, however, only possible through either extension of agriculture onto previously virgin lands such as grasslands, wetlands, and marginal farmlands, or through the increased use of capital-intensive inputs like fertilizers and more powerful farm machinery. Since the latter is a more expensive option, most farmers opt for the former, improving drainage conditions on poorly drained lands and creating better environmental conditions for higher production levels. In this process of draining previously uncultivated land, farmers, with the help of modern mechanical diggers, and often with the encouragement of financial assistance by governments, have greatly expanded the land base for agricultural development. In addition to Europe and North America, other regions such as the Soviet Union, China, the Near East, and North Africa have also benefited from extensive drainage programs.

The agricultural sector in the Ijsselmeerpolders of Holland is beyond doubt a classic example of increased productivity and economic efficiency due to agricultural drainage (Table 1). The increased productivity undoubtedly benefited every level of the Dutch economy including employment, wages, services, industry, marketing, research and development, and the general well-being of society.

Table 1
Increased agricultural productivity due to land drainage
in the Ijsselmeerpolders, the Netherlands.

Crop	Average Yields (T/ha)	
	Ijsselmeerpolders	Netherlands
Sugar beets	57.0	47.5
Potatoes		
– feed	50.2	38.5
– seed	31.0	25.0
Onions	40.0	36.5
Winter Wheat	5.9	5.4
Spring Barley	4.3	4.2
Oats	5.5	4.4

Source: Bradshaw and Chadwick, 1980

A simplified demonstration of this macro-economic phenomenon can be expressed in the following example. A farm community (say a district or a township) consists of k farms, as a subset of the N farm communities which comprise the agricultural sector of the country or region as a whole. These k farmers sell their output (Y_{ki}) to each other or to a group of proprietors (P_{ki}) that include brokers, agro-food processing industries, wholesalers, distributors and retailers. The proprietors then distribute farm products either as raw materials or processed foods. However, to produce those primary farm products, k farmers require a number of inputs that range from basic necessities in their households to a number of complex goods and services produced by a multitude of primary and specialized firms. This dynamic economic system (at k level) is influenced by a number of factors such as farmers' production levels and efficiency, among other things. Because agricultural drainage can improve farmers' production functions and net benefits (Equation 1), it can have a positive impact on this dynamic macro-economic system. To demonstrate these chain effects, let us use a simplified macro system which is comprised of a market with two players only (Figure 3), that is, the kth farmer who produces the ith agricultural commodity, and the jth consumer who demands the same ith commodity.

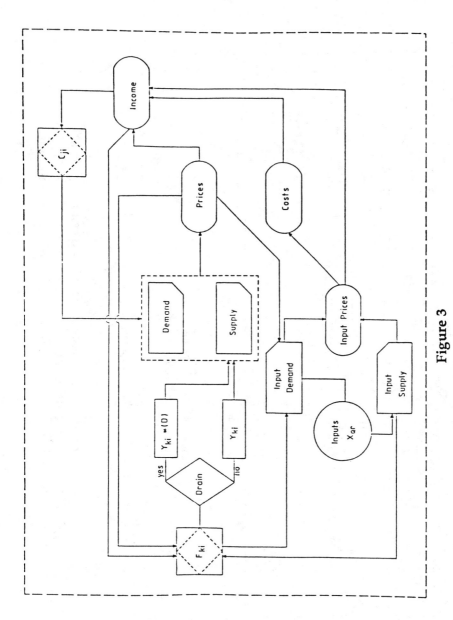

Figure 3

A simplified macro system representing a market with two players

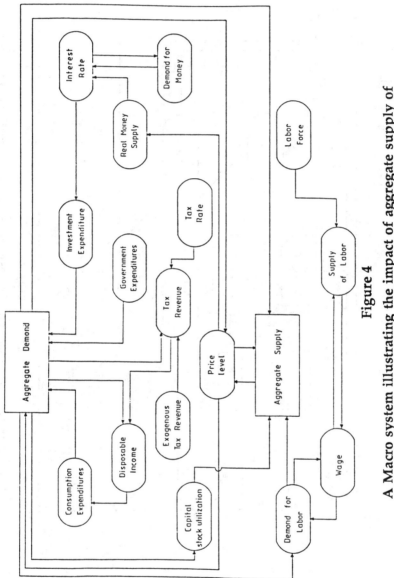

Figure 4

A Macro system illustrating the impact of aggregate supply of agricultural commodities on prices, employment, balance of payments, government budget, consumers' disposable income and the aggregate demand

Analysing this simplified model, it can be observed how a farmer's decision concerning drainage and its impact on the production of agricultural commodities (Y_{ki}) supplied to the market can affect agricultural commodity prices and the players' income levels through revenues (farmer's) and expenditures (consumer's). The fluctuations in the income levels not only influence the consumer's demand for farm products, but they also affect the farmer's ability to purchase the required inputs for production of the ith good. Extending this model to a larger sector of the economy which includes more than two players and a market would produce a complex macro-economic model. Assuming this macro-economic system includes three markets (namely, goods and services, money, and production and labour) and three sectors (namely, households, business, and government), it is possible to determine the effect of a drainage program on variables such as levels of national income, interest rates, prices, and wages (McNertney, 1980). Using such a model (Figure 4), one can analyse the impact of drainage programs on the aggregate supply of agricultural commodities and its further effects on items such as prices, employment, balance of payments, government budget, consumers' disposable income, and finally the aggregate demand. This model can also be extended further (with modifications) by including additional sectors of the national economy.

As a final note, it must be mentioned that in dealing with economic efficiency of local and regional drainage projects one must be aware of the temporal aspects of these projects. That is, factors such as technological breakthrough, inflation, employment, and societal goals must be taken into account. For example, some of the parameters used 30-40 years ago for determining the economic efficiency of a major drainage and reclamation project in a region may not be holding by today's standards. In other words it is possible that the question of economic efficiency of drainage projects in most developing countries would be addressed differently in the year 2000 and beyond.

2.3.2 Employment

Drainage investment affects employment in the following ways.

2.3.2.1 Primary Source of Employment

Primary-employment groups include both private and public organizations that are directly involved in (a) planning, administration and management, (b) materials and machinery manufacturing and handling, and (c) implementation of drainage projects. This includes all the specialized consulting firms, drainage contractors, manufacturers, distributors, and public offices at various municipal, county, provincial and federal levels.

2.3.2.2 Secondary Source of Employment

A more general category includes all the additional manpower required in a region after drainage projects are completed, that is, both the manpower required for management of the projects as well as the additional manpower needed as a result of the higher productivity and economic efficiency. For example, the Eastern Ontario Drainage Program in Canada (Cecile et al., 1985) not only enabled some of the low-income farmers of the region to increase their productivity (through better soil-water conditions), but it also expanded economic activities in that region. This expansion provided more employment opportunities for the local population. The Ijsselmeerpolders in Holland are another example of how a major drainage and reclamation project can generate employment opportunities at the regional and national level. Whether a major regional or a limited farm-level drainage project, the cumulative impact of such projects on employment is undoubtedly positive.

2.3.3 Reclamation and Augmentation of Land

Drainage and reclamation have been important societal goals in the low countries of Europe since the Middle Ages. To augment the land base for agricultural and non-agricultural uses, the Dutch used earth embankments (dikes) to enclose shallow coastlands of the North Sea. With windmills they pumped water from the enclosed area and drainage channels to facilitate the reclamation process through shrinkage, crack formation, and finally soil ripening (Schultz, 1982). Thousands of hectares of prime agricultural land in Holland originated this way (Veen,

1982). Currently, a complex network of drainage systems is being used in the newly reclaimed Dutch polders to control the water-table level and seepage (Kienhuis, 1982).

Bradshaw and Chadwick (1980) noted that reclamation of coastal salt marshes has been carried out in eastern England over many centuries. After enclosure with dikes, the areas were left for a few years to allow rain water to leach out salts through drainage ditches. This process permitted many communities in eastern England to augment their arable land base.

In addition to coastal lowlands, many inland wetlands have been reclaimed for agricultural as well as non-agricultural uses. At present, part of Haarlemmermeerpolder is being used by the Schiphol development project (the Schiphol International Airport). The Holland Marsh, north of Toronto, Ontario, Canada, can be cited as another example. This lowland was previously a large marsh that, because of its location and agricultural potentials, was reclaimed and eventually became one of the major vegetable-producing areas in Ontario. There are numerous other locations around the world that have benefited from agricultural drainage and reclamation. Framji et al. (1981) have reported the drained areas in the world as 158.4 million hectares. However, in a report by Rangeley (1987) the gross drained and flood-protected areas are recorded as 144 million hectares. Despite a nearly 10% discrepancy in their estimates, both studies have indicated North America, Asia, and Europe as the major drainage areas. This increase could partly be due to the abrupt increase in oil prices and its impact on commodity prices in the early 1970s on one hand, and the Green Revolution during the 1960s on the other. Both these phenomena favoured production of high-yielding varieties that require intensive use of inputs along with effective soil-water management including drainage.

2.3.4 Balance of Payments

The increased economic activities associated with higher export earnings have a significant impact on public and private economies. Export earnings have a special significance in the balance of payments as they generate foreign exchange to offset deficits created by imports. In some regions agricultural products are among the major export items, particularly in North

America and Europe (Table 2).

Table 2
Export of total agricultural products in selected countries in $100,000

Country	1981	1982	1983	1984	1985	1986
Algeria	1323	717	377	479	558	630
Argentina	63775	48636	58902	60604	56578	45632
Brazil	96878	80786	90389	104626	96739	77957
Canada	78425	80470	82269	85115	69956	66568
Denmark	50622	49193	46621	45301	47279	58287
Egypt	7405	6729	7264	7520	6656	6436
France	179012	158332	160376	160111	165207	197725
German DR	6086	4890	4027	3868	4254	4978
German FR	106152	101166	95830	98298	100391	130720
India	26980	23095	24035	23791	23449	24619
Iran	1590	1337	1556	1770	1501	1385
Iraq	433	565	504	260	322	295
Israel	9427	9024	8261	9042	8613	8662
Kenya	6150	5914	6324	7467	6760	8908
Netherlands	156375	151377	147361	150558	152102	192538
Pakistan	12607	8464	7958	7832	6955	10276
Syria	2361	2906	2789	4109	2063	1961
Turkey	25488	25901	24091	23947	22064	23396
UK	79353	73837	67471	67474	69870	86118
USA	450529	382426	375426	393505	305836	280713
USSR	29733	28087	23668	22024	22119	24639

Modified from Table 6. Agricultural products, total exports. FAO Trade Yearbook. Vol. 40. Pp. 42-44.

A series of events in the early 1970s (i.e., mainly rising income in certain countries such as OPEC member countries, devaluation of the U.S. dollar, and poor weather conditions in specific grain-producing countries) caused farming in North America and Europe to expand rapidly to meet the increasing demand for food products. This expansion took place in two ways: first, by extension of croplands through forest clearing and drainage, among other things; and second, by intensification of farming through intensive use of fertilizers and pesticides (UNEP, 1987). In Canada, the increasing trend in crop land was nearly 5% during the period 1971-1976; the same trend in Ontario was 15% (Hansen, 1981; Statistics Canada, 1981). With these expansions, Canadian farmers were able not only to provide enough food for the growing domestic consumption, but made major contributions to Canada's balance of payments. During 1985 Canadian farmers earned nearly $20 billion. In the amounted to CDN $700 million (FAO, 1985).

In addition to increasing export earnings from surplus agricultural production, drainage can also improve a country's balance of payments through import replacement. For example, considering the agro-climatic conditions of Canada, vegetable growing is one of the important sub-sectors of the Canadian economy because of its import-replacement potentials. The delta areas of British Columbia, and the marshland areas of Montreal, and Central and Southwestern Ontario are the dominant vegetable-producing centres of Canada. Some of these areas, such as the Holland Marsh in Ontario, could not have been developed without drainage. During 1984, Canadian vegetable growers received over 523 million dollars in farm cash receipts. In the same period, Canada imported over 500 million dollars of fresh vegetables (Statistics Canada, 1987). Thus, had these resources for producing vegetables in various parts of Canada not been developed, Canadian consumers would have had to spend an additional 500 million dollars on imports of fresh vegetables, or reduce their consumption of these foods.

3. THE FRAMEWORK

Decisions are choices among alternatives in the face of scarcity and uncertainty. Decision makers, implicitly or explicitly, evaluate the expected performance of a project of interest in response to several alternatives. Having set forth agricultural outlooks on drainage and its economic linkages from farmers, and societal perspectives, it is established that agricultural drainage can be considered as an important technological component of agricultural development and food security in developing countries. Systematic analysis of decision problems on agricultural drainage investment, particularly in developing countries, seeks to determine the most feasible alternative that the NGO and the donor agency can consider.

This section will discuss a model to estimate the statistically expected incremental crop yield resulting from agricultural drainage. The model provides a reliable methodology to predict the potential incremental crop yield due to drainage under different agroclimatic conditions. This model is based on the inferred plant-soil moisture regime relationship (agro-hydrology) and probability analysis. Before discussing the model, a brief technical background is provided.

3.1 Technical Background

Some preliminary aspects of the multifactor relationship involved in agricultural drainage have already been developed by a number of scientists from different disciplines.

Agronomists and soil scientists have adopted methods to determine the effect of wet soils, groundwater level, high water-table and water and heat on crop growth (e.g., Wesseling, 1974; Van Hoorn, 1958; Gupta and Larson, 1979; McBride, 1983; Feddes, 1971).

Engineers have identified and tested important variables that influence removal of excess moisture from soil such as depth of drains, drain diameters, drain spacing and drain material (e.g., Dierickx, 1980; Fouss, 1974; Irwin, 1986; Fitz et al., 1980).

Agricultural economists and engineers have developed methods to quantify a representative average incremental crop yield to be used in financial analysis of drainage benefits (e.g., Found et al., 1976; Colwell, 1978; Jorjani and Irwin, 1983, Lembke et al., 1982; Van Vuuren and Jorjani, 1986; Van Vuuren and Jorjani, 1984).

Engineers and drainage scientists have developed simulation models to evaluate the effect of various components of agricultural drainage (biological and physical) on plant growth and crop production (Wind, 1972; Van Wijk and Feddes, 1981; de Wit, and Goudrian, 1978; Skaggs, 1980).

3.2 Estimating Crop Yields Emanating from Drainage

3.2.1 Background

A model is a symbolic representation of a system. The bulk of modelling in agricultural economics has involved symbolic models or systems. A symbolic model is that which requires mathematical or logical operations and which can be used to formulate a solution to the problem at hand.

Design, synthesis, and analysis may be viewed collectively as steps in the process of developing a sufficient understanding of a system for construction of a model. Hence, these activities may system for construction of a model. Hence, these activities may be interpreted as steps essential to scientific inquiry, isolating parameters and concepts or relationships and weaving them into a representation of the system which is consistent with the theory, its perceived appropriateness (fitness) and the research objectives of these modelling activities.

With these in mind, and the theoretical criteria provided by various disciplines, the concepts and relationships involved in agricultural drainage can first be identified and then relevant variables chosen according to their importance. Subsequently these important variables and their interrelationships are woven into a system model which will determine the combined effect of these variables on the increased (crop) productivity due to agricultural drainage. A graphical presentation of this process is given in Figure 5.

Figure 5

A Schematic presentation of a framework to assess the economic value of agricultural drainage under different agroclimatic and soil conditions.

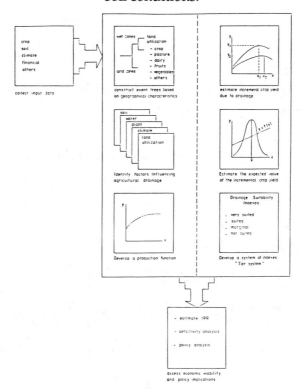

3.2.2 The Model

Changes in physical production resulting from agricultural drainage can be estimated either as the difference in the total physical productivity (TPP) of two production functions (e.g., drainage and no-drainage), or simply as the difference in physical yields obtained from drained and undrained lands (Jorjani, 1982; Jorjani and Irwin, 1983). This change in physical production can be translated into monetary values using specific agricultural commodity prices.

Review of the relevant literature suggests that a model to estimate these changes must include at least soil, climatic, and management factors. Such a model has been suggested by Jorjani (1982). The general form of this model can be written mathematically as:

$$Y_d = q(S, C, M) + e \qquad 2$$

$$S = w(ST, SND) \qquad 3$$

$$C = u(PPT, PET, HU) \qquad 4$$

$$M = v(FRT, PEST, MCH, COR, TIL) \qquad 5$$

Where:

Y=Crop yield

d=Yield code,

if d=01 then Y=drained

if d=02 then Y=undrained

S=Soil factor:

ST=Soil type; SND=soil's natural drainage classes

C=Climatic factor:

PPT=Precipitation level; PET=Potential evapotranspiration;

HU=Heat units (an index or mean temperature values)

M=Management factor:

FRT=fertilizer application rates; PEST=Pesticides application rates;

MCH=Machinery use; COR=Cropping practices; TIL=Tillage practices

3.2.2.1 Application Procedure

- Assemble into a computer data base crop yield, soil, and climatic input data collected from the study area,
- Estimate Y_d using a simultaneous system of equations or a simple regression model.

3.2.3 Probability Analysis

For this analysis the underlying assumption is that with constant management (controlled by sample selection), the most important factor in the soil-water-plant interrelationship is the climatic fluctuation. This is particularly true during crucial stages of crop growth.

In wet zones, annual crop yield differences between drained and undrained land are expected to fluctuate because of variation in annual precipitation levels. If high precipitation levels prevail during crucial periods of the growing season, higher yield differences are expected compared to relatively dry years. In a dry year, drainage may not be needed in wet zones.

In dry zones, however, annual crop yield differences between drained and undrained land are expected to fluctuate because of variation in irrigation amount and frequency, soil water depth, and finally soil salinity level. If high temperature and dry periods prevail during crucial periods of the growing season, more irrigation water would be required to balance crop moisture requirements. More irrigation water in turn will raise the ground water table and harm the crop with waterlogging and saline conditions.

Consequently, higher incremental crop yields are expected from drained irrigated crop lands under dry conditions. Theoretically, this can be expressed as follows:

If:

$$Y_d = f(C) \qquad 6$$

And,

$$I = Y_{01} - Y_{02} \qquad 7$$

Then:

$$I = h(C) \qquad 8$$

Hence:

$E(I)=h(E(C))$ 9

Where:

I=Incremental crop yield resulting from drainage

C=Climatic factor

E(I)=The expected value of I

E(C)=The expected value of C

Thus, the calculated incremental crop yield must give a representative picture of the distribution of drainage benefit (incremental crop yield) under all possible climatic conditions that can be expected during the economic lifetime of a drainage system. Given the above assumption, it can be ascertained statistically how often the calculated incremental crop yield will occur over the life time of the drainage project (Figure 6).

Figure 6
The expected value of I with respect
to the expected value of PPT over 50 years.

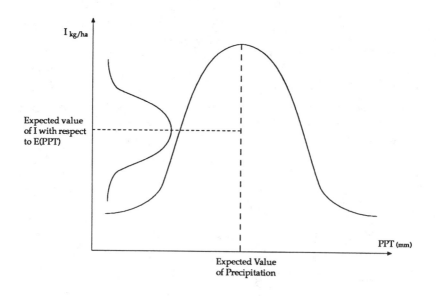

3.2.3.1 Application Procedure

- Test the climatic data for normal distribution,
- Estimate the expected value of climatic variable(s),
- Retrieve the estimated Y_d from the previous section,
- Estimate the expected value of Y_d with respect to climatic pattern in the study area.

3.2.4 Financial Analysis

Financial analysis is the process of determining the profitability of an investment or comparing the viability of alternative options. In order to estimate the profitability of a drainage system as a soil-water management technique in an area, one requires information concerning: 1) net cash revenue from drainage investment, and 2) cost of installing subsurface drainage. The method to be used for this investment analysis is the internal rate of return (IRR). The net cash revenue from drainage investment can be estimated as follows:

$$NR=\{[E(I)*PY]-E\} \qquad 10$$
$$NPV= NR/(1+i)^t \qquad 11$$
$$IRR= NR/(1+i)^t=0 \qquad 12$$

Where:

NR=Net cash revenue in \$/ha/year,

P_Y=Price of the commodity in \$/Kg,

E=Costs associated with I in \$/ha/year,

i=The discount factor in percentages,

IRR=Internal rate of return which is NPV set equal to zero

and solved for the i, the discount factor.

3.3.1 Application Procedure

- Assemble average investment costs for each area,
- Estimate costs associated with the I,
- Estimate net cash revenues,

- Calculate **IRR**. This step will also involve a series of sensitivity analysis that would provide answers to some "WHAT IF" questions. These include the examination of certain policy issues such as cost of borrowing, government subsidies, and changes in commodity prices at the local and international markets.

4. Data Requirement

- Annual crop yields representing the study area*,
- Records of climatic parameters from the study area,
- Data representing soil characteristics of the study area,
- Records or estimates of the agricultural chemicals and machinery used, and information concerning cropping and tillage practices in the study area,
- Financial data (e.g., commodity prices and costs).
* In some developing countries these input data may not be available. Under such circumstances yield records may be simulated before hand.

5. SUMMARY

Soil and water comprise a major part of our ecological system. For many years human beings have used these resources for agricultural, urban, industrial, infrastructure, and recreational purposes. Because of the importance of these resources in our lives, man soon realized that the key to his survival was devising certain norms and methods that would sustain the usefulness of soil and water resources. However, not many generations actually respected this basic notion of sustainability. Archeological evidence from the Middle East and other ancient sites of human civilization reveals that poor soil water management was one of the causes of the decline of several civilizations.

Today more than ever man is preoccupied with the wise use of these resources. After nearly four decades of rapid expansion of farming, with the help of modern technology, in industrialized countries a surplus agricultural sector and an over burdened environment have become a major topic of debate among scholars, planners, farmers, and the public at large. The wasteful and unwise use of these resources and the residue of agrochemicals have led to a growing awareness of the limitations of our ecological system.

Yet, on the other side of the global village, non-industrialized countries are hastily beginning to adopt a similar approach in order to achieve food security and economic growth. While the plight of these countries and their quest for self sufficiency in food production is understandable, it would be a self-defeating prophecy if they did not learn from earlier mistakes of industrialized countries.

To avoid these problems non-industrialized countries (and some donor agencies who are supporting agricultural development programs in those countries) need to reassess their agricultural programs by developing a new set of guidelines that would integrate expansion of agricultural output and environmental protection.

Because of the unique agroclimatic conditions in most non-industrialized countries, soil-water management is crucial to agricultural growth and productivity in those countries. Without adequate irrigation and/or drainage, no significant increase in agricultural output can be expected in a number of non-industrialized countries. However, most soil-water management projects are costly programs that require an in-depth economic assessment prior to project undertaking. Failure to incorporate biophysical cause-effect structure and impacts of such projects may result in a total loss for the host country and the donor agency (if any). For example, if an irrigation project in an arid zone does not incorporate a complementary drainage scheme, it is bound to be a technical disaster and a financial burden.

Decisions concerning allocation of funds for such projects necessitate access to appropriate tools to quantify the stream of forthcoming benefits. While there are numerous resources for economic analysis of irrigation projects (e.g., Hexema and Heady, 1978), very few studies are known for estimating benefits of agricultural drainage investment. A few methods that are available estimate benefits of drainage in terms of annual differences of crop yield between drained and undrained farm lands without any consideration for variations in soil, climate and management factors.

Recognizing this shortcoming, the present study focussed on a comprehensive framework that may provide accurate information for a precise economic judgment of drainage projects under different agroclimatic and soil conditions. The proposed framework is fairly simple and requires a combination of time series (crop yield and climatic data) and cross-section data (e.g., soil information and management data). Most of these input data can be obtained either from government agencies, and some international organizations (e.g., FAO, the World Bank, etc.) or through questionnaires. The application of this framework can demonstrate to government planners and donor agencies the economic viability of different projects under various soil, climate and management conditions.

REFERENCES

Abrol, I.P. 1987. Salinity and food production in the Indian subcontinent. Pp. 109-113 *In* W. Jordan (editor), Water and Water Policy in World Food Supplies, Conference Proceedings. Texas A&M University, College Station, Texas.

Aceves-Navarro, E. 1987. Salinity problems in food production of the Mexican irrigation districts. Pp. 129-133 *In* W. Jordan (editor), Water and Water Policy in World Food Supplies, Conference Proceedings. Texas A&M University, College Station, Texas.

Adams, R.M. 1962. Agriculture and urban life in early South-Western Iran. Science. 13: 109-122.

Armstrong, A.C. 1986. Drainage benefits to land workability. Pp. 589-598. *In* K.V.H. Smith and D.W. Rycroft (editors), Hydraulic Design in Water Resources Engineering: Land Drainage, (Proceedings, 2nd International Conference, Southampton University, U.K.) Springer-Verlag, New York.

Barrada, Y. 1987. Salinity management in Nile delta food production. Pp. 115-120 *In* W. Jordan (editor), Water and Water Policy in World Food Supplies, Conference Proceedings. Texas A&M University, College Station, Texas.

Bradshaw, A.D. and M.J. Chadwick. 1980. The restoration of land, the ecology and reclamation of derelict and degraded land. Studies in Ecology. Vol. 6., Blackwell Scientific Publications, Edinburgh: 317.

Briggs, D.J. and F.M. Courtney. 1985. Agriculture and Environment - The Physical Geography of Temperate Agricultural Systems. Longman, New York: 442.

Brooks, S.E. 1971. A study of the agricultural drainage outlet assistance program in eastern Ontario. ARDA Branch, Ontario Department of Agriculture and Food, Ontario, Canada.

Bryant, G.J., R.W. Irwin and J.A. Stone. 1987. Tile drainage discharge under different crops. Canadian Agricultural Engineering 29: 117-122.

Buttel, F.H. 1984. Socioeconomic equity and environmental quality in North American agriculture: alternative trajectories for future development. Pp. 89-106 In G.K. Douglass (editor), Agricultural Sustainability in a Changing World Order. Westview Press, Boulder, Colorado.

Cecile, C.P., M.J. Bardecki, and E.A. Snell. 1985. The Eastern Ontario Subsidiary Agreement Drainage Program: Impacts on the Land Resource and Initial Evaluation. Working Paper No. 40. Lands Directorate, Environment Canada, Ottawa: 58.

Chisci, G. and C. Zianchi. 1981. The influence of different tillage systems and different crops on soil losses on hilly silty-clayey soil. Pp. 211-217 In R.P.C. Morgan (editor), Soil Conservation: Problems and Perspectives, Wiley, Chichester.

Chowdhury, A. and E.O. Heady. 1980. World crop production variablity and U.S. export. Pp. 1473-1478 In W.G. Vogt and M.H. Mickle (editors), Modeling and Simulation, Vol. 11, part 4, Proceedings of the Eleventh Annual Pittsburgh Conference. School of Engineering, University of Pittsburgh, Pittsburgh.

Colwell, H.T.M. 1978. The economics of increasing crop productivity in Ontario and Quebec by tile drainage installation. Canadian Farm Economics. 13: (3).

de Wit, C.T. and J. Goudrian. 1978. Simulation of Ecological Processes. Simulation monographs, Centre for Agricultural Publishing and Documentation, Wageningen, The

Netherlands.

Dierickx, W. 1980. Electrolytic analogue study of the effect of openings and surrounds of various permeabilities on the performance of field drainage pipes. National Institute for Agricultural Engineering, Belgium.

Eichner, A.S. 1985. Toward a New Economics, Essays in Post-Keynesian and Institutionalist Theory. M.E. Sharpe Inc., New York.

El-Gabaly, M.M. 1977. Problems and effects of irrigation in the Near East region. Pp. 239-249. *In* E.E. Worthington (editor), Arid land irrigation in developing countries. Pergamon Press. Elmsford, New York.

El-Guindy, Samia. 1983. Economic evaluation of tile drainage projects. Pp. 186-202. *In* Proceedings on amelioration and development of deteriorated soils in Egypt. FAO technical report EGY/79/020.

FAO. 1985. FAO Trade Yearbook. Vol. 39, FAO Statistics Series No. 72. Food and Agricultural Organization of the United Nations, Rome.

FAO. 1986. FAO Trade Yearbook. Vol. 40, FAO Statistics Series No. 78. Food and Agricultural Organization of the United Nations, Rome.

Feddes, R.A. 1971. Water, heat and crop growth. Doctorate thesis. Agricultural University, Wageningen, The Netherlands.

Fitz, J.C., G.L. Horner and J.H. Snyder. 1980. The economic feasibility of installing tile drainage in Panoche Water District, San Joaquim Valley. Giannini Foundation of Agricultural Economics, Information series 80-3, Bulln. No. 1397, University of California, U.S.A.

Fitoussi, J.P. (editor). 1983. Modern Macro-economic Theory. European University Institute, Florence. Basil Blackwell, England.

Found, W.D., A.R. Hills and E.S. Spencer. 1976. Economic and environmental impacts of agricultural land drainage in Ontario. Journal of Soil Water Conservation. 31: 20-24.

Fouss, J.L. 1974. Drain tube materials and installation. Drainage for agriculture, No. 17, Agronomy, Madison, Wisconsin,

U.S.A.

Framji, K.K., B.C. Garg, and S.D.L. Luthra. 1981. Irrigation and Drainage in the World. International Commission on Irrigation and Drainage. 48, Nyaya Marg, Chanakyapuri, New Delhi, India: 491.

Friday, R.E. and D.J. Allee. 1976. The environmental impact of American agriculture. Pp. 213-239 *In* J.W. Watson and T. O'Riordan (editors), The American Environment: Perceptions and Policies. John Wiley and Sons, Toronto.

Galloway, J. and J.R. Johnston. 1982. Drainage benefits for field crops. Presented to the American Society of Agricultural Engineering. No. 82-2545, St. Joseph, Michigan.

Gupta, S.C. and W.E. Larson. 1979. Estimating soil water characteristics from particle size distribution, organic matter present and bulk density. Water resource research. 15: 1633-1635.

Hansen, J.A. 1981. A research note on a land use study of Canada, the United States and U.K., C. 1951-1971. Area. 13: 169-171.

Hexema, R.W. and E.O. Heady. 1978. Water production functions for irrigated agriculture. Center for Agricultural and Rural Development. The Iowa State University Press, Ames, Iowa.

Hill, A.R. 1976. The environmental impacts of agricultural land drainage. Journal of Environmental Management. 4: 251-274.

Hoffman, K.C. and Dale Jorgenson. 1978. Technological-economic models for strategic planning. Pp. 1477-1485 *In* A. Niemi, B. Wahlstrom, and J. Virkkunen (editors), A Link Between Science and Applications of Automatic Control: Reprints of the Seventh Triennial World Congress of the International Federation of Automatic Control, Helsinki, Finland.

IFPRI. 1987. International Food Policy Research Report. Washington, D.C., U.S.A.

Irwin, R.W. 1986. Drainage Guide for Ontario. AGDEX 752, Publication No. 29, Ontario Ministry of Agriculture and Food. Ontario, Canada.

Jorjani, H. 1982. A Multidisciplinary Approach to Economic Feasibility of Tile Drainage in Southern Ontario.

Unpublished M.Sc.thesis, University of Guelph, Guelph, Ontario.

Jorjani, H. and R.W. Irwin. 1983. A comparative analysis of corn yields from drained and undrained land in Ontario. Report under Ontario Ministry of Agriculture and Food, Project 43-507. Ontario Agricultural College, University of Guelph, Guelph, Ontario.

Jorjani, H. and R.W. Irwin. 1985. A simplified model for drainage benefits. Presented to the American Society of Agricultural Engineers, paper No. 85-2555, Chicago, Illinois, December: 17-20.

Jorjani, H. and P. Groenevelt. 1988. An economic assessment of the biophysical cause-effect structure of drainage impacts in the context of the SWEEP Program. Presented to the Annual Meeting of the Canadian Society of Soil Science, Calgary, Alberta, August 1988.

Jorjani, H. 1988. Biophysical cause-effect structure of drainage and its impact. A poster presentation commemorating the graduation of 1000 Cultuurtechniek students from Department of Land and Water Use (Vakgroep Cultuurtechniek), Wageningen Agricultural University, Wageningen, The Netherlands.

Kienhuis, J.H.M. 1982. The management of polders in the Netherlands. Pp. 175-185 In Polders of the World (keynotes), International Symposium, Lelystad, the Netherlands.

Leitch, J.A. and D. Kerestes. 1981. Agricultural land drainage: Costs and returns in Minnesota. Staff paper P81-15. Department of Agricultural and Applied Economics, University of Minnesota, St. Paul, Minnesota.

Lembke, W.D., C.J.W. Drablos, J.G. Arnold and J.N. Scarborough. 1982. A model for drainage benefits. Transactions of the American Society of Agricultural Engineers. 25: 1329-1332.

Luthin, J.N. 1957. Drainage of irrigated lands. Pp. 344-371. In J.N. Luthin (editor), Drainage of agricultural lands. American Society of Agronomy, Madison, Wisconsin.

Marsh, C.L. 1980. A general microeconomic theory simulation model. Pp. 1479-1481 In W.G. Vogt and M.H. Mickle (editors), Modeling and Simulation. Vol. 11, Part 4, Proceedings of Eleventh Annual Pittsburgh Conference.

School of Engineering, University of Pittsburgh, Pittsburgh.

McBride, R.A. 1983. Agronomic and engineering soil interpretation from water retention data. Unpublished Ph.D. thesis, University of Guelph, Guelph, Ontario.

McNertney, E.M. 1980. Economic modeling with NDTRAN: a three market macroeconomic policy analysis model. Pp. 1485-1490 In W.G. Vogt and M.H. Mickle (editors), Modeling and Simulation. Vol. 11, Part 4, Proceedings of Eleventh Annual Pittsburgh Conference. School of Engineering, University of Pittsburgh, Pittsburgh.

Mashali, Amin. 1983. Soil deterioration and role of the executive authority for land improvement projects in its control. Pp. 31-42. In Proceedings on amelioration and development of deteriorated soils in Egypt. FAO Technical Report EGY/79/020.

Rangeley, W.R. 1987. Irrigation and drainage in the world. Pp. 29-36 In W. Jordan (editor), Water and Water Policy in World Food Supplies, Conference Proceedings. Texas A&M University, College Station, Texas.

Rayment, A.F. and D.J. Cooper. 1968. Drainage of Newfoundland peat soils for agricultural purposes. Proceedings of 3rd International Peat Congress, Quebec, Canada.

Reeve, R.C. and N. Fausey. 1974. Drainage and timeliness of farming operations. Pp 55-66. In J. van Schilfgaarde (editor), Drainage for Agriculture. American Society of Agronomy, Madison, Wisconsin.

Schultz, E. 1982. From natural to reclaimed land, land and water management in the polders of the Netherlands. Pp. 17-42 In Polders of the world (keynotes). International Symposium, Lelystad, the Netherlands.

Shoven, J.B. and J. Whalley. 1984. Applied general-equilibrium models of taxation and international trade: an introduction and survey. Journal of Economic Literature. 22: 1007-1051.

Skaggs, R.W. 1980. A water management model for shallow water table soils. Water Resources Research Institute of the University of North Carolina, Technical Report No. 134. Raleigh: North Carolina State University.

THE WORLD FOOD CRISIS

Skaggs, R.W. 1987. Drainage. Pp. 329-324 *In* W. Jordan (editor), Water and Water Policy in World Food Supplies, Conference Proceedings. Texas A&M University, College Station, Texas.

Smith, L.P. 1972. The effect of weather, drainage efficiency and duration of spring cultivations on barley yields in England. Outlook on Agriculture. 7: 79-83.

Statistics Canada. 1981. Canada Year Book 1980-1981. Statistics Canada, Ottawa.

Statistics Canada. 1987. Canadian Statistical Review. Statistics Canada, Ottawa.

UNEP. 1987. Environmental data report. United Nations Environment Program, Nairobi, Kenya, Basil Blackwell, New York.

Van Hoorn, J.W. 1958. Results of a groundwater level experimental field with arable crops on clay soil. Netherlands Institute of Agricultural Science. 6:1-10.

Van Vuuren, W. and H. Jorjani. 1984. Estimating yields for a cost-benefit analysis of subsurface drainage in Southern Ontario. Canadian Agricultural Engineering. 26: 15-20.

Van Vuuren, W. and H. Jorjani. 1986. Impact of income tax regulations on profitability of subsurface drainage investment in Canada and the United States. Transactions of the American Society of Agricultural Engineers. 29: 1284-1296.

Van Wijk, A.L.M. and R.A. Feddes. 1981. A model approach to the evaluation of drainage effects. Land drainage seminar, Cambridge, U.S.A.

Veen, J.V.D. 1982. Agricultural aspects in polder areas in the Netherlands. Pp. 121-135 *In* Polders of the World (keynotes), International Symposium, Lelystad, the Netherlands.

Wesseling, J. 1974. Crop growth and wet soils. Chapter 2 *In* J. van Schilfgaarde (editor), Drainage for Agriculture. American Society of Agronomy, Madison, Wisconsin.

Wind, G.P. 1972. A hydraulic model for simulation of non-hysteric vertical unsaturated flow of moisture in soils. Journal of Hydrology. 15: 227-246.

Whithey, M. and N. Hanley. 1986. Problems of agriculture externalities: a conceptual model with implications for research. Journal of Agricultural Economics. 37: 1-11.

Chapter 12

THE BLUE REVOLUTION:
THE MODERNIZATION OF FISHERIES

Janet Marie Huddle

The best known attempt to revolutionize food production is the Green Revolution. However, alongside the Green Revolution, another food-related revolution has been taking place: the "Blue Revolution," an attempt to increase food production through development of the global fishing industry. Technological developments facilitated a tremendous expansion of fishing since World War II. These technologies have been coupled with development planning. Small scale fishing has been seen as only an inefficient, transitory stage in the development of large-scale fishing.

Using a very narrow definition of fishery development (namely, increased fish production), industrialization and technology have spread throughout the world. Globally, the annual catch of fish has increased steadily. It reached a stabilization point in the 1970s. The sustainability of this growth-oriented development started to be questioned in the 1970s, prompting research into the feasibility of aquaculture and small scale fisheries. The definition of fisheries development has since been expanded to include concerns about conservation, employment, and domestic food production.

The development of the earth's oceans has been regarded as a promising endeavour for humanity, particularly during the middle of this century, when development was almost synonymous with extraction. B.R. Sen (Director General of FAO) noted with respect to the Second World Fishing Boat Congress held in 1959 that "it was part of a very much larger plan of attack on one of the most crucial problems that face the world: that of

385

increasing food production." In the 1950s and 1960s popular magazines featured numerous articles on the subject of ocean development, chronicling such diverse topics as inhabiting the sea, and vacuuming minerals off the sea-bed (Cloud 1963, Fleming 1959). In the area of food production, one author suggested that the raising of whales for food might have a significant effect on the future of mankind (Clarke 1960). The potential fish harvest from the ocean was considered to be between 200 million and 1,000 million metric tons/year, yields which could only be wrought through developing harvest technology. The hope placed in this technology — and its linkages to agricultural modernization — is summarized below:

> The application of science and modern techniques to the improvement of agriculture has yielded highly beneficial results, both to the producer and the consumer. The same process could make the fishing boat more efficient, thereby producing more food for the world while bringing to the fishermen a higher standard of living.

> Fishing throughout the world is going through a period of intense change in which we are taking the "maybe" and "could be" out of it, and making it into a hard science, realizing that "world fishing is world feeding."

The success of the new technology was to be measured through increased yields. The pathway to bettering the quality of life throughout the planet was to be found through international co-operation for ocean development (Commercial Fisheries Review 1967). The predominant notion of ocean development was the increased use of technology to extract resources efficiently and effectively.

In hindsight, the equating of ocean and fishery development with increased production and technology, appears oversimplified. Fisheries development is a multidimensional process revolving around economic, socio-political, and ecological objectives. Its socio-political nature is seen in the way resources and benefits are allocated to different groups (FAO 1983c, Diegues 1983). Economically, fishing must be profitable and ecologically it must be sustainable. As well, fisheries development is by its very nature international, as demonstrated by the migratory habits of tuna and other fish and the existence of shared stocks (Ronquillo 1983, Mitchell 1985).

Government and development agency planners now seek to list various objectives of fisheries development as an aid to planning and management. FAO suggests the following as a comprehensive collection of fishery development objectives. They are in no particular order as one of the tasks of planners is to rank them in order of priority.

i)   employment, job creation;
ii)   increased food production:
      a) export for foreign currency,
      b) food for domestic consumption;
iii) higher wages for fishing industry personnel;
iv)   increased efficiency for vessels of fish farms:
      a) better production per unit,
      b) better production investment costs,
      c) reduced fuel consumption per fish produced;
v)   development of region in question by any
      profitable means;
vi)   proper management of resources including fish
      and water;
vii) development of local shipyards and marine
      engineering industry (FAO 1983b).

These objectives are considered not only in relation to each other but also in terms of the relationship between fishing and the overall national development priorities. The fishing objectives are required to be priorized on a national level and also a regional level (FAO 1983b).

This is a difficult task as these objectives are often conflictual, reflecting the interests of different groups. For example, producers desire a high price for their product, while urban consumers demand a low priced product (Smith 1979). Employment and job creation have frequently been inversely related to increasing fish exports, because the fish exporting business and associated industry have generally been capital intensive, requiring little labour. The fishing sector also competes with other sectors for use of the ocean — tourism and industry for instance. Industrial pollution may reduce the sound management of marine resources, but at the same time increase employment.

Not only are these objectives difficult to rank, and reconcile with each other, but particularly in LDCs these objectives are subject to a number of constraints. These constraints include 1) lack of information about resources, 2) weakly developed institutions, 3) lack of financing, 4) pollution, 5) stock depletion, 6) inappropriate technology, and 7) lack of fishermen participation (FAO 1983b, Gaudet and Parker 1986).

In addition to the above aspects of fisheries development, the following more general issues must also be dealt with: the role of government and private sector, co-operation with other LDCs, external assistance, training and extension work and the strengthening of physical infrastructure (FAO 1983b).

This multifaceted definition of fisheries development has only recently been articulated. The events of the Blue Revolution took place in a context where fisheries development was synonymous with the increased extraction of fish from the sea. This will become evident as the history of the Blue Revolution is reviewed.

Post World War II Fisheries

The expansion of world fisheries following World War II has been tremendous: the average annual catch rising from 22 million metric tons in the late 1940s to over 75 million metric tons in the 1980s. International trade in fish and fish products increased fivefold by volume between 1950 and 1980. In terms of current dollars this increase represented over 15 billion $US, almost a thirtyfold increase (Ceres 1984).

This expansion has been attributed to general economic growth following World War II and technological developments in the fishing industry. Two major technological developments were the capacity for on-board freezing and the hardware allowing for larger purse seines (Ceres 1984). In order to facilitate the increased catch brought about by these developments, in 1960 the British restored two aircraft carriers (13,000 tons each) to service 50 trawlers each. This venture which cost $7 million US at the time, involved the use of helicopters to transfer the fish from the trawlers to the aircraft carriers where the catch would be frozen. The development of factory ships allowed the fishing fleets of Japan to expand their foreign fleets during this time, and be represented in Brazil, Fiji, and India to name a few places. The expansion did not bypass the LDCs. The governments of South East Asia for example were promoting mechanization and rapid expansion of the fishing industry (Panayotou 1985). The bottom trawl net which was introduced into Thailand in the 1960s, soon spread to Malaysia and Indonesia where it facilitated a great increase in catch. In Thailand the number of trawlers went from 99 in 1961 to 5,204 in 1976, an increase of 520%. By the 1970s a luring purse seine with a light was also being used in Thailand. In the LDCs generally, other modernization efforts were taking place, such as the use of nylon gill nets, and an increase in the number of motorized boats (Menasveta 1983).

Several interrelated factors favoured the development of large scale fisheries.[1] During this time of expansion and technological development, development planners and governments regarded industrial or large scale fishing, as more efficient than small scale or artisanal fishing and considered small scale fishing a transitory stage in the development of large scale fishing (CIDA 1986). The efficiency of large scale fishing would increase food production and fight malnutrition. This prompted Western aid donors, through their Official Development Assistance (ODA), to provide money and services for large scale fisheries. Between 1974 and 1983, worldwide ODA increased with respect to fisheries by over 100% in real terms (CIDA 1986). Contributors of ODA tried to ensure the success of their ventures by providing the services of expatriates, experienced in the management and development of large scale fishing. The financing and expatriates were well received by the governments of the LDCs and investment was made in capital intensive schemes (Diegues 1983).

Industrialization was also promoted by governments and international agencies because it was predicted to bring benefits to the rest of the fishing community, particularly the small scale fishermen. Small scale fishermen would either become industrialized themselves, be employed by the industrial fishing industry, or be gainfully employed in some other occupation that emerged as a direct consequence of the increased economic growth brought about by the industrial fishing industry. The small scale fishing industry would gradually disappear allowing the natural progression to large scale fishing (Panayotou 1982a). These ideas can be represented in the growth oriented model of fishing development.

An illustrative case of this type of industrial oriented growth is found in Peru. In a matter of a few years Peru grew from minimal fish exports to the largest fish exporter in the world (by volume). This phenomenal growth was due to a single species of fish — the anchoveta. Virtually all of the anchoveta caught was converted into fish meal and exported, until the stocks collapsed in 1972. This offers a heuristically valuable, though perhaps exaggerated, example of the Blue Revolution.

Peruvian Case Study

The Peruvian anchoveta stocks have not been the only fish stocks to collapse this century (i.e., California sardines and Norwegian herring), however they have been the largest. At the height of the industry in 1970-71, an estimated 11-12 million metric tons were taken. In the following year a meagre 4.5 million metric tons were caught and in 1973 only 1.5 million metric tons were caught. The stocks are still decimated, yielding only 1.7 million metric tons in 1982 (George 1985, Thompson 1981).

Ecology

The coast of Peru is one of only five major areas in the world characterized by high organic productivity due to upward vertical currents known as upwellings. In areas of upwelling, cool nutrient rich water from below rises up, providing nutrients to the phytoplankton (plants) above, that are the most basic elements in the marine food chain. Consequently, areas of upwelling are able to support significantly more marine life than other areas (Thompson 1981). The proliferation of phytoplankton has facilitated the large numbers of anchoveta found in Peru. In turn the anchoveta constitute the primary food of three types of birds, three types of tuna, and contribute to the diet of other fishes, whales, porpoises, squids and sea lions (Murphy 1954).

R.C. Murphy's words penned in 1954 are hauntingly prophetic in light of the subsequent developments in the Peruvian anchoveta industry. He cautioned against an uninformed and unrestricted exploitation of anchoveta stocks, because the capability of humanity to extract fish for meal posed a great threat to the resources. He said: "It must be remembered that men who are eager to tap natural resources are not inclined to be sympathetic toward an adequate weighing of the pros and cons. Their attitude is usually more vociferous than judicious" (Murphy 1954).

Fifteen years after the collapse of the anchoveta stocks, it can be stated that the collapse was due to the type of exploitation Murphy warned about, in combination with the natural phenomenon known as El Nino. Although minor occurrences of El Nino are frequent, it occurs severely only rarely (i.e., 1972 and 1983). This phenomenon consists of the influx of warm nutrient poor water (the exact cause is unknown) resulting in a chain of biological events (Paulik 1971). One consequence of El Nino, particularly in its most severe manifestations, is a reduction in the number of anchoveta. Therefore this occurrence in 1972 would have resulted in a decrease in the anchoveta catch. However, at the same time anchoveta fisheries had been extracting record high catches at a level of questionable sustainability. Together, El Nino and overexploitation caused the depletion of stocks.

Industrial Development

The rise and fall of the anchoveta industry in Peru has been particularly dramatic. In 1950 the first fish meal factory was constructed along the coast of Peru, and in 1951, 7.2 thousand metric tons of fish meal were produced. By 1963 with a total of 1.2 million metric tons of fish meal produced, Peru was the largest meal producer in the world (Paulik 1971). In 1970, the amount of fish meal from Peru was 2.25 million metric tons, accounting for 42% of the world total. This was the highest level Peru ever achieved; in 1973 only 0.5 million metric tons were produced (Vondruska 1981).

It is apparent that the anchoveta fishery in Peru grew at a very rapid rate, and the question arises how did such growth occur. One factor certainly was the increased demand for fish meal after World War II, as the field of animal nutrition expanded. Animal feed is costly, and fish meal provides a way to increase the productivity of feed conversion for a relatively inexpensive price. Thus countries of the developed world began importing fish meal for use in animal feed. Those countries importing the most were Japan, USSR, USA, UK, and West Germany. In the US approximately 80% of imported fish meal is used in chicken feed; the other 20% being distributed between livestock, fish, mink, lab animals and household pets. After the 1972 El Nino, Peru attempted to increase its fish meal through the use of other fish. Japan and the USSR also increased their production, reducing the impact of the Peruvian anchoveta collapse (Vondruska 1981).

More than 20,000 full-time fishermen and 3,000 factory workers were employed in the Peruvian anchoveta industry at its peak. The number of purse seiners used in the catch were 1300, and 125 fish meal plans existed (Paulik 1971). Today only 10 plants are in operation, and commercial fishing is extremely limited (George 1985).

The plants and vessels far exceeded the number required to obtain and process the annual recommended 9.5 million metric tons. Even a reduction by 25% would have left an excess of plants and vessels. This excess encouraged further excess. The quota of 9.5 million metric tons could be fished in about 130 days. In order to try and operate plants at full capacity, plant operators would increase the capacity of their boats or add additional ones in order to secure a larger share of the catch. Moreover, catches were often substantially underreported, a situation which led to more overfishing (Instituto del Mar del Peru 1970).

Thus the Peruvian anchoveta industry was characterized by a) production of fish meal for export to developed countries and b) overcapitalization of the industry. Government fishery policy, or lack thereof, can be seen to be a factor in both of these areas.

Government Involvement

Prior to the 1968 military takeover, direct government involvement in fisheries was minimal. However, as much as 35% of Peru's foreign exchange was earned through the fish meal industry, thus making it the number one foreign exchange earner in the economy. Government promotion of the industry occurred more through inaction than decisive policies because although the government under President Belaunde had expressed interest in developing fishing for food, no policy initiatives were taken in this area. Consequently investors chose to be involved with the rapidly expanding fish meal industry. No one government department or agency was responsible for making decisions with respect to fishing, rather a multiplicity of agencies made various decisions which reflected a variety of often conflictual interests. The most important decisions were made by the Ministry of Finance and Congress (Hannergren 1981).

While the government left industrial development to the private sector, it was concerned with gaining revenue through import and export taxes. These were of particular importance to the fish meal industry: large exporters of meal and importers of equipment. The government did become involved in other areas such as credit and conservation, but these were largely in response to lobbying and not the result of government initiative (Hannergren 1981).

With respect to conservation, in 1966 the government limited access to fisheries by closing the fisheries during certain seasons. However, by not establishing quotas, as technological improvements increased and factories and fleets increased, more fish were taken. By the time of the first military takeover in 1968 (General Velasco Alvarado) the industry was plagued by 1) overexpansion, 2) reliance on a single vulnerable resource (with no real measures to preserve it), 3) pressure for further growth, 4) wastage of resources due to gross inefficiency of some factories, and 5) the potential for bankruptcies, closures and unemployment at the onset of a bad season (Hannergren 1981).

The 1968 government was not much concerned with fisheries other than fish meal. A Ministry of Fisheries was created in early 1970, but the predominant view of the industry was to generate revenue (which went for example to help fund the new Ministry of the Air Force). The Ministry of Fisheries expanded rapidly (from less than 200 employees in 1970 to 1300 in 1973), largely with inexperienced people; in fact the head of the new ministry's only fishing experience was in sports fishing (Hannergren 1981).

One of the first products of this expanded bureaucracy was a 5 year development plan, which included more than 50 specific policy objectives. A government organization was created to take over fish meal and oil marketing domestically and externally. The production however remained in private hands (until 1973).

The monitoring of anchoveta catch was minimal at this time due to disorganization and the inexperience of the administrators. As well the government was naively optimistic about the size of anchoveta stocks even in light of indications to the contrary (Hannergren 1981).

In 1972, after the crisis of the recent El Nino a decision was made to nationalize the fish meal industry. This was seen as a way to restructure the overexpanded, debt-ridden industry. After 1975 and the second coup (General Morales Bermudez) the number of boats had been reduced to 530, and there were only 51 factories, although the work force was still 23,000. The fishing fleet was returned to the private sector (although the vessels were too expensive to convert to other types of fisheries), and through a program offering benefits for voluntary resignation the number of factory workers was eventually reduced to 7043 in 1978. At that time only 42 factories remained. Concurrently the Ministry was reduced to 800 employees and, with the collapse of anchoveta and privatization, more investment began in other areas of fisheries such as canning and food fishing (Hannergren 1981).

In terms of general trends the Peruvian example follows the model of the Blue Revolution. It was characterized by rapid industrial expansion, and a marked increase in fish production. This production however was all geared to export, and so the distribution was not to the people who caught the fish or other local Peruvians. Only 23,000 people out of a total labour force of more than 4 million were employed in the industry (Weeks 1985). Recently there has been more attention paid to small scale fishermen, and the production of fish for domestic consumption. Peru, due to its ecological marine environment, cannot be said to be a `typical' LDC with respect to fisheries, although its development has been similar in many respects to that of other countries. In terms of industrialization Peru embarked on a course that ended in disaster. Other LDCs have also followed the same general course of industrialization, but have changed direction before large scale disaster occurred. Peru is representative of the ocean development through extraction theory, disregarding many other aspects of fishing development.

The fall of the Peruvian anchoveta occurred almost thirty years after the Blue Revolution began. At the global level of analysis, the loss of the anchoveta stock occurred simultaneously with a plateau in global fish catch and a subsequent change in perspectives with respect to fishery development. A series of events in the 1970s and 1980s have been instrumental with respect to the fishing industry and in effecting this change. The first significant event was the collapse in the Peruvian anchoveta described above. Previously, biologists had warned about the possibility of overexploiting fish stocks; the case of the Peruvian anchoveta was the most dramatic display to date of the consequences of exploitation and a reminder that the sea is not an infinite resource.

The oil crisis in the early 1970s also had significant effects on the fishing industry. The sudden increase in fuel costs made the recently mechanized boats very expensive to run and resulted in reduced profits. The third significant event was the establishment of the Law of the Sea in 1982. Signed by representatives from over 100 coastal states, this law allowed for national jurisdiction in water 200 miles from shore, and accounted for more than 90% of the area currently fished (CIDA 1986). In addition to granting the rights of Exclusive Economic Zones (EEZ), the state was also given the responsibility of managing the marine resources in that area. If the coastal state lacked the capacity to harvest the Maximum Sustainable Yield (MSY), then they must grant access to other states (Mitchell 1985).

Thus the governments of the LDCs were confronted with the realities of stock depletion and increased production costs, while at the same time being called on to review and manage their current plans for fishing development. The first two problems really called into question the growth-oriented model of fishing. Previous assumptions and theories about small and large scale fisheries were questioned and as a result 1) criticisms began to emerge with respect to large scale fishing, 2) alternatives for production increases such as aquaculture were considered and 3) the role of small scale fishing was examined more closely.

Large scale fishing efforts were criticized for the amount of fish wasted and the energy expended, while man-made cultivation was attempted to increase production of certain species beyond what could be obtained naturally. Both of these areas were aimed at efficiently increasing the amount of available fish. Therefore although the growth model was questioned, an emphasis on increasing production and technology was still evident. Concurrently the relative importance of small scale fishing was being realized.

Wastage of fish

Numerous accounts of fish wastage have been articulated. There is the waste of fish through overfishing — that is the exploitation of stocks until they diminish in size, or conversely, fish may be wasted through underfishing. The use of fish in livestock feed and fertilizer has been considered wasteful. Out of 35.5 million tons of pelagic fish caught in 1981, 14 million tons were used for fish meal for animals. The use of energy in capturing fish has been questioned and considered wasteful, as it sometimes takes more energy to harvest fish than the fish yield (Kent 1984).

While wastage in these areas gives cause for legitimate concern, the sheer volume of wastage that occurs in the shrimp industry has virtually eclipsed these other areas. Referred to as by-catch, this area of wastage concerns lower valued species that are caught alongside species of higher commercial value (primarily shrimp) during trawling. By-catch fish generally are either discarded or spoiled. An estimated 20% of total marine catch is lost this way, mainly via large scale fishermen (Menasveta 1983). CIDA estimates that small scale fishermen on average discard less than 5% of their catch, whereas industrial fishermen dispose of approximately 45% (by weight).

More specifically, in Mexico, the annual by-catch of 3,000 shrimp trawlers is estimated at 7×10^5 tons. A 1980 study in Guyana indicated that although the largest quantities of shrimp were caught in water 22-39 fathoms, the largest amounts of by-catch occur in water considered shallow (<15 fathoms). The shallower waters are continually fished however because they are home to the large shite shrimp, a highly valued species not found in deeper waters. This shrimp, however, at most makes up 5% of the total catch of trawling in these shallow waters — indicating an immense wastage of other fish in the pursuit of these shrimp (Furnell 1982). In some areas of Malaysia, the shallow fish stocks have been overexploited by trawling, whereas farther away from shore, the fish stocks are underexploited (Menasveta 1983).

The ratio of fish by-catch:shrimp is highly variable. For

example, in Guinea the ratio is 20:1, in the North Central Gulf of Mexico it is 19:1, and the Pacific coast of Mexico varies from 1.3:1 to 33:1 (Slavin 1982). In general, temperate or subtropical areas average 5:1 and tropical areas 10:1 (FAO/IDRC 1982).

This variability in by-catch is due to physical conditions such as water temperature, current, and sea bottom, as well as man-made factors such as the length of the shrimp season and market demand for fish. If the shrimp season is short, virtually all the by-catch will be discarded. If the season is longer, more fish will be utilized (FAO/IDRC 1982).

Various efforts have been made to reduce by-catch. Preventable measures involve a system for selectively catching shrimp instead of fish. Selectivity devices include light, sound or electrical current. The use of sound is the most promising method, as fish are much more sensitive to sound than shrimp. The cost of using electrical current is too prohibitive, and not enough is known about light responses to make its use feasible at present (Sternin and Allsopp 1982).

If the fish are not selectively eliminated but instead caught, they can be sorted on board and the marketable species kept in chilled seawater (CSW) or refrigerated and circulated seawater (RSW) to prevent spoilage (Pariser 1982). Alternatively these fish could be transferred to another collector ship, or processed at sea to prevent spoilage (FAO/IDRC 1982). Unfortunately to date no feasible method has been developed for processing these fish at sea. These fish are often only 12 cm, and are therefore too small to be headed, tailed and gutted by traditional methods (Pariser 1982).

The limitations on the processing and marketability of these fish serve as a reinforcement for shrimpers to discard the by-catch. They consider it unprofitable to retain the fish because the fish are more bulky than shrimp and market at about 1/5 the price of shrimp. Therefore, in a ship with a limited carrying capacity of approximately 30 tons, it is far more profitable to store shrimp and cast away fish (FAO/IDRC 1982).

Currently, the wastage of by-catch is a foregone conclusion. There is not enough intrinsic demand to make marketing profitable, and the structures of the food system have been unable to generate demand, or develop low cost means of production. The market demand for shrimp is encouraged by

LDCs wishing to increase foreign exchange, further decreasing the incentive to market by-catch. However cultural values have led some groups to demand the better use of by-catch. These groups include, among others, developers concerned about the huge protein source wasted, and biologists concerned about the reduction of juvenile fish which forms a part of the by-catch.

The demands for aquacultural development have likewise come from biologists (who see aquaculture as a method of reducing the reliance on capture fishing) and developers who regard it as a method of providing available high quality protein.

Aquaculture

Large scale aquaculture is the most efficient type of aquaculture, but it usually means having hatcheries, disease prevention and treatment systems and in some cases fish processing as well. The extent and expense of these inputs yields a product that is also expensive (Ben-Yami 1986). One of the most successful examples of this type of aquaculture is Japanese mariculture (salt water aquaculture). The cultivation of fish through mariculture has been consistently increasing, although it currently accounts for only 17% of the total mariculture production. Providing 10^6 tons of fish/year, mariculture provides 10% of the Japanese fisheries production (Kuronuma and Fukusho 1984). In comparison, aquaculture in South East Asia accounted for 7.2% of the total fisheries production in 1978 (Menasveta 1983).

Due to the unreliability, expense, and unavailability of natural fish larvae, the Japanese have begun artificial production of larvae. The larvae are obtained from broodfish which have been raised for two to three years in floating net cages in the sea or concrete land tanks. The rearing of these larvae gives an idea of the intensiveness of this operation. They are initially raised on live food in indoor or outdoor concrete tanks, holding 0.5-200 tons of water. From there the larvae are moved to floating net cages and fed processed food. When the larvae have grown to sufficient size they are used for marketing, restocking, or are returned to the sea (Kuronuma and Fukusho 1984).

An essential feature in fish cultivation is diet. Good diets result in higher production, better disease recovery, and better ability to deal with environmental stress, whereas poor diets can result in nutrient deficiencies and toxicoses. The diet is also important in maintaining the same body composition as wild fish, an important factor in marketability. Producing a high quality diet is an expensive process requiring attention not only to the actual content of the diet but proper storage and transportation of the food to prevent microbial infestation, fat rancidity and other problems. These problems are best overcome through refrigeration and or freezing (Cho et al. 1985).

These capital intensive methods which concentrate on production contrast with aquacultural endeavours in China which have been operating since the 11 century B.C. Chinese feed includes compost, aquatic plants and naturally occurring food in the water. These foods are supplemented with antibiotics to reduce disease (Committee 1981).

Although the Chinese system may look relatively simple and easily adopted, upon closer examination some of the barriers to even this type of aquaculture are seen. Aquaculture can be divided into three stages, procurement, transformation and delivery. Procurement includes obtaining the necessary inputs such as stock, feed, land, water, labour, fertilizer, and some managerial or technical expertise. Transformation is the actual process of raising the fish to a marketable size and delivery is the aspect of selling the fish through the market, either directly to consumers, or to middlemen (Smith 1982).

Each of these stages produces a multitude of barriers, most of which have been more prohibitive to smaller farmers than larger. Larger farmers have more access to capital, credit and technical knowledge, three essential components of the procurement and transformation stages. Consequently, in the past larger operations have been more profitable. Therefore large farmers have a greater chance to get into aquaculture and once they are in, a greater probability of success (Wattanutchariya and Panayotou 1982). Other barriers include the system of land tenure/ownership (Panayotou 1982b), failure of past projects, and lack of government support (Gaudet and Parker 1986).

Government support has led to some successful aquacultural development in Thailand. The Thai government selected target areas in which to begin a fish pond development program in the early 1980s. Poor villages were able to request the Department

399

of Fisheries to prepare and seed ponds for them. The ponds were then managed by village committees, who received diminishing financial support from the government until the fourth year of the program when they received only advisory support. Over a five year period more than 500 ponds were built, and the project has been so successful in providing affordable fish to local populations, that the project has now been expanded to a national basis, and will include pond establishments at schools (Kent 1986).

This type of government support is crucial if aquacultural development hopes to provide benefits to the poor. Otherwise the preliminary capital required and efficiency of larger scale operations will result in an intensification of aquaculture and a final product that is too costly (Ben-Yami 1986).

Small Scale Fishing

Small scale fishing is not a transitory stage in the development of large scale fishing. Estimates range from 25%-50% of all fish landings used for human consumption, is caught by small scale fishermen. Regionally the figures are even higher. As much as 75% of the domestic fish supply is landed by small scale fishermen in parts of Africa and Asia (Ceres 1984, CIDA 1986). In some areas small scale fishing has yielded greater efficiency of production than large scale efforts. In Senegal for example small scale fishing yields a 50-70% return on capital whereas industrial fishing yields only 3-7% and the cost of creating a job in the industrial sector is greater (CIDA 1986). In West Africa sheer numbers illustrate the importance of small scale fishing. Approximately 176,000 fishermen are employed in small scale fisheries, whereas only 8,307 are employed by the industrial sector. These small scale fishermen provide more than two thirds of the fish catch in this region, (excluding the Ivory Coast and Guinea who were net importers of fish), according to Mitchell (1985).

These figures only partially reveal the extensiveness of this sector. Fishermen are often considered as those who actually catch the fish, but as Emmerson points out this is really misrepresentative, and development efforts based on such a definition are not useful. Referring to a fishing community in the Philippines, Emmerson (1980, p. 51) states:

> Excluding the shopkeeper who sold supplies for the
> fishing trip, the officials who taxed the catch, persons who
> added value to the fish by processing it, those who bought
> and sold the processed product, and those who finally
> purchased the fish retail and consumed it, nearly 50 people
> enjoyed in cash or kind, at least a small portion of the catch.
> From a bioanthropological point of view, just as a
> development project's impact on the marine ecology of fish
> must be considered, so must the effects on the crowded,
> fragile network of human interdependence in the maritime
> community that receives the catch. To focus on fishermen as
> physical producers only and to try to change their fishing
> effort on behalf of production or conservation without regard
> for the intensely distributive local ramifications of such
> changes is to distort, if not doom, artisanal fisheries
> development.

This passage indicates the highly labour intensive nature of
small scale fishing. It is difficult to envision, as planners at the
time did, how the capital intensive large scale fishing industry
would provide gainful employment for all these people.

The Social Basis
for the Technological "Revolution"

The current management of fisheries has largely developed
within an American/European paradigm.

> All wild stock fisheries are common property natural
> resources. Since no single enterprise has to pay for the use of
> fishery resources, they are often overexploited...with a
> common property fishery resource, each acting on its own
> leads not to a social optimum, as Adam Smith envisioned, but
> to a private market failure and thus to overfishing. The
> fundamental reason why the fisheries need management is
> economic inefficiency and waste (Bell 1978 p. 198).

In other words the sea has been considered to be common
property (Cycon 1986) and consequently it must be managed
and controlled. If the sea is not managed then physical and
economic wastage occurs. Physically, the resource will become
overexploited if there is no ownership or limitation to
access—the tragedy of the commons as articulated by Garett

Hardin — because if anything is left, it may be taken by someone else. Economic waste occurs because if fishing is profitable it will attract more investors and stocks will decrease. In order to maintain yields, an increased effort must be made by the fishermen (see Figure 2). In order to prevent either of these types of wastage from occurring, the sea is managed through limiting quantity of fish, limiting gear type and style, and limiting entry to the industry. This whole system of management could be referred to as Common Property Management. The overall result of this type of management strategy is described this way: "In order to achieve economic efficiency, the western model encourages concentration of capital into fewer, more modern vessels and technologies, with a consequent limitation on the overall labour devoted to a fishery" (Cycon 1986, p. 4). This paradigm embodies the assumption that small scale fishing was only a transitory inefficient state, prone to exploitation.

This Common Property Management paradigm did not take into account two differences found in LDCs; abundant labour and multispecies fisheries. The highly industrialized fishing industry was not labour intensive and processing plants were not always appropriate for the tropics or multispecies catches. This paradigm also gave highest priority to increasing production, defining fishery development in a very narrow way. Moreover, highly valued species (like shrimp) were given priority because operating costs were so high and foreign exchange was important. Export-oriented development increased while domestic development remained pretty much the same (Diegues 1983).

The ideas of production and conservation are woven into this western thought. However, this contrasts and is in some ways incompatible with the traditional methods of fishing found in coastal areas of LDCs and their system of Distributional Management. In these communities the distribution of food to community members was the primary concern. Within each given area a system had developed for determining the use of the sea (Cycon 1986). Although in most cases this system included restrictions on access it was motivated by different values. Whereas the western model promotes regulation to achieve economic efficiency, traditional fishing communities in LDCs controlled access to allow an optimal number of fishermen and distribution (see Figure 3). The coming of the Blue Revolution introduced the western mode of fisheries development into the areas of predominantly subsistence fishing.

An example of Distributional Management is provided by a study of a Brazilian fishing community (Cordell 1978). This community had, over a long period of time, developed a very complex system of temporary territorial rights, and was characterized by non-competitive, co-operative behaviour. While keeping up with population growth this arrangement allowed for a very gradual expansion of fishing operations in a fixed area. A decision was made by fishery planners to upgrade fishing in the area, and no nylon nets were introduced. Unaffordable to the local fishermen they were intended for, the nets were purchased by wealthier members of the community, such as merchants and factory bosses who subsequently employed some of the fishermen to work the nets for them. Meanwhile, many fishermen who had not been employed by the entrepreneurs, moved elsewhere, dismissing their crews. The competitive entrepreneurial group of net owners disrupted the previously established fishing rights and territories. Unregulated, the number of nets increased beyond what the area could accommodate.

This case is a clear example of a production/technological oriented planning scheme that failed because it overlooked the Distributional Management and modalities of production and distribution that were already in existence. Numerous other specific examples exist of areas where the western conceptualization of fisheries development disrupted, in a negative way, well established fishing operations.

In Peru the development of local fish for food was basically put on hold, while investors, and anyone else who could, jumped on the band wagon of large scale industrial fishing development. This was the beginning of Peru's competitive fishing industry and by and large it followed the path predicted in Common Property Management. The fishing stocks were exploited economically and physically and although regulatory measures were initiated they were not far reaching enough and came too late. Peru lacked the necessary information and the infrastructure to regulate the existing stocks, and the infrastructure to regulate the industry once the information was available. The Common Property Management model really relies on information about stocks, and the assumption that capital intensive large scale fishing is the road to fisheries development. On a smaller scale than Peruvian anchoveta, other examples question the efficiency of widespread mechanization because of the increasing costs of production.

The Costs of Production

While it could be argued that the goal of increased production has been achieved through mechanization, this increased production has not always been dramatic especially when compared to the increased costs of production for small fishermen. Increased production as a primary goal of the western paradigm, has proved in some cases to be rather costly, and not as economically efficient as it proposes.

A recent comparative study of Caribbean fisheries (Berkes and Shaw 1986) considered fishery development in Jamaica and the Barbados. In the Barbados mechanization of fishing boats began in the 1950s and 1960s, and by the 1970s the small 10 HP engines were replaced by engines of 80-180 HP. The trend of increasing mechanization was encouraged because the larger boats went further, faster, and brought back more fish. In 1978, ice holds were introduced to these boats so that more fish could be brought back, helping to offset the increased cost of these boats. The onshore infrastructure did not keep pace with these other developments and the increased production caused a glut on the market. One boatload of fish could glut the market, acting as a disincentive for some fishermen to even take out their boats since selling their fish became extremely difficult if not impossible.

In Jamaica the situation is very different. Trap fishing occurs from dugout canoes, some of which are motorized (up to a maximum of 40 HP). The local fishermen enforce a strict territorial system, and intruders run the risk of having their traps removed or damaged. Over 90% of the boats are owner operated and in areas of non-mechanization the fishermen are virtually self-sufficient, making their own canoes and traps.

Comparing the fish yield/ton of fuel used, Berkes found that in the Barbados the ice boats yielded 2.7 tons fish/ton fuel, and day boats (non-iced, motorized) yielded 1.1 ton fish/ton fuel. The motorized boats of Jamaica yielded 2.5 tons fish/ton fuel, almost as much as the ice boats, and significantly more than the day boats. The investment cost/job created ranges from $500 for non-motorized Jamaican boats to $44,000 for Barbados ice boats. It costs four times as much to run an ice boat as a day boat, or 100 times that of the non-motorized canoes, but the yield is only just over twice as much in both cases.

In this study, large production increases occurred but the costs of production also increased, making the production gains less profitable for the fishermen. The co-operative production in Jamaica, although less in absolute terms was as profitable as the highly technological Barbados fleet. Librero et al. (1985a) also concludes from a study in the Philippines that non-motorized boats yielded a greater net income than motorized boats due to high cash costs, especially fuel costs and the depreciation of motorized boats.

The infrastructural problems mentioned by Berkes are also recorded elsewhere. In many West African coastal states where running water and ice are lacking, processing of fish occurs on the beach. Because of this an estimated 20-40% of the fish are lost due to spoilage. To try and prevent this spoilage, a lot of the fish is smoked. Unfortunately this process lowers the protein content of the fish due to dehydration (Mitchell 1985).

The Effects of Technology

The examples used so far have pointed to the fact that the technology brought in through western fishery development has been value laden. One effect of this is that economic values (profit) have become more important than "traditional" values of assuring access to fishing areas and co-operative sharing. The promotion of production-oriented values has been common to both agents of international assistance and government policymakers, influenced by their foreign education, need to increase foreign exchange, and the power of elites who stand to benefit from such policies. This has led to "structural problems and policy distortions which pose serious threats to the majority of those employed in the fisheries sector" (Bailey, Cycon, and Morris 1986).

When evaluating the Blue Revolution and the effects of Common Property Management, the role played by technology and production centred development cannot be overemphasized. In another Philippino study, in the early 1970s (Emmerson 1980) the government made financing available in a particular area allowing a total of 84 out of 8,000 households to mechanize. This allowed a small number of fishermen to increase their catch and also the value of their catch since the fish were fresher when landed. The fishermen without access to the technology felt that their way of life, based on sharing, was in jeopardy as was the resource itself. By 1977, government financed large scale motor driven purse seines were selling their catches directly to canneries in an auction hall on the beach. The small scale middlemen were excluded from the whole selling process at this point because the fish were sold in lots that were too large, and cash was demanded for all sales. Additionally, women and children who previously had been permitted occasional fish from the catch were now likewise excluded. The increased production that accompanied this technology also brought some economic changes. In 1977 the income of 600 households had quadrupled to approximately $2.00 a day, while the rest remained at the previous level of 0.50 a day. Considering inflationary effects, this puts the vast majority of fishermen in a worse position than before.

This example indicates the potential for conflict among large and small scale fishermen and indeed this has emerged as a constraint in current fisheries development planning. In some cases the catch of large scale fishermen is interfering with that of small scale fishermen. For example the fishing has declined for small scale fishermen in San Miguel Bay, Philippines (Bailey 1985). Before 1970 there were only a few trawlers in this bay, by 1982, there were 75 small and 20 medium trawlers in operation. One person owns 25% of these trawlers, and 8 people own another 34%. The trawlers in total employ 500 people and catch 47% of the fish in the bay (by volume). The other 5,000 small scale fishermen catch the remaining 53%. Although trawlers are restricted from this area, they are not made to leave, and the economic incentives to be gained by them "invite violations." Current government policy in this region is to try and improve the life of the small fishermen by providing more access to credit so that boats and sophisticated gear such as that in use by the trawlers may be purchased. Despite the fact that the government is securing 80% of the loans, the banks are requiring loans to be guaranteed by a current trawler operator. This has allowed for trawler operators to control more boats and become more powerful.

Overall, the Blue Revolution has been selectively beneficial and divisive. It has increased the income disparity in community fishing villages, has broken up traditional patterns of production and distribution, and has caused conflicts between large and small scale fishermen. Its production increases have been accompanied by increased costs economically, socially, and biologically. The western conceptualization of the fishing industry has been for the most part inappropriate in LDCs, ignoring different values evident in social relationships and distributional patterns. This conceptualization resulted in a narrow definition of fishery development where production and technology were emphasized to the exclusion of other considerations such as existing distributional patterns in small communities and small scale fishing.

Conclusion

The Blue Revolution failed in its attempt to significantly affect malnutrition through modernizing the fishing industry. Trusting that a direct causal relationship existed between production and distribution, increased production of fish (and fish products) became an important means of reducing malnutrition. Thus fishery development became synonymous with extraction, and technology provided the tools for efficient extraction. This perspective meshed well with the then popular Common Property Management paradigm.

Despite production increases, malnutrition was not significantly affected by the Blue Revolution, and indeed the Blue Revolution challenged some previous assumptions. The efficiency of large scale fisheries was questioned, and the importance of small scale fisheries was recognized. Many examples illustrated that technological innovations alone were not enough to secure fishery development. Consequently fishery development began to be viewed as more comprehensive than extraction, and fish production began to be viewed more in relation to other socio-political variables, and the food system as a whole.

The developments of the Blue Revolution are remarkably similar to those of the Green Revolution, largely because each "revolution" was based on the same assumptions regarding the use of technology and the relationship between production and distribution.

The technologically-oriented food production strategy of the Blue Revolution was quite similar to that of the Green Revolution. While the Green Revolution attempted to revolutionize food production through the implementation of HYV crops, the Blue Revolution attempted to do the same through intensified efforts to harvest the sea. In each case it was assumed that the increases in food production would bring benefits to those people suffering from malnutrition, because of an assumed causal relationship between production and distribution. This relationship was not evident in either situation. In the case of the Green Revolution the benefits of increased production went primarily to the larger, wealthier farmers, and in the case of fisheries, benefits were accumulated by those with access to credit and technology — a very small minority.

The similarities of these two revolutions have been noted by numerous authors. Bailey (1985, p. 259) states:

The introduction of new fishing technologies over the pasttwo decades has brought about a radical transformation of the fisheries sector in many third world countries. The impact of this "Blue Revolution" has gone largely unnoticed by rural sociologists and other social scientists, who instead have focussed attention on parallel and nearly simultaneous changes wrought by the Green Revolution.

The similarities of these revolutions are demonstrated by parallel technological solutions implemented in both. The same model served as the underlying conceptualization for both. This dovetailed with the Common Property Management paradigm of the Blue Revolution because its emphasis on efficiency and regulation encouraged the maximization of efficient production through technology.

The Green Revolution has received a tremendous amount of attention. Problems have been pointed out by various critics. The newer stream of thought emphasizes social, political and economic problems. Holding the Blue Revolution up to the same type of critical scrutiny received by the Green Revolution reemphasizes the inability of purely technological solutions to significantly decrease malnutrition.

By considering the food system as a whole, it can now be ascertained more clearly how production and distribution are related. Food production is a necessary but not sufficient condition for food distribution, and that is why they are only indirectly related. Food production may be increasing, but other components of the food system, such as those described above, may be affecting distribution in a way that causes it to become more inequitable. The choices made by government officials (and others in the food system) sometimes impose barriers to equitable distribution of food, even in areas of increasing production. Hence, the attempts that have been made to revolutionize the global fishing industry in order to increase equitable distribution of food have not always been based on an adequate conceptualization of the complex factors involved.

ENDNOTE

[1] By way of definition, the terms large and small scale fishing will be used in the following context throughout this paper. Large scale fishermen are those who capture fish primarily for commercial markets. They generally operate larger boats, and have access to more resources in terms of finances and fish. Small scale fishermen, on the other hand, sell the fish they catch to local markets through small-scale buyers. Their smaller, less mechanized craft limit their fishing grounds to those areas found close to shore.

REFERENCES

Allsopp, W.H.L. 1985. *Fishery Development Experiences*. Surrey: Fishing News Books.

Bailey, Conner, Dean Cycon and Michael Morris. 1986. "Fisheries Development in the Third World: The Role of International Agencies." *World Development*. 14(10): 1269-1275.

Bailey, Conner. 1984. "Managing an Open Access Resource: The Case of Coastal Fisheries" in Korten, David D. and Rudi

Klauss (eds.). *People Centered Development: Contributions Toward Theory and Planning Frameworks.* Connecticut: Kumarian Press: 97-103.

Bailey, Conner. 1985. "The Blue Revolution: The Impact of Technological Innovation on Third World Fisheries." *The Rural Sociologist.* 5(4): 259-266.

Bell, Frederick W. 1978. *Food From the Sea: The Economics and Politics of Ocean Fisheries.* Boulder, Colorado: Westview Press.

Ben-Yami, M. 1986. "Aquaculture: the Importance of Knowing Its Limitation." *Ceres* No. 112. 19(4): 15-19.

Berkes, Fikret and Anthony B. Shaw. 1986. "Ecologically Sustainable Development: A Caribbean Fisheries Case Study." *Canadian Journal of Development Studies.* 7(2): 175-196.

Borgstrom, Georg. 1973. *World Food Resources.* New York: Intext Publishers.

Brown, Lester with Erik P. Eckholm. 1974. *By Bread Alone.* New York: Praeger Publishers.

Ceres. 1984. "Cerescope: Better boats, gear being designed for Brazilian fisheries." *Ceres.* 17(1): 8-9.

Ceres. 1984. "The New Regime for fisheries: prospects, policies, practices." *Ceres.* 17(1): 8-9.

CIDA. 1986. *Canadian Assistance and Third World Fisheries.* Hull: CIDA.

Cho, C.Y., C.B. Cowey and T. Watanabe. 1985. *Finfish Nutrition in Asia: Methodological Approaches to Research and Development.* Ottawa: IDRC.

Clarke, Arthur C. 1960. "Will a Hungry World Raise Whales for Food?" *Popular Science.* November: 74-76, 216.

Cloud, Wallace. 1963. "The Race for the Bottom of the Sea." *Popular Science.* July: 35-40, 164-165.

CFR. 1967. *Commercial Fisheries Review.* "Aircraft Carriers as Fishing Factoryships." 22(5): 67-68.

CFR. n.d. *Commercial Fisheries Review.* "Speech by Director of Commercial Fisheries." 30(6): 1-5.

CFR. 1967. *Commercial Fisheries Review.* "Fiji Islands: Tuna Cannery with Japanese Interests." 22(10): 56.

CFR. 1967. *Commercial Fisheries Review.* "Fishing Operations by Japanese Criticized." 22(7): 52.

CFR. 1967. *Commerical Fisheries Review.* "India: Japanese to Aid in Development of Fisheries." 22(12): 78.

CFR. 1967. *Commercial Fisheries Review.* "Japanese-Malayan Tuna Firm Slow Getting Started." 22(2): 84.

Committee for the Collection of Experiences in the Culture of Freshwater Fish Species in China. 1981. *Science of the Culture of Freshwater Fish Species in China.* Ottawa: IDRC.

Commoner, Barry. 1975. "How Poverty Breeds Over-Population (and not the other way around)." *Ramparts.* Aug-Sept.: 22-25, 58-59.

Cordell, John. 1978. "Carrying Capacity Analysis of Fixed Territorial Fishing." *Ethnology.* 177(1): 1-24.

Cushing, David. 1975. *Fisheries Resources of the Sea and Their Management.* London: Oxford University Press.

Cycon, Dean E. 1986. "Managing Fisheries in Developing Nations: A Plea for Appropriate Development." *Natural Resources Journal.* 26(1): 1-14.

Diegues, Antonio Carlos S. 1983. "Policies and Strategies for Fisheries Development: Some Relevant Issues for Developing Countries." In "Case Studies and Working Papers presented at the Expert Consultation on Strategies for Fisheries Development (with particular reference to small-scale fisheries) Rome, 10-14 May 1983." *FAO Fisheries Report* (295) Supp.: 1-15.

Emmerson, Donald K. 1980. "Rethinking Artisan Fisheries Development: Western Concepts, Asian Experiences." *World Bank Staff Working Paper* No. 423. Washington: World Bank.

FAO. 1983a. "Case Studies and Working Papers presented at the Expert Consultation on Strategies for Fisheries Development (with particular reference to small-scale fisheries) Rome, 10-14 May 1983." *FAO Fisheries Report* (295) Supp. Rome: FAO.

FAO. 1983b. "Report on the FAO/LKIM Workshop on Strategic Fisheries Development and Manpower Planning in Malaysia, Kuala Lumpur Malaysia 25-27 October 1982." *FAO Fisheries Report* (286). Rome: FAO.

FAO. 1983c. "Report of the Expert Consultation on Strategies for Fisheries Development (with particular reference to small-scale fisheries) Rome, 10-14 May 1983." *FAO Fisheries Report* (295). Rome: FAO.

FAO/IDRC. 1982. *Fish By-Catch...Bonus from the Sea: Report of a Technical Consultation on Shrimp By-Catch Utilization held in Georgetown, Guyana, 27-30 October 1981.* Ottawa: IDRC.

Fleming, Roscoe and Fleming, W.N. 1959. "Can We Vacuum-clean the Sea Floor for Valuable Ore?" *Popular Science*. July: 102-104.

Furnell, Donald J. 1982. "By-Catch from Shrimp Trawling in Guyanese Waters." In FAO/IDRC *Fish By-Catch...Bonuses from the Sea: Report of a Technical Consultation on Shrimp By-Catch Utilization held in Georgetown, Guyana, 27-30 October 1981.* Ottawa: IDRC.

Gates, C.C., J. Adamczewski and R. Mulders. 1986. "Population Dynamics, Winter Ecology and Social Organization of Coats Island Caribou." *Arctic*. 39(3): 216-222.

Gaudet, J.L. and D. Parker (eds.). 1986. "Summary of proceedings and selected papers. Symposium on the planning and implementation of fisheries management and development programmes in Africa. Lusaka, Zambia, 7-11 October 1985." *FAO Fisheries Report* (360). Rome: FAO.

George, Carl J. 1985. "Notes on the Peruvian Fisheries." *Fisheries*. 10(3): 13-17.

George, Susan. 1977. *How the Other Half Dies: The Real Reasons for World Hunger*. New Jersey: Allenheld, Osmun & Co.

George, Susan. 1984. *Ill Fares the Lane: Essays on Food, Hunger and Power*. Washington: Institute for Policy Studies.

Glantz, Michael H. and J. Dana Thompson (eds.). 1981. *Resource Management and Environmental Uncertainty: Lessons from Coastal Upwelling Fisheries*. New York: John Wiley & Sons.

Hannergren, Linn A. 1981. "Peruvian Political and Administrative Responses to El Nino: Organizational, Ideological, and Political Constraints on Policy Change." In Glantz, op. cit.

Hopkins, R. and D. Puchala (eds.). 1978. *The Global Political Economy of Food*. Madison: University of Wisconsin Press.

Instituto del Mar del Peru (IMARPE). 1970. "Panel of Experts Report on the Economic Effects of Alternative Regulatory Measures in the Peruvian Anchoveta Fishery." In Glantz, op. cit.

Kent, George. 1984. *The Political Economy of Hunger: the Silent Holocaust.* New York: Praeger.

Kent, George. 1986. "Aquaculture: Motivating production for low-income markets." *Ceres* No. 112. 19(4): 23-27.

Keohane, R.O. and J.S. Nye. 1977. *Power and Interdependence: World Politics in Transition.* Toronto: Little, Brown and Company.

Kuronuma, Katsuzo and Kunihiko Fukusho. 1984. *Rearing of Marine Fish Larvae in Japan.* Ottawa: IDRC.

Lappe, Frances Moore and Joseph Collins. 1977. *Food First.* New York: Ballantine Books.

Librero, A.R., Diego Ramos and Lustina Lapie. 1985a. "Mechanization: Its Impact on Productivity, Cost Structure, and Profitability of the Philippine Municipal Fishery." In T. Panayotou (ed.) *Small-Scale Fisheries in Asia: Socioeconomic Analysis and Policy.* Ottawa: IDRC: 151-162.

Librero, A.R., Rebecca F. Catalla and Rital M. Fabro. 1985b. "Socioeconomic conditions of small-scale fishermen and fish farmers in the Philippines." In T. Panayotou (ed.) *Small-Scale Fisheries in Asia: Socioeconomic Analysis and Policy.* Ottawa: IDRC: 36-45.

Menasveta, Deb. 1983. "A Regional Approach to the Development of Living Aquatic Resources in the Southeast Asian Region." In Johnston et al. (eds.) *International Symposium on the New Law of the Sea in Southeast Asia: Developmental Effects and Regional Approaches.* Halifax: Dalhousie Ocean Studies Programme: 35-51.

Mitchell, Carlyle L. 1985. *Implementation of the New Law of the Sea in West Africa.* Halifax: Dalhousie Ocean Studies Programme.

Murphy, Robert Cushman. 1954. "The Guano and the Anchoveta Industry." In Glantz, loc. cit.

Nef, J. 1985. "Violence and Ideology in Latin American Politics: An Overview." In Marcel Daneau (ed.) *Violence et conflits en*

Amerique Latine. Québec: Centre Québécois de relations internationales.

Panayotou, T. 1982a. "Management concepts for small-scale fisheries: economic and social aspects." *FAO Fisheries Technical Paper* (228).

Panayotou, T. 1982b. "Social Welfare Economics and Aquaculture: Issues for Policy and Research." In IDRC *Aquaculture Economics: Research in Asia Proceedings of a Workshop Singapore 2-5 June 1981*. Ottawa: IDRC: 103-116.

Panayotou, T.(ed.). 1985a. *Small-Scale Fisheries in Asia: Socioeconomic Analysis and Policy*. Ottawa: IDRC.

Panayotou, T. 1985b. "Small-Scale Fisheries in Asia: An Introduction and Overview." In Panayotou (ed.) *Small-Scale Fisheries in Asia: Socioeconomic Analysis and Policy*. Ottawa: IDRC: 11-29.

Pariser, E.R. 1982. "By-Catch for Human Consumption." In FAO/IDRC *Fish By-Catch...Bonus from the Sea: Report of a Technical Consultation on Shrimp By-Catch Utilization held in Georgetown, Guyana 27-30 October 1981*. Ottawa: IDRC: 37-41.

Paulik, Gerald J. 1971. "Anchovies, Birds, and Fishermen in the Peru Current." In Glantz, op. cit.

Ronquillo, Inocencio. 1983. "The Law of the Sea and its Impact on the Development of Fishing Resources in Southeast Asia" in Johnston et al. (eds.). *International Symposium on the New Law of the Sea in Southeast Asia: Developmental Effects and Regional Approaches*. Halifax: Dalhousie Ocean Studies Programme: 54-64.

Sinha, R. 1976. *Food and Poverty: The Political Economy of Confrontation*. London: Croon Helm.

Slavin, Joseph W. 1982. "Utilization of the Shrimp By-Catch." In FAO/IDRC *Fish By-Catch...Bonus from the Sea: Report of a Technical Consultation on Shrimp By-Catch Utilization held in Georgetown, Guyana, 27-30 October 1981*. Ottawa: IDRC: 21-28.

Smith, Ian R. 1979. *A Research Framework for Traditional Fisheries*. Manila: International Centre for Living Aquatic Resources Management.

Smith, Ian R. 1982. "Microeconomics of Existing Aquaculture Production Systems: Basic Concepts and Definitions." In

IDRC *Aquaculture Economics: Research in Asia: Proceedings of a Workshop held in Singapore 2-5 June 1981.* Ottawa: IDRC: 15-25.

Sternin V. and W.H.L. Allsopp. 1982. "Strategies to Avoid By-Catch in Shrimp Trawling." In FAO/IDRC *Fish By-Catch...Bonus from the Sea: Report of a Technical Consultation on Shrimp By-Catch Utilization held in Georgetown, Guyana 27-30 October 1981.* Ottawa: IDRC: 61-64.

Thompson, J. Dana. 1981. "Climate, Upwelling and Biological Productivity: Some Primary Relationships." In Glantz, Michael H. and J. Dana Thompson (eds.) *Resource Management and Uncertainty: Lessons from Coastal Upwelling Fisheries.* New York: John Wiley & Sons.

Traung, Jan-Olof (ed.). 1960. *Fishing Boats of the World: 2.* London: Fishing News Books.

Vondruska, John. 1981. "Postwar Production, Consumption, and Prices of Fish Meal." In Glantz, op.cit.

Wattanutchariya, Sarun and T. Panayotou. 1982. "The Economics of Aquaculture: The Case of Catfish in Thailand." In IDRC *Aquaculture Economics Research in Asia: Proceedings of a Workshop held in Singapore 2-5 June 1981.* Ottawa: IDRC: 26-24.

Weeks, John. 1985. *Limits to Capitalist Development: The Industrialization of Peru, 1950-1980.* London: Westview Press.

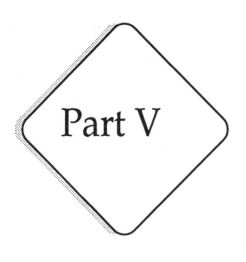

Part V

FOREIGN DONOR ASSISTANCE, FOOD AID, AND FOOD SECURITY

"MEN PLOWING"
Two men in Central America use a modified type of harness and levelling board to prepare the land near their homes.

Photo courtesy of IDRC.

Chapter 13

FOOD AS ECONOMIC STATECRAFT:
CANADIAN AND AMERICAN FOOD AID/TRADE WITH AFRICAN COUNTRIES

Robert D'Arcy Henderson

As of mid-1985, nineteen African countries (more than a third of the continent) were listed by the United Nations Office for Emergency Operations in Africa (UNOEOA) as experiencing severe food shortages due to either a continuing deficit or a serious drop in their domestic agriculture production (UNOEOA 1985: 8-9). Of these, only six countries had received sufficient emergency food assistance to cover the gap between their domestic consumption needs and the reduced local production; the latter resulting from a combination of factors, e.g., continuing drought, poor climatic conditions, and internal conflict. In addition to those countries which were suffering from immediate starvation and famine, a number of other African countries continued to suffer from various levels of malnutrition.

At the same time, the major Western grain exporting countries were experiencing record harvests. The world grain situation at the beginning of 1985 was placed at nearly 190 million tons of surplus grain stocks, while the entire grain shortfall by the drought-ridden Sahelian countries in Africa was estimated at only three to four million tons (Insel 1985: 905). Over the past decade, world wheat supplies have risen 69 percent while prices have plunged 45 percent (Lewis 1986). Between 1984 and 1986 the world price of wheat declined by 23 percent and that of maize (corn) by 31 percent (F & D 1986: 45).

This paper attempts to place the American and Canadian food trade/aid linkages with African countries (i.e., a set of North-South food relations) within the emerging dominant set of food relations in the 1980s: West-West competition in global food trade (i.e., the United States and the Europe Economic Community — EEC). Prior to considering the implications for Africa of both the West-West and North-South contexts, it would be useful briefly to review two recent critiques of the utilization of economic instruments of foreign policy. It will also be relevant subsequently to appraise any "countervailing" economic policy options which might be available to African countries, individually or jointly. Finally, an attempt will be made to suggest prospects for this set of North-South food relations into the 1990s.

REVIEW OF RECENT LITERATURE

David Baldwin, in his recent book *Economic Statecraft*, called for a reassessment of the utility of economic techniques of statecraft. He defines "economic statecraft" as:

> ... government influence attempts relying primarily on resources that have a reasonable semblance of a market price in terms of money (Baldwin 1985: 30).

It is seen by Baldwin as the capacity of a state to utilize economic "resources," such as: primary/manufactured goods, financial investment, and aid transfers, to influence another state. But such an attempt to influence is essentially an act **within a political relationship** between two state-actors, in which one initiator state seeks to alter the behaviour of a target state.

Including both positive (e.g., economic assistance) and negative (e.g., economic denial) sanctions as constituting the "arsenal" of economic techniques, Baldwin argues that, when used in combination, they can provide key indicators of a state's capability, intent and commitment to a specific foreign policy objective: "... economic assistance and denial serve a useful purpose as a conduit of policy whether or not the means themselves have much economic impact on the target country"

(Baldwin, 1985: 205). Such economic techniques are perceived by him as a valuable means of communicating messages of approval and/or disapproval to friendly and hostile states alike. While suggesting that the impact of imposed costs on the target state for non-compliance can be considered a measurement of success, in so far as it forces a choice between those costs and compliance, in implementing a sanctions policy, he points out that "economic sanctions may have diplomatic, psychological, political, military, or other effects even when their economic effect is nil" (Baldwin 1985: 63).

Comparatively, Robert Paarlberg, in his monograph on *Food Trade and Foreign Policy*, examined the "presumed" connections between food trade and foreign policy. In particular, he questioned "the popular notion that nations seek to manipulate their food trade in search of external advantages, and that food exporters gain the most advantage in the event of such manipulations" (Paarlberg 1985). Based upon a three-country study of American, Indian and Soviet food relations, he explored American failures to implement "food power" in terms of the three key areas in his proposed food power process: the domestic system of the exporting state, the international food-trading system, and the domestic system of the 'target' country. In the first area, he suggests that "the only means to accomplish denial abroad may be to incur economic costs at home (Paarlberg 1985: 215), possibly an unacceptable political decision. And even where such a "food denial" strategy has succeeded at the first two areas, it may still prove difficult to implement it due to factors such as national prestige which are inherent to the target country's own domestic food system. These findings bring into question whether "food power" can actually constitute a base of power in the study of inter-state relations? An earlier study on *Food in the Global Arena*, while discussing food power in terms of "the uses of food by national or even transnational, actors as a political or economic instrument," also acknowledged that "the promotion of 'food power' policies is not without domestic costs" (Hopkins 1982: 82).

As such, Paarlberg's conclusions, contrary to popular views, are that "national food trade policies most often evolve as an extension of an outward expression of inward-looking domestic food and farm policies" and that the so-called "world food system" (or what other writers have referred to as the

421

"international food regime") was "little more than the residual external consequences of many separately determined, inward-looking national food and farm policy actions, suggesting that it may not be a `system' at all" (Paarlberg 1985: 215). His country-examples appeared to consider the world food system as only an "after-thought," using it either "as an outlet for surplus production brought on by domestic farm subsidy programs or as a supplementary source of supplies when domestic consumption could not be met from home production" (Paarlberg 1985: 215).

Based on the above studies, it would appear that economic techniques of statecraft continue to retain a utility for policy-makers in terms of interstate influence even if they have a questionable degree of effectiveness. Neither of the authors, however, dwells upon the **issue of mutuality of influence** between an initiator state and a target state.

With regards to food relations with African countries, food sanctions would appear to have a capacity to achieve an initiator state's foreign policy goals in specific issues, such as human rights records, if compliance required a low level of reform, or as a means of helping to destabilize a target government. But as a means to bring about major structural policy changes, such as economic reforms, by a foreign government, this appears to be less likely for a number of reasons. Those reasons include: (1) domestic political demands on the grain-exporting countries (farm export subsidy programs, cost of stored surpluses); (2) world moral and humanitarian objections to using food as a "weapon"; (3) alternative sources of grain supply (i.e., "commodity leakage") (4) international prestige of the initiator state and weakness of target state (i.e., "bully" image); and (5) ability of target states to play donors and/or exporters against each other.

For the purposes of this paper, these various reasons need to be considered in terms of Africa's position with regard to both the West-West and the North-South food relationships. It is this overlapping relationship which needs to be highlighted in order to be able to review possible countervailing options available to African states.

WEST-WEST FOOD RELATIONS
(domestic policy and food trade)

According to one analyst, the cost of financing the whole 1985 Sahelian drought shortfall in grain was approximately US$500 million, at a time when American agricultural export credits and food aid programs were totalling US$7 billion annually and comparable European Community programs were approaching US$1 billion (Insel 1985: 905).   American Administration under President Ronald Reagan supported agricultural export policies which attempted to ensure that American grain exports retain their "traditional" market share of world sales.   These policies were declared to be "countervailing" actions against the European Community's subsidized grain exports, though both exporting regions have encouraged over-production (Butler 1983: 105-122).

In June 1985, the Reagan Administration implemented a new export subsidy program under which selected countries would be approved to buy a predetermined amount of American wheat which would include a quantity of surplus wheat released from Government storage and given to American exporters at no cost. This "bonus" amount would permit the exporters to receive a larger payment than their own portion would realize.   When the "export enhancement" program was announced on May 15th, 1985, then Secretary of Agriculture John R. Block stated that "the first criterion is to sell more product" abroad while "the second criterion is to target markets where we [the Administration] believe that unfair trading practices have victimized the American farmer" (Pear 1985).   The US Congress authorized the Agriculture Secretary to spend US$1 billion over three years in cash or commodities to promote export markets and another US$500 million to spend at his discretion; a further US$325 million was allocated to use export subsidies as a means for combatting foreign competitors deemed to be using unfair trading practices (Greenspon 1986).

In addition to offers of subsidized grains to such major importers as the Soviet Union, which subsequently accepted the EEC's lower subsidized deal, the United States has currently offered subsidized grain or wheat flour sales to over 30 selected Middle East and African countries, such as Algeria, Egypt, Saudi

Arabia, Syria and Zaire. Many of these Third World countries also received American food aid and food at concessionary prices under U.S. development assistance and/or the Economic Support Fund. As of 1985, more than 40 percent of American grain exports were going to less developed countries. This was greater than the volume being exported to industrial countries which had slipped from over 50 percent to less than 40 percent in three years. Reduced demand from the European Community accounted for a significant part of this slide (Shaffer 1986).

The U.S. Department of Agriculture estimated that farm exports in 1986 would amount to only US$27.5 billion, almost 12 percent lower than 1985 exports. In order to prevent any further rise in the 182 million tons of grain surplus in mid-1986, American farm exports would have had to have risen by 90 percent. Yet Department estimates expected only a 25 percent growth in export sales (Economist 1986: 19). The surplus was forecasted to rise to 217 million by mid-1987.

But the rising costs of its export subsidies and domestic farm support forced the Reagan Administration to make sweeping changes in the US domestic farm support programs in its 1987 budget proposal. During the 1986 fiscal year, the farm programs cost the US Government more than US$25.5 billion, according to James C. Miller III, the Director of the Administration's Office of Management and Budget. Those programs had become politically unsustainable. Although the agricultural lobbies continue to have considerable strength in American politics, particularly in the Midwest, the proposed cutbacks in the farm budget reflected the Congres-sional pressure for a cross-the-board cuts in government expenditure under the Gramm-Rudman amendment. The proposed changes were estimated to save more than US$16 billion over a five-year period (1987-1992).

In the case of the EEC, its Common Agricultural Program (CAP) subsidies have almost bankrupted the Community's budget. Those subsidies cost the Community US$21 billion in 1986, 72 percent of the total budget. In the twelve months prior to September 1985, its stocks of unsold surplus cereals trebled, at a time when its agricultural stock price was valued at about US$1 billion annually for storage. (Globe 1986: 8 Jan.). By 1986, it had in storage almost 17 million tons of grain, with a projected rise to 36 million tons by mid-1987. Further it was committed to spending a further US$3.6 billion in 1987 — money which the

European Community did not have. Recently there have been attempts to reduce some EEC farm prices, though critics say that no less than a 30 percent slash in EEC guaranteed farm prices is necessary for Europe to put its CAP house in order. The reason for continuing such financially disastrous policies is the same as in the United States: very strong farm lobbies. Basically, European politicians have not been prepared to cut off financial support to their over-producing but politically powerful agricultural sector (Lewis 1986: 48-52).

These competitive patterns of subsidized over-production and export have resulted in a global grain surplus and resultant price drop: a downward spiral of falling prices and decreasing income in both the United States and the European Community, as well as for other traditional grain exporters, such as Canada, Australia, Argentina and even Thailand. The sharp fall in the price of wheat, maize and other coarse cereals between 1984 and 1986 was crucial, in that wheat accounts for 12 percent of Argentina's export earnings, 7 percent of Australia's and 5 percent of Canada's, while maize accounts for 11 percent of Argentina's, 5 percent of Thailand's and 4 percent of Zimbabwe's (F & D 1986: 145).

With regard to Canada's position on food trade, it has attempted like the United States to maintain access to the European Community while cultivating other major grain buyers like the Soviet Union and China. More recently, it has promoted increased agricultural trade with such Third World countries as Algeria, Syria and Saudi Arabia; three countries which have accepted subsidized grain sales under the US export enhancement program. While this program was intended to "combat" the European Community's subsidized grain sales, it has heavily undercut Canadian sales in each of these countries. For example, at the end of 1986 the United States was able to sell 225,000 tons of durum wheat to Algeria at US$111.50 a ton. This was 30 percent below the world market price and US$30 a ton below Canadian break-even price (Globe 1986: 22 Dec.).

At a time when the Canadian farming sector was rocked by drought and uneven harvests, the undercutting of the world grain price further reduced Canadian grain exports and farming income. Unlike the European Community which has increased its subsidies and engaged the United States in "a head-to-head price war," Canada lacks the financial resources to pay the level of export subsidy which its wealthier allies are maintaining. As a result of this price cutting competition, the Canadian government was forced to provide its farmers with a Can$1 billion special assistance support to cushion their drastic 30 percent drop in farming income during the second half of 1986. To provide for this two-part support, the Mulroney government acknowledged that it would have to cut spending in a number of other areas. This practice of forcing other grain exporters to lower their prices accordingly or lose their market share has also hurt other American and European allies, such as Australia and Thailand, which receive a substantial portion of their foreign earnings from agricultural exports.

The Reagan Administration, in its attempt to maintain its domestic agricultural sector and its share of the world wheat export market, further undercut the world price for wheat and other cereals at the cost of inflated American domestic and export subsidies; while the European Community continued to stagger under the burden of its CAP subsidies and its growing grain surpluses. At Canada's request, the so-called Big Five grain exporters held a ministerial conference in British Columbia in June 1986 to discuss the sharp drop in the world price of grain and other problems caused by the escalating grain export subsidy competition between the United States and the European Community. But the participating countries failed to reach an agreement on how to stem the price slide or on solutions to deal with increasing trade protectionism by the industrial countries (Globe 1986: 16 Dec.). Further meetings met with no more success.

But the French Minister of Agriculture François Guillaume called for a concerted global management of grain supplies similar to those imposed by a cartel. He proposed an institutional approach: "a world market organization" for grains (Globe 1986: 5 Dec.). This French call for management of world grain supplies runs contrary to the call of the United States and the so-called "Group of 14" (non-subsidizing agricultural exporting countries, including Canada) at the current round of GATT talks in Uruguay for the elimination of agricultural subsidies and trade barriers. Such economic policy contradictions further reduced the likelihood that the Western exporting countries would be able to liberalize their agricultural exports. Rather for the foreseeable future, the United States and the European Community continue to heavily pay for export subsidies to undercut each other and, in the bargain, undercut the agricultural export earnings of a number of their Western allies.

NORTH-SOUTH FOOD RELATIONS
(food trade and aid)

As a result of widespread agricultural production deficits, African countries have further increased the level of foreign penetration of their economies and, in this case, their dependence upon Western agricultural surpluses. Over the past decade, almost every African country has increased its volume of cereal imports (see Tables 1 and 2). And most countries, though not all, have also had to increase their receipt of food aid in cereals (see Table 1). A few African countries, though, have managed to maintain food production ahead of their population growth (see Table 3).

Such growing reliance upon food imports and aid from Western exporting countries can only increase the vulnerability of African countries to sanctions affecting not only their already weak international economic strength but also (and perhaps more importantly) their domestic economies and political structures. It is evident, in the current African situation, that negative economic sanctions would only further hurt their already crisis-ridden economies. In some cases, such pressure could be seen as punishment for a country taking a hostile attitude to American interests. For example, terminating assistance to Mozambique in 1981 was the first food aid decision taken by the Reagan Administration, due to the FRELIMO government's policies regionally and at the United Nations which were considered hostile to American interests. More recently, in July 1986, Zimbabwe's Prime Minister Robert Mugabe accused the United States of using its foreign aid to coerce other countries "to toe its line" (Times 1986: 17 July).

Most African governments view their economies as being a "dependency" of the world capitalist system. Within this perception, there is a sense of being dominated, despite the retention of substantial social and political ties to Western countries (quite often very strong ties with the former colonial power). This mutuality is partly based on factors, such as a common language (e.g,. the English language), previous and ongoing education of national leaders and professionals in the ex-colonial power, personal relationships, etc. But it is also based upon the need of African states themselves for transfer of technology, professional training, development assistance, and, increasingly, food supplies. In the North-South context, such dependence for basic needs increases the vulnerability of African countries to economic influence within their political relationship with industrial countries, both East and West (Henderson and Kerr 1985).

While promoting increasingly costly subsidized grain export sales to the Third World, the Reagan Administration placed significant diplomatic and economic pressure on African countries, *via* its foreign assistance, to encourage internal economic reform, particularly towards private enterprise. The reforms sought include reducing the role of the public sector, encouraging greater development of private agriculture, and greater emphasis on a "free market" approach in their national economies. A declaration of this U.S. policy objective was made at the 1986 UN Special Session on the Critical Economic Situation in Africa by U.S. Ambassador Joseph Verner Reed, who stated that:

> Africans' experience with the public sector has been disastrous. Their governments must examine the efficiency of public sector institutions and reform or eliminate them in favor of the private sector (Hoeffel 1986: 5).

With a view to strengthening agricultural production in the private sector, two new assistance programs were implemented in 1985. The "Economic Policy Reform" program, according to Assistant Secretary for African Affairs Chester Crocker, was created "to provide additional support for those African countries which are in the process of implementing policy changes or have indicated a willingness and ability to establish a growth-oriented policy framework" while the "Food for Progress" initiative "would use food aid to support African countries which have made commitments to reform in the key agricultural sector, stressing market approaches in agricultural pricing, marketing, and input supply and distribution." (Crocker 1985: 3).

Speaking in Geneva three months later at a UN Conference on the Emergency Situation in Africa, then Vice-President George Bush stated:

Almost half of the countries on the [African] continent have started the journey to open and free agricultural markets.... The United States is encouraging such progress with a 5-year [US] $500 million African economic policy reform program and a 'Food for Progress' program under which nondisaster food will be provided to countries undertaking reform, (Bush 1985: 2).

By October 1986, nine African countries were receiving support under the reform program and two countries (Guinea and Madagascar) under the "Food for Progress" initiative. But such U.S. foreign policy pressure utilizing non-disaster food aid can only further undercut American (and other Western exporters') grain sales to African countries.

By comparison, Canada's food aid program (for 1984-85) amounted to almost Can$400 million, over 60 percent of which was provided in the form of cereals; for Africa alone, food assistance amounted to almost Can$100 million (CIDA 1985: 35). Under the International Food Aid Convention, Canada has agreed to provide a minimum of 600,000 tons of cereals annually. As 80 to 85 percent of the food assistance budget must be spent on Canadian procurement, these cereals are purchased from Canadian grain farmers.

As a result of the mid-1980s African famine relief, Canadian food aid to African countries has increased. According to CIDA President Margaret Catley-Carlson, that famine and the one in 1974-75 has brought about a "change in our (Canadian) thinking about African development needs." This change is to place greater emphasis on the private sector in African economies: support for "privatization" rather than "countless parastatal agencies and authorities." Within this process, food aid is seen as providing "adjustment assistance to help put the economy on an even keel."

Such assistance has been a special focus of our (CIDA) cooperation with, for example, Ghana — and with Mali, where, along with other donors, we are using food aid to support the government's attempt to modify its food policy and restructure the grain market so that farmers will have stronger incentives to grow more food. (Catley-Carlson 1986: 4).

Like the United States, Canada appears to be prepared to use its grain surplus as an aid incentive to encourage African countries to reform their economies. But in view of the depressed world market for Canadian grain exports and the lack of sufficient government revenues to competitively subsidized foreign sales, this use of food assistance also acts to support domestic farm incomes and reduce surplus stocks.

So in the North-South context, food aid and subsidized food sales are available to food-exporting countries to provide incentives to influence African states in their policy choices in such areas as economic planning. But it appears that such economic techniques lack the power to enforce compliance to a specific policy, probably due to the necessity of the exporting countries to sell at below world prices or dispose of increasing amounts of their surplus grains. Rather food as a technique of economic statecraft appears better used as an incentive for following a specific policy and/or to strongly communicate a particular point of view of the exporting country. Even if food is a "weak" technique of economic statecraft, do African states possess any countervailing options? Would such options assist economic development and reduce vulnerability to pressures from countries holding agricultural surpluses?

AFRICAN COUNTERVAILING OPTIONS

International consideration of global issues has placed substantial emphasis on world agriculture, in particular the economic crisis in Africa. During the U.N. Special Session on the Critical Economic Situation in Africa in May, 1986, member-states of the Organization of African Unity accepted the point that their economic problems (particularly in agriculture) were partly of their own making and committed themselves to making the hard choices necessary to reform their economies "and get them moving in the right direction." They agreed to commit 20 to 25 percent of their public investments to agriculture. For their part, Western donor countries pledged to support the African effort toward adopting medium-and long-term strategies to develop private enterprise, though making no specific commitment to further amounts of aid (Sciolino 1986).

At the same time, the World Bank devoted a substantial portion of its *World Development Report 1986* to an analysis of "trade and pricing policies in world agriculture." The report argued that the "whole world would be better off if industrial countries were to stop protecting their farmers and liberalize agricultural trade." Based on a simulation model, a simultaneous liberalization of North and South agricultural policies (i.e., an end to agricultural surpluses in the industrial countries and the abolition of price controls in the developing countries) would increase food prices and encourage agricultural output in the Third World, which could result in a US$18.3 billion income gain (World Bank 1986: 127-132). Its 1985 report had earlier pointed out that nearly 30 percent of developing countries' agricultural exports to the industrial countries were restricted by quota restraints or non-tariff barriers, as was nearly 20 percent of their manufactured exports (Farnsworth 1985).

In view of this "mutuality of interest," African governments should view their North-South food relations as essentially part of a political relationship rather than just an *economic* one. Domestic demands on Western grain exporting countries overlap with their own domestic needs and internal demands. In the long term, African countries need to implement agricultural policies which ensure adequate funding to generate agricultural production for domestic consumption, if not surplus for export as well. In the short term though, solutions are only likely to be found which take into account the dynamics of the domestic processes in both the exporting countries and their own country, and where they overlap. What "countervailing" options do African countries have in the short-term?

One option has been "triangular" food transfers. This is where the donor countries are encouraged to use their development funds to buy up any African grain surpluses, which various regional producers may have from time to time available, and use it as food aid. In 1985, seven African countries (Benin, Ivory Coast, Kenya, Malawi, Sudan, Togo and Zimbabwe) produced enough to export part of their agricultural production. Such an approach would assist the surplus-producing African country by strengthening its agricultural sector (by providing increased incentive for its farmers to grow in excess of local consumption), as well as the recipient African country which could use the food aid to meet its food deficit and thus save its scarce foreign exchange for development efforts (Africa Emergency Report 1986a: 5).

This approach would appear to satisfy part of the U.S. Administration's calls for greater incentives for the private sector to increase African agriculture production. But such an approach does conflict with domestic demands within Western exporting countries to increase their grain sales overseas or, at the least, dispose of part of the government-stored surpluses as food aid. A recent example was the European Community, where EEC ministers were unable, prior to the U.N. Special Session, to agree on a joint statement on the African situation. This was reputedly due to disagreement over utilizing such triangular food operations, rather than such aid being "taken from Community food surpluses" as it "was likely to anger the powerful (Community) farm lobby" (Africa Emergency Report 1986a: 12). In this latter case, a donor country which wished to dispose of an accumulated grain surplus could alternatively transfer a portion to a centrally-placed regional African producer to free local stocks for rapid assistance to neighbouring countries which might suffer from a poor seasonal harvest or an annual grain deficit. A portion of Western donor aid funds have been allocated to the construction of such a regional "food security" storage scheme for the SADCC countries in Southern Africa.

Two further factors need to be considered in this approach. First is the prevailing national and regional conflicts within Africa. Such ongoing violence and socio-economic disruption will continue to hinder any attempts to strengthen agricultural production in a number of African countries (e.g., Ethiopia, Chad, Angola, Mozambique, Sudan, etc.). As outright military solutions seem presently unlikely in the current conflicts, political solutions would appear to be necessary and possibly more viable, in which case, effective agricultural policies would constitute an important support for solidifying and maintaining any political solution.

Second is the possibility that such food transactions could counteract attempts at **regional** economic statecraft. For example, in the case of the Southern African region, South Africa is able to exert a degree of inter-state influence on its neighbouring, independent African states by providing various levels of maize exports to make up for their deficit agricultural production. This dependence upon South African agricultural surpluses is partly due to underfunded domestic agricultural programs, urban-biased food pricing policies, and poor climatic conditions but also, in a number of cases, to South Africa's aggressive regional destablization policy of cross-border military raids and support for anti-government rebels (Henderson 1983: 38-52). However, since 1984, Zimbabwe has regained its capacity to produce agricultural surpluses for export, reducing the strength of this economic technique of South African pressure.

Another possible option for African countries is to exchange their projected short-term need for food transfers from Western grain exporting countries for greater access for their own exports into those countries. The most likely forum for such an approach would be during the discussions on agriculture at the current round of the GATT talks in Uruguay. This "political" approach would capitalize on the Western exporting countries' domestic need to dispose of their mounting agricultural surpluses as a countervailing pressure to liberalize the Western markets (i.e., reduce tariff and non-tariff barriers) to increased African primary and semi-processed imports, and possibly for manufactured and light industrial goods in the future. This "political" solution would increase export earnings for the debt-ridden African countries while enabling them to continue to receive food imports at below domestic agricultural costs over the transitional period needed to strengthen their agricultural production. Such a strategy, in the *short term*, could make an asset out of what is currently a liability.

PROSPECTS FOR THE 1990s

This analysis of American/Canadian food relations with African countries (in both the West-West and North-South contexts) lends support for Baldwin's argument that techniques of economic statecraft have a place in inter-state relations. But more emphasis should be placed upon the point that such statecraft is part of the political relationship between sovereign states, in which mutual benefits from peaceful managing of overlapping state interests outweigh possible advantages gained by resorting to overwhelming inter-state pressure. If we assume that paramount importance rests with reciprocal *political* and not with economic relationships, the target state will also possess some countervailing techniques of statecraft, such as economic, diplomatic and moral strategies, by which to influence or at least moderate the foreign policy options (including economic) of the initiator state.

Though the African continent as a whole is unlikely to be self-sufficient in food production throughout the remainder of the 1980s (see Table 3), regional African producers should be able in good years to have exportable surpluses either to trade to a neighbouring country or to utilize as part of a "triangular" sale with a donor country. Such intra-continental co-operation should be encouraged by African states and supported by Western donor countries as a primary short-term objective.

Concurrently, Western exporting countries, as long as they continue to pursue domestic programs of agricultural support, are likely to produce in excess of the demands of their "traditional" export markets or, alternatively, of the capacity of importing countries to pay. The resultant effect of this surplus production and decreased demand will perpetuate a contradictory process. First is that the world price of grains will continue to weaken, encouraging those African (and other Third World) countries which can pay to continue to import food though probably only at subsidized prices. And second, as they continue to produce grain surpluses, Western exporters will be forced to further implement surplus disposal policies if only to reduce their storage costs.

Such policies, whether at concessionary prices or *gratis*, will discourage efforts to improve agricultural production by those African countries which can afford to pay for cheaper food imports than they can produce themselves. While those African countries which lack the resources to develop their own agricultural sector will have to continue to accept food aid with donor-imposed conditions. Basically in either case, African governments will be faced with the prospect of Western food imports undercutting any financial incentive (e.g., higher prices to farmers) for increasing their domestic agricultural production.

While continuing surplus production by American exporters will further result in expensive government export subsidy or disposal costs, such a situation of agricultural over-production (i.e., in excess of export demand) is unlikely to be translated into a significant degree of economic statecraft. The primary reason is the increase in global agricultural production both by previous major food importers such as India and China, and by secondary food exporters, like Canada, Australia, Argentina and Thailand. Such "commodity leakage" reduces the ability to use economic pressure. Large-scale food exports did not have the political impact they might have been thought to have given the U.S. Administration in its foreign policy dealings in the 1980s. This would tend to support Paarlberg's conclusions (1985) with regard to the primacy of domestic policy (i.e., support for the American agricultural sector) over foreign objectives (i.e., bringing about compliance of a target state). But it does not negate Baldwin's argument (1985) that economic statecraft will continue to be a foreign policy option of some utility. In terms of influence and communication, food as economic statecraft, even if of little effective power because there is no mechanism to enforce compliance, will continue to be a significant factor.

The world food crisis is complex in part because of the continued significance of the use of food for political and economic goals. This analysis of the use of food aid and trade has concentrated on Africa but it could be repeated for other continents. The role of the U.S. in the global food system will continue to be as significant in the 1990s. Unfortunately, the internal logic of the dynamics of international statecraft is not always likely to lead to improvements in food security for individuals and households. When domestic and foreign policy options are debated in the U.S. and Canada, the issue of the extent to which policy decisions will contribute to the amelioration of world hunger and malnutrition is often given low priority.

TABLE 1: FOOD - SELECTED AFRICAN COUNTRIES*

(1,000 tonnes)

	Volume of imports			Aid cereals		
	Year 1983/84	1974	1981	1984	1974/75	1980
Angola	149	244	375	0	2569	
Benin	8	93	65	9	12	6
Botswana	21	NA	59	5	11	32
Burkina Faso	99	71	89	28	51	57
Burundi	7	19	14	6	12	11
Cameroon	81	106	121	4	9	1
Cen. Af. Rep.	7	14	30	1	3	8
Chad	50	14	74	20	14	69
Congo	34	56	113	2	2	1
Ethiopia	118	207	506	54	228	172
Ghana	177	256	311	33	94	74
Guinea	63	134	186	49	34	43
Ivory Coast	172	619	545	4	0	0
Kenya	15	534	560	2	173	122
Lesotho	49	95	141	14	44	50
Liberia	42	111	109	3	26	47
Madagascar	114	268	172	7	26	74
Malawi	17	113	20	–	17	3
Mali	281	102	367	107	50	111
Mauritania	115	182	277	48	106	129
Mozambique	62	368	392	34	155	297
Niger	155	89	45	73	11	13
Nigeria	389	2,441	2,351	7	0	0
Rwanda	3	16	20	19	15	25
Senegal	341	458	698	27	153	151
Sierra Leone	72	58	61	10	12	16
Somalia	42	432	330	111	330	177
South Africa	127	476	3,240	–	–	–
Sudan	125	305	530	46	195	450
Tanzania	431	265	364	148	237	136
Togo	6	62	95	11	4	9
Uganda	37	37	20	0	57	10
Zaire	343	538	246	1	17	53
Zambia	93	295	236	5	84	76
Zimbabwe	56	21	334	0	18	76
TOTAL	3,901	9,099	13,096	888	2,225	2,568

* Countries of Subsaharan Africa with populations of more than 1,000,000.

SOURCE: World Bank, World Development Reports, 1983 and 1986.

Table 2

Average production per capita 1982-84
(1974-76=100)

Angola	81
Benin	97
Botswana	61
Burkina Faso	94
Burundi	106
Cameroon	83
Cen. Af. Rep.	94
Chad	95
Congo	96
Ethiopia	100
Ghana	73
Guinea	93
Ivory Coast	110
Kenya	82
Lesotho	78
Liberia	91
Madagascar	89
Malawi	100
Mali	101
Mauritania	95
Mozambique	73
Niger	113
Nigeria	96
Rwanda	112
Senegal	66
Sierra Leone	95
Somalia	69
South Africa	83
Sudan	93
Tanzania	100
Togo	92
Uganda	98
Zaire	92
Zambia	74
Zimbabwe	69
Total	90

SOURCE: World Bank, World Development Report, 1986

Table 3

Food Production Per Capita in Selected African Countries*

Average index of food production
per capita, 1982-1984**
(1974-1976 = 100)

Angola	81
Benin	97
Botswana	61
Burkina Faso	94
Burundi	106
Cameroon	83
Can. Af. Rep.	94
Chad	95
Congo	96
Ethiopia	100
Ghana	73
Guinea	93
Ivory Coast	110
Kenya	82
Lesotho	78
Liberia	91
Madagascar	89
Malawi	100
Mali	101
Mauritania	95
Mozambique	73
Niger	113
Nigeria	96
Rwanda	112
Senegal	66
Sierra Leone	95
Somalia	69
South Africa	83
Sudan	93
Tanzania	100
Togo	92
Uganda	98
Zaire	92
Zambia	74
Zimbabwe	69
Total	90

*Countries of Subsaharan Africa, with population of more than one million.

**Average (mean), weighted by population.

SOURCE: World Bank 1986: 190-191.

REFERENCES

Africa Emergency Report. 1986a. "African Grain for Aid."*African Emergency Report* no. 8 (June-July): 5.

Africa Emergency Report. 1986b. "No EEC Statement on Local Food Purchases." *Africa Emergency Report* no. 7 (April-May): 12.

Baldwin, David. 1985. *Economic Statecraft*. Princeton, N.J.: Princeton University Press.

Bush, George. 1985. "U.S. Pledges One-half of Africa's Food Aid." *Current Policy* no. 673 (11 March): 2.

Butler, Nicholas. 1983. "The Ploughshares War Between Europe and America." *Foreign Affairs*. 62 (1): 105-122.

Catley-Carlson, Margaret. 1986. "The Famine in Africa: A Turning Point for CIDA?" *Communique* (Autumn): 4.

Crocker, Chester H. 1985. "U.S. Assistance and Africa's Economic Crisis." *Current Policy* no. 648 (17 January): 3. [*Current Policy* is published by the U.S. Department of State.]

CIDA. 1985. *Canadian International Development Agency Annual Report 1984-1985*. Ottawa: CIDA.

Economist. 1986. "Only the Russians are Smiling: Farm Surpluses." *The Economist* (16 August): 19.

Farnsworth, Clyde. 1985. "Export Curbs on Third World Cited." *New York Times* (3 July).

F&D.1986."The Sharp Fall in Commodity Prices, 1984-86." *Finance & Development*. 23 (4): 45.

Globe & Mail. 1986. "Cartel-like Clout Urged to Stabilize Grain Prices." *Globe & Mail* (5 December).

Greenspon, Edward. 1986. "Subsidies to Farming Sector Raised to Record Level." *Globe & Mail* (31 March).

Henderson, Robert D`A. 1983. "The Food Weapon in Southern Africa." *International Affairs Bulletin*. 7 (3): 38-52.

Henderson, Robert D'A. 1987. "Who Will Feed Africa?" *International Perspectives* (May-June): 12-16.

Henderson, Robert D'A. and William A. Kerr. 1985. "The Theory and Practice of Economic Relations Between CMEA Member States and African Countries." *Journal of Contemporary African Studies*. 4 (1-2): 3-35.

Hoeffel, Paul Heath. 1986. "The Donor Perspective." *Africa Emergency Report* no. 8 (June-July): 5.

Hopkins, Raymond F. et al. 1982. *Food in the Global Arena: Actors, Values, Policies and Futures*. New York: Holt, Rinehart and Winston.

Insel, Barbara. 1985. "A World Awash in Grain." *Foreign Affairs*. 63 (3): 892-911.

Lewis, Paul. 1986. "Food Surplus May Bankrupt European Bloc." *New York Times* (27 December).

Paarlberg, Robert L. 1985. *Food Trade and Foreign Policy: India, the Soviet Union, and the United States*. Ithaca, N.Y.: Cornell University Press.

Pear, Robert. 1985. "U.S. Helps Grain Sale to Algeria." *New York Times* (5 June).

Sciolino, Elaine. 1986. [Various Articles]. *New York Times* (28 May, 29 May, 2 June).

Shaffer, Ralph. 1986. "U.S. Farm Exports Shift to 3rd World." *Christian Science Monitor* (15 December).

UNOEOA. 1985. "A Summary Profile of Emergency Unmet Needs, as of 1 July 1985." *Africa Emergency Report* no. 4 (September-October): 8-9.

World Bank. 1986. *World Development Report 1986*. New York: Oxford University Press. Part II: 127-132.

Chapter 14

FOOD AID AS A STRATEGY FOR FOOD SECURITY IN POOR HOUSEHOLDS:
A REVIEW

Olga B. Martinez

E.A. Cebotarev

Introduction

Since its inception in the 1950s, food aid to developing countries has undergone considerable conceptual modification. While disposal of surplus agricultural production was the main impetus for its initiation, food aid is increasingly viewed as a potential resource for development and as an important contributor to food security, both nationally and at the household level (FAO, 1985; Singer et al., 1987, p. 38).

The change in emphasis of food aid has been paralleled by changes in the institutional mechanisms for food aid distribution, the number of both donors and recipients, the quantities and geographical destination of food, and the ways in which it is expected to be used.

It is not our intention in this chapter to discuss the intricacies of how food aid works (For details see Singer et al. 1987). Rather, we wish to focus on an aspect of food aid that has been largely neglected: the impact of food aid at the household level. (For details on the development of food aid see Appendix 1.)

This chapter will focus on why food aid is considered a necessary measure in the alleviation of food "insecurity." Evaluations suggest that food aid can be regarded as a flexible resource and that it can contribute to food security at the household level. This chapter surveys the potential benefits of food aid as income transfer to households and the important role of women in this context.

Role of Food Aid in Food Security

The role of food aid in food security is something of a paradox. If the long-term objective of food security is self-sufficiency with acceptable nutritional standards on household and on national levels, then the notion of food aid is inconsistent with this objective, since it presupposes both household and national dependency. From this point of view, the use of food aid is an admission that food security is unobtainable and that some degree of self reliance has to be given up in the face of overwhelming needs (Stewart, 1986).

Another inconsistency is the place of food aid. If food aid is a means of surplus disposal, if it represents political or other vested interests such as benefitting the agricultural, fishing and dairy industries of developed countries, or if it interferes with local food production, its role as a developmental resource may be compromised.

Nevertheless, from a more practical viewpoint, food aid can be an important factor in alleviating short-term food insecurity in emergencies and in programs targeted to the most needy. Moreover, within this perspective, food aid may also be considered as an additional resource, a part of a general aid package, to support policies to sustain and increase food production and to provide stability (FAO, 1985).

Many criticisms have been raised against food aid. Some claim that it is an inferior type of aid compared to financial aid (Singer, 1987). However, defenders of food aid see its potential as another resource which, if used properly, offers an opportunity to attain, though not automatically guarantee, food security (Singer, 1987). Others claim that foreign financial aid is not likely to grow (CIDA, 1986: 20). While food aid is more readily available at a lower cost (and no constraints in the level of food aid have existed in the recent past (Reutlinger, 1987). Food aid is more politically acceptable to the public in many donor countries. Whether this view would be changed with the present decline in food available is to be seen. Nevertheless, warnings against the potential detrimental effects of food aid have been made (Stewart, 1986).

Criticisms apart, it would seem that food aid is here to stay (Singer et al., 1987, p.ix). Considering food security in its narrow sense, that is, of increasing local food production and decreasing its variability, is a long term process. In the present economic recession, given the increasing food insecurity and the past neglect in food production in Africa, it is expected that food aid will be needed for decades just to prevent deteriorating food situations in that continent (Cassen, 1986: 164).

The present economic crisis affecting many developing countries, especially in Latin America and in Sub-Saharan Africa, and the application of structural policies such as structural adjustment lending (SAL) have exacerbated poverty levels through increased unemployment, wage restrictions, increased food prices and a reduction in social service programs by governments (Stewart, 1988) affecting overwhelmingly women and consequently household members. Unacceptable hardships have been created for some groups of people in the population, especially poor women and children (Jolly and Cornia, 1984; Antrobus, 1989).

This social stress has been manifested by increasing levels of child malnutrition, negating previous improvements in rates of infant and child mortality throughout Latin America, Africa and some parts of Asia (Cornia et al., 1988). Other symptoms of social stress, such as high rates of child abandonment, child delinquency and school dropout, have also increased. Diseases thought to have been eliminated such as yellow fever in Ghana and malaria in Peru have reappeared (Stewart, 1988).

In the face of this intolerable situation, it has been proposed that structural economic adjustment should be accompanied by measures to protect the most vulnerable: adjustment with a human face (Cornia et al., 1988). A new role for food aid has been advocated in the process jointly by the WFP and UNICEF (UNICEF/WFP, 1986). This necessitates a more flexible use of food aid to provide short-term food security to the poor (feeding the poor) while supporting long-term goals of self-reliance for households and nations.

Program versus Project Food Aid

The case for the continuation of food aid seems clear. The question is how could it be used more effectively? Normally two forms of food aid are distinguished: program food aid and project food aid. Program food aid is generally provided bilaterally, from a donor country to a recipient government. It is an indirect form of financial assistance or balance of payments support, using commodities that the country might normally have to purchase commercially, to save foreign exchange (Singer, et al. 1987: 41-46). The saved foreign exchange could be theoretically used for development purposes. In practice, the bulk of this type of food aid comes in the form of concessional sales; donor and recipient agree for the latter to sell the commodities on the local market through government outlets; the revenue from such sales ('counterpart funds') is used for agreed beforehand developmental purposes. However, there is no certainty that the local benefits derived from program food aid reach those most in need (UNICEF/WFP, 1986: 10) and donors do not have real control over the foreign exchange made available to recipient governments. The potential disincentive effects on local agriculture production and on changing food preferences away from locally produced commodities such as sorghum or millet in favour of imported wheat and rice is a subject of considerable debate and has been thoroughly reviewed. (For example, Maxwell, 1986).

Project food aid is provided to benefit the poor directly through both bilateral (country to country) or multilateral channels (mostly through the WFP or regional institutions). While in the past most of food aid has been provided in bulk for sale (as for example PL 480 Title I) over the years the share of project food aid has increased and today constitutes about 30 percent of total food aid (FAO, 1985). There is a wide spectrum of uses to which project food aid may be put: from direct distribution in emergencies (disasters, refugees, etc.), to providing targeted food to vulnerable populations such as mothers and children; to institutional feeding (schools, clinics, etc.); to food for work and to human settlement programs (virgin land development; see Singer et al., 1987: 93) Much criticism of project food aid has been directed to the appropriateness of the food commodities used as aid, to logistical problems (timing, transportation, storage) and the administrative and distribution difficulties associated with it. (Jackson and Eade, 1982; Tagle, 1980).

Project food aid is, at present, almost exclusively intended for the food deficit and low income countries and with priority to the least privileged groups (Singer et al., 1987: 94). Its administration is carried out by the WFP and the non-governmental organizations (NGOs) or private voluntary agencies (PVOs). NGOs/PVOs may range in size from small local charities to large internationally funded groups such as The Red Cross, CARE (Cooperative for American Relief Everywhere), CRS (Catholic Relief Services), Save the Children, etc. Most of Title II food aid is distributed by CARE and CRS which together with the WFP constitute the larger donors. While NGOs were initially organized to provide relief in emergencies, over the last few decades their contribution has been increasingly slanted toward developmental activities. Their small size, flexibility and involvement at the grass-roots level, in addition to considerable experience gained in the field, have made them particularly useful to official agencies for the implementation of food aid projects for emergency and development.

Nevertheless some NGOs are becoming reluctant to distribute food aid. CRS itself has reduced the volume of food aid programmed for Sub-Saharan Africa. A series of factors are responsible for this such as the difficulties in arranging financing of in-country logistic costs, the stringent accountability to the U.S. government, and questions concerning the effectiveness of some programs, especially those including a nutritional component.

Flexible Use of Food Aid

Currently, two contradictory views appear to have emerged among the food aid planners. Some food donors seem to advocate a greater role for program food aid wherever possible and to reduce assistance to particular groups in need of higher food assistance or income earnings, mainly because of the lack of infrastructure (particularly in sub-Saharan Africa), and the administrative burden that project food aid forces upon recipient countries (Reutlinger, 1987; Cassen, 1986: 166). The special "low food aid absorption" capabilities of sub-Saharan Africa have emphasized the need for "a more packaged approach," that is a greater integration of food aid with other aid resources and better co-ordination among donors (FAO, 1985). Program food aid is distributed through existing market or ration systems and unlike project food aid, it does not have a high administrative overhead (CIDA, 1988). Bilateral donors believe that well planned, nutritional benefits could be derived from programs using program food aid (CIDA, 1988). In addition, bilateral donors feel better equipped to deal with the problems of disincentives created by food aid and with the delicate issue of commercial vs concessional food imports by recipient countries.

Other organizations propose increased assistance to the most vulnerable. Prompted by the dramatic findings of UNICEF, they have come to appreciate that providing people, especially the most vulnerable (poor children and mothers) with adequate consumption is a good investment and that developing the human resources of a country is a basic requirement for implementing sustainable adjustment reforms (Reutlinger, 1987). Thus programs that would provide food aid directly to the most vulnerable would seem important to facilitate SAL.

An eloquent call for more flexible and imaginative utilization of food aid in order to help children directly and indirectly has been made by UNICEF/WFP. Their suggestions would lead to the integration of the different types of food aid (program, project and emergency). Such flexibility would involve: 1) the monetization of project food aid, 2) the use of counterpart program food aid funds to help the poor directly, 3) the use of project food aid as income transfer to households (not only as a nutritional supplement), and 4) the increase of food entitlements for the poor through food subsidies supported by food aid.

Project food aid has been customarily provided requiring direct delivery to and consumption by the target populations ideally, to the last grain (Singer et al., 1987: 136) to ensure that it meets the intended purpose of upgrading the nutritional status of targeted groups. Selling these commodities by donor agencies or recipients has been forbidden.

Experience has shown this to be inefficient because cheaper food could be bought locally; or to have undesirable effects if it would compete with locally available food supplies; or it may not be what is most needed, because other factors such as clean water or health clinics may be more conducive to health. Especially in remote areas, cash payments may be much more efficient than food packages because of difficulties and costs associated with delivering commodities. Increased efficiency of food aid could be achieved if it could be sold (monetized) to provide poor people with needed cash or finance transport, storage and cover other administrative costs (Reutlinger, 1987). Food aid would also be used for the creation of rotating funds through sale in small co-operative groups to provide capital for income generating ventures. The sale of reconstituted food aid commodities by recipients to increase income is another possibility.

The WFP activities have been greatly hampered because of the inability to sell food aid in recipient countries' markets (World Bank, 1986). While a portion of multilateral contributions is provided for non-food purposes (for example logistical expenses, etc.), these have traditionally been smaller than the one third cash contribution the WFP estimates would be needed to optimize its programs. The monetization of at least 10% of the commodities to finance the inland transport, storage and handling costs of commodities for distribution and for needed non-food project inputs is mandatory for PL 480 Title II programs since 1985. Partial and full monetization is also allowed to implement income generating projects, community development, health and nutrition projects, agricultural programs and other development activities (USAID, 1988). Nevertheless, concerns regarding monetization of food aid have been raised in relation to the potential disincentives that this may cause to local production; and, in the case of religious organizations, a concern that the involvement in commercial transactions of this type may distort their charitable image.

While restrictions have been put on monetization, counterpart funds generated from the sale of program food aid have not been used to benefit the poor directly. A more immediate contribution to food security would be to use counterpart funds to provide the poorest in rural and urban areas with adequate food, to increase their purchasing power, and to provide opportunities for them to expand their capacity to produce more food. Counterpart funds could be used to provide the target population with money, or with some appropriate and often much cheaper locally produced foods, or with production inputs, services, or infrastructure (Reutlinger, 1987). Counterpart funds from Title III are used along these lines, but the magnitude of this program is small and its effects largely unsuccessful (Hopkins, 1983).

Program food aid could also be used to increase the purchasing power of recipient households through its distribution in food subsidy schemes. General (or non-targeted) subsidies may be more appropriate in rural areas where most people are poor and therefore benefits could be more evenly distributed (Singer and Longhurst, 1986). Targeted food subsidies may be easier to implement in urban centres. These include subsidies of self-targeting foods (i.e., staples of lower prestige unlikely to be used by better-off households) produced locally and purchased with the proceeds of food aid commodity sales at current market prices. This seems possible since the chief aid commodity is wheat, which is considered superior in many recipient countries. Other forms of targeted subsidies include fair-price shops (where foods are sold at subsidized prices) and food stamps. Difficulties with these schemes are the administrative difficulties of targeting food aid and that benefits may not accrue only to the neediest groups.

Underlying these innovative ways lies the view of direct food transfers to the poor as income-transfer which rather than directly combatting, may indirectly improve people's nutritional status. The income-transfer value of food aid commodities is now generally recognized. Analyses incorporating this concept are widespread in agencies involved with food aid. Food aid's functions have also been extended to include incentives, subsidies, wages, creation of funds, and budget support for institutions such as schools. A recent report on the potential food aid interventions to provide household food security in Sudan emphasized the use of food aid in most of these modalities (Katona-Apte, 1988).

Food and Women

Emphasizing the continuum between the productive and reproductive roles of women, UNICEF/WFP has stressed the need to increase women's incomes and improve their health. Accordingly, food aid as income-transfer directed specifically and systematically to women, especially women heads of households, to support their productive, marketing and household activities has been strongly advocated by these agencies.

Income controlled by women is more likely to benefit children and improve intra-household distribution. UNICEF/WFP acknowledges the need for additional studies to find appropriate channels to accomplish this efficiently. The benefits sought would involve time saving of overworked mothers and provision of opportunities to pursue productive and child care activities. The need to reorient food aid programs from simple relief toward the improvement of the physical productive capacity of women has also been recognized. This could be done through supplementation programs of a preventative nature, that is, before women engage in heavy food for work projects or during the pre-harvest or "hungry" season where food intake is at its lowest and caloric expenditure at its highest (Hammam and Youssef, 1986).

In conclusion, UNICEF/WFP would like to see an expansion of the multilateral programs, a closer integration of food aid with financial aid and a closer integration of food with other developmental activities through a monetization process which would effectively bring food aid into the mainstream of developmental activities (Singer et al., 1987: 204; UNICEF/WFP, 1986: 53). The emphasis on helping women in order to protect children is also of particular importance. However, proposals to allow the WFP to expand its program of food aid activities in the context of SAL have not been well received by its governing body, although the use of food aid to alleviate the impact of SAL on the poor is being evaluated by the USAID Title II program (Pines et al., 1988).

No conceivable program of food aid provided directly to the poor is likely to do more than scratch the surface of world malnutrition. Assuming that the recipients are correctly targeted (which they are not) and under other optimistic assumptions, it has been estimated that no more than 20% of those in need are reached by project food aid (Maxwell, 1978). More recently, a new orientation to reach more of the poor more efficiently has been proposed (Reutlinger, 1988). This would involve the creation of a new institution administered by the WFP and the World Bank with assistance from other international institutions and NGOs and which would operate with food and cash donations.

This institution would be in charge of sponsoring programs involved in income-transfer in the form of food coupons (food "money") to "income tested" households (that is, poor households that meet certain selective criteria) especially if they include educational and health services components, or if they create incentives to local agricultural production, generate productive employment (for example, marketing services) or result in environmental improvement.

If only the most efficient income transfer programs are funded, it is estimated that 40-45 million people's annual income could be augmented by approximately $20. If benefitted households would spend half of the additional income in food, it would augment their per capita daily diet by 300-400 calories and increase substantially their other essential non-food expenditures.

An advantage to this system is that food would be handled through existing and improved food marketing systems and there would not be a need for developing expensive, parallel public food distribution channels. The experience of three countries with food coupons (Sri Lanka, Jamaica and Colombia) suggest that food stamps effectively transfer income, but problems of targeting may persist and their nutritional effects on recipients are not known (Pinstrup Andersen, 1983; Uribe Mosquera, 1983). Elsewhere, an important obstacle to the implementation of an income-tested food coupons scheme is the absence of administrative capability to handle it.

Project Food Aid

Project food aid covers a wide range of activities. These include targeted projects, where food aid is intended for a particular beneficiary and projects where food rations are not targeted.

Non-Targeted Food Aid

Non-targeted food aid is commonly used to provide employment and to develop economic and social infrastructure in Food For Work (FFW) projects where food is used as partial wage. This is the main outlet for WFP food aid. In essence most FFW is targeted to poor households since only the very poor and landless participate in such projects as opposed to targeting to individuals within households. Nevertheless restrictions in the use of food commodities have been made with the expectation that such food would translate into nutritional benefits within the household.

FFW projects include road building, and land development and improvement. For example in Bangladesh FFW a nationwide program pays workers in wheat for rural construction, water protection works (such as raising school grounds to protect them from floods) and other rural infrastructure. FFW is also provided as an incentive for people to invest their labour in conservation of natural resources. In Peru, FFW from Title II is used to employ people to plant trees to decrease soil erosion in denuded areas (Doughty et al., 1984). In Guatemala FFW has contributed to an "impressive" agroforestry project leading to increased yields, and community tree nurseries which continue to operate after food support ends (Pines et al., 1988). In these projects food is used to encourage innovation by reducing risks and to maintain family food intake while farmers invest in terracing and tree planting and help community building of nurseries and related capital improvements. FFW has been also used for the construction of compost piles to improve the environment, reduce cultivation costs and increase farm income.

FFW is also used in urban settings. Many urban projects provide food packages for sweeping streets and other routine tasks with little permanent consequence (Doughty et al., 1984). Nevertheless, major construction work requested by participating communities are now underway and the results have been so far encouraging (for example, in Guatemala; Pines et al., 1988).

Non-targeted food aid is also used in land settlement and agrarian reform where families, displaced to new sites or the clearing of virgin land, are provided with a family ration until they are able to bring the land into production. For example, in

Indonesia where large numbers of Javanese, Balinese, Sundanese and other groups are "transmigrated" into less populated areas, Title II rice has been given to long-distance resettlers for clearing new land, building roads and other infrastructure. (Bryson et al., 1984).

The effectiveness of FFW programs has been mainly evaluated from the point of view of number of persons employed and the rural infrastructure constructed. This type of aid has been severely criticized largely because it often is a stop gap measure of short duration with no long-term beneficial effects. Often the products derived from an FFW project have benefitted the better off. In some cases, FFW projects have been associated with rampant corruption (Deaton and Siaway, 1988).

More recent evaluations of Title II FFW projects however, have endeavoured to assess their outcome in terms of long-term benefits to the participants and their impact in encouraging community collaboration leading to development. Where local initiative and leadership exists, FFW can act as a positive incentive towards community development, even when food support ceases (for example, in Peru). In such cases food is provided not as a wage but as economic support in projects where the main inducement for work is the value of the project to participants (Doughty et al., 1984 and Pines et al., 1988). Whether capital accumulation is taking place and sustainability of the projects ensured when food aid ceases, is also evaluated.

The socio-economic impact of FFW programs at the household level has not been thoroughly evaluated nor their impact on the nutritional status or the quality of life of participating household members assessed. Difficulties encountered in accomplishing this include the absence of baseline information and adequate monitoring. It has been assumed that food earned as part of the wages is consumed in addition to the normal diet (Kennedy and Pinstrup-Andersen, 1983). Nevertheless, FFW is often bartered or sold. In Bangladesh, sale or barter of such food resulted in families meeting only 50% of their calorie requirements (United Nations, WFP, 1976). Similar findings have been reported for FFW programs in Tunisia (Grissa, 1973).

Some argue that FFW projects may be detrimental because they may divert labour from local farm production and reduce local food production. This question has been recently addressed in an evaluation of an FFW project in a food deficit labour surplus area in the Baringo District in rural Kenya (Bezuneh et al., 1988).

The WFP supported project was initiated in 1981 with the objective of meeting the food needs of low income people and of utilizing the labour surplus to build rural infrastructure. It was designed to employ 800 workers per month to work 5 hours a day, twenty days per month on FFW activities. All participants were adults, mostly males, who received rations of 4.5 kg of maize, 4 kgs of beans and 1.5 kg vegetable oil for very 100 hours of work.

Evaluation data were collected during August 1983 to February 1984 from 300 representative households in the area, 100 of which were participants in FFW. Monthly visits were made to each household to obtain recall information on crop and livestock inputs used, quantities and prices of foods harvested and disposed of, food and non-food items consumed and labour use by activity.

Using a two year linear programming model, the study shows that net income for FFW project households was 52% higher than for non-participating ones. The former met the minimum nutrient requirements largely through food aid commodities and shifted crop production from maize to millet, a less nutritious but more profitable crop. FFW households earned more cash from selling millet, goats and beans, than non-participating ones and were able to save 891 Kenyan shs., whereas the latter were not. By the second year participants had reduced hours devoted to FFW activities, hired more labour because millet is a more labour intensive crop, and increased own-farm production.

The model also showed that participants spent a larger proportion of increased income on maize, beans, millet, sorghum, milk, eggs and fish than non-participants. Non-participants, however, spent a higher portion of income on non-food items and leisure. (This was attributed to a reduced opportunity cost of their leisure due to their limited income generating activities.)

This study shows that FFW did not cause production or labour disincentives and suggests that increased income improved nutritional provision to households. It further suggests that FFW may have encouraged a transition from FFW dependence to greater own-farm production through capital accumulation and own-farm investment, resulting in increased self-sufficiency. However, this is only one example of a successful FFW project whose success may have been a factor of its integration into existing agricultural and developmental projects and of the high priority given it by the Government of Kenya (Bezuneh et al., 1988).

Supplementary Programs

Targeted projects include supplemental feeding programs for mothers and pre-school children who are the most vulnerable to malnutrition. Food is distributed at feeding centres (on-site feeding) or more often given to recipients to take home (take-home mode). About 75% of Title II and two-thirds of WFP food is given on a take-home basis (National Research Council, 1982). Distribution is carried out through Mother and Child Health Centres (MCH) or Nutritional Rehabilitation Centres (NCR) (for severely malnourished children), clinics or hospitals. Food often acts as an incentive for mothers to bring their children for immunization, growth monitoring to detect malnutrition, and for nutrition education and family planning information (Singer et al., 1987).

Another targeted food aid project type is school feeding (SF) in elementary and secondary schools; these projects may range from a snack of milk and biscuits for primary school children (especially in rural areas where children may have to walk long distances and often go without any food) to full board in a residential secondary school.

Until recently, the feeding of school children predominated over mother-infant feeding even though the latter groups are the most vulnerable (Anderson et al., 1981: 7). By 1976, for example, only 8% of WFP financial commitment since 1963 had been devoted explicitly to preschoolers and mothers (Gongora and Shaw, 1977), although these groups comprised slightly over 20% of the total number of WFP food beneficiaries. In comparison, WFP invested twice that amount in the primary school age group because of the political gains that local governments hoped to obtain by showing concern for the well-being of the nation's children, especially in urban areas where school feeding programs are visible, popular and easy to deliver.

On the basis of global evaluations of PL 480 Title II in 1972, the USAID designated preschool nutrition schemes as a top priority. Likewise, WFP increased substantially food supplementation programs directed towards preschool age children and mothers (Anderson et al., 1981: 7). However, use of food for FFW and land settlements predominates, accounting for 81% of non-emergency food volume in 1987. Table 1 shows the volume of PL 480 Title II food channelled through CARE, CRS and WFP and the approximate number of beneficiaries by program type (refers to Title II only).

Table 1

VOLUME AND DISTRIBUTION OF TITLE II (1986)[1]

Number of recipients (thousands)

Sponsor	Volume[2] -tonnes-	MCH	SF	FFW	OCF[3]
C R S	363,678	5114	1008	922	394.5
C A R E	351,920	5320	7121	5096	203.3
W F P	260,281	6634	1761	3424	359.0
I E F R	230,009	0			

[1] Food for Peace. 1986 Annual Report on Public Law 480 (from Table 17)

[2] Data as of December 1988 (PL480 Title II. Fiscal Year 1988, Agency for International Development (FFP/POD, 1989), from Table 18

[3] OCH: other child feeding and preschool feeding

Effectiveness of Targeted Projects

The benefit of supplementary feeding programs has traditionally been seen as their potential for alleviating protein-calorie malnutrition. Thus, numerous evaluations of changes in nutritional status with supplementation mainly through growth monitoring of school children, infants and pre-school children have been undertaken. The results of these evaluations have not been very encouraging. (For a recent comprehensive and annotated review of such evaluations see Figas-Telemance, 1985.)

Positive effects of programs directed to infants and preschool age children have been small and mostly confined to well managed pilot projects where a great commitment of resources and personnel has been employed. Large scale supplementary feeding programs have not been so successful. Positive effects have not persisted after discontinuation of the program. For example, an evaluation of an infant feeding program in the Philippines showed that 59% of the children had regressed after program discontinuation (Stewart, 1986).

In a few carefully monitored pilot studies, supplementation of pregnant women has been shown to reduce the number of low infant weight births; infants of supplemented mothers with higher birthweights have shown less growth retardation at 36 months of age than infants born of unsupplemented mothers (Mora et al., 1978) and a positive effect on mental development was observed in children born of supplemented mothers in contrast to that of children supplemented after birth (Klein et al., 1975). Supplementation of lactating mothers is desirable because malnutrition affects the quantity of milk produced and the duration of lactation (the quality of milk remains fairly stable except under severe food deprivation).

In practice, few supplementation programs have included pregnant or lactating mothers. In the Harvard Institute for International Development survey of 201 preschool-focussed programs, 79% of which included a feeding component (Austin, 1978), only one third enrolled pregnant or lactating women. In the 1976 worldwide survey of the American Public Health Association, only 15% of the nutrition projects had mothers enrolled as beneficiaries (Karlin, 1976). Some programs that have attempted to feed pregnant mothers have had considerable difficulty in doing so, partly for cultural reasons. For example, in India pregnant women do not feel that they require an increased dietary intake and deliberately try to consume as little as possible in order to have a smaller baby and an easier delivery. Nevertheless, participation of mothers can be higher if mother and child are included as a unit as has been the experience of projects in India and Africa (Anderson et al., 1981, p.29).

The failure to document nutritional successes of targeted food aid projects is to a large extent the result of poorly conceived and designed projects, often discontinued after a short time (Sahn, 1984). It has been assumed as a matter of course that it is feasible to identify those at greater nutritional risk in a community. However, effective targeting of programs to the most vulnerable, children 6 months to 3 years of age, especially those with most severe malnutrition, and to pregnant and lactating mothers of low income is costly and not easily achieved. It is now argued that targeting should be directed to households where vulnerable children are found rather than to individuals within such households (Singer and Longhurst, 1986).

It has also been assumed that the nutritional status of target groups could be improved by the provision of food commodities, without due consideration to other factors, such as sanitary conditions and health, or to the behaviour of households living in poverty. As well, it has been assumed that any nutritional effect should translate into growth improvement (Sahn, 1984) and other possible benefits, such as increased school attendance (Gupta and Hou, 1984), have not been considered.

The most successful supplementation programs for children and mothers have been those that have included a primary health care component (Kennedy and Pinstrip-Andersen, 1983: 40; Beaton and Ghassemi, 1982) where they resulted in reduced morbidity, mortality and to a lesser extent growth (Beaton and Ghassemi, 1982). It is now recognized that well managed supplementation programs can be effective when applied within a broad health context (Singer and Longhurst, 1986).

Little attempt has been made, until recently, to understand the mechanism through which the impact of a nutritional supplementation intervention is effected or of the additional factors that may contribute to such an impact especially the response of households (Pinstrup-Andersen, 1983). The phenomenon of intrahousehold "leakage" of food commodities has forced agencies concerned with food aid to focus on the behaviour of households living in poverty with respect to the use of food commodities given as aid.

Significance of Leakage

One of the most significant factors affecting the success of supplementation programs results from not all the provided food being consumed by the target population. "Leakages" of the supplemented food occur when the food is shared by non-target family members (take-home mode) or when the food, instead of adding calories to the usual diet, is substituted for other food that normally would be consumed (on-site feeding). Food supplements may also be used for feeding small household livestock, or may be bartered or sold, in cases where recipients cannot afford to buy complementary foods with which to use the food commodities (Nieves, 1988) or distrust of the commodities for cultural or other reasons (Fleuret, 1985). Other types of leakages may and often do occur. "Leakages in process" are those which occur before the food is delivered to the recipients (FAO, 1985) and the leakages that occur due to the opportunity cost of time spent travelling to and/or waiting to receive food commodities (Knudsen, 1981).

Data of on-site and take-home programs directed to children showed that food sharing accounted for a substantial proportion of foods distributed in take-home programs; displacement of food normally consumed at home was greater in supervised feeding programs (Beaton and Ghassemi, 1982). Overall leakages amounted to between 30 to 80% of the food distributed; however no apparent characteristic differences between the net energy intake in "take-home" and "on-site" food programs were found. The average net increase in intake by the target recipient oscillated between 45% to 70% of the food collected, with a range of 10% - 70%.

The supplementary feeding programs filled only 10-25% of the apparent energy gap in the target population, even though they had been planned to meet about 40 to 70% of the gap. This may have been an important reason for the small size of the observed increases in the children's growth. Even so, these authors were unable to account for the increased energy ingested by the beneficiaries in terms of growth. They concluded that physical growth probably was not the only nor the most important benefit of supplemental feeding. An increase in voluntary activity which may affect cognitive development might have been a positive result of additional food (Chavez and Martinez, 1978); or calories might have been diverted towards fighting infection, or the increased purchasing power available to the family might have been conducive to home improvements, benefitting the child. (Figure 1)

Figure 1
Net increase in food supply
in the household

Net increase in
food intake by target

Body functions   Growth   Voluntary
(immune system)   activity

Resistance   Psycho-social
to infection   development

Household environment

Figure 1.   Some potential benefits to the individual from food aid (adapted from Beaton and Ghassemi, 1982).

Using the size of the estimated energy gap as a measure of need by other members of the household, Beaton and Ghassemi (1982) could not conclude that family need was a major determinant of leakages. Similar patterns were found in a take-home supplementation study of pregnant women in Colombia where extra food was provided for all other family members; the women actually consumed about 58% of the supplement, but food displacement accounted for the equivalent of 42%, reducing the net benefit to only 16% of the food ration (Mora et al., 1978).

Another interesting observation was that about 30% of the total final energy intake of children came from "on-site" feeding; in "take-home" programs only 10% was thus utilized (Beaton and Ghassemi, 1982). This implies that while leakages were equivalent in terms of energy, regardless of program model, the leakages in terms of nutrients could be more pronounced in the take-home mode, if the nutrient composition of the food distributed is higher than that of the foods displaced (National Research Council, 1982).

Nutritional Cost Effectiveness
of Food Commodities

These findings, and the realization that intrahousehold leakages are inevitable, has given rise to a thorough review of the nutritional cost-effectiveness of food commodities provided by PL 480 Title II. Since the immediate objective of Title II food distribution programs is to improve the energy and nutrient intake of beneficiaries, food commodities should be chosen according to appropriate criteria to maximize their nutritional benefit in spite of leakages (National Research Council, 1982).

Two pathways by which food supplements exert a nutritional effect have been identified (Figure 2). A direct pathway in which foods distributed to and consumed by recipients directly influences their nutritional and energy intake, allowing for foods displaced (that is, that would have been eaten in the absence of this supplement) and an indirect pathway by which food commodities benefit individuals indirectly through an income-transfer effect to the household by displacement of foods usually purchased. In on-site feeding both direct and indirect pathways operate while in the take-home mode the dominant pathway is the indirect effect.

Selection of nutritional cost-effective commodities requires the definition of both the program mode, (on-site or take-home) and the nutritional objective (energy or specific nutrient increase) (Nutritional Analysis).

The nutritional effectiveness of the indirect pathway would depend on the magnitude of the increased purchasing power accruing to the household from a particular food commodity or package, referred to as the *income-transfer efficiency* (Reutlinger, 1984) and the marginal propensity to spend on nutrition of that particular household and not on the nutritional quality of the food commodity (Reutlinger and Katona-Apte, 1984).

Figure 2
Pathways by which food supplements
may exert a nutritional effect.
(Adapted from Katona-Apte, 1983)

FOOD COMMODITIES MADE
AVAILABLE TO HOUSEHOLD

(additional to)   in lieu of

Food purchases and   Food purchases and
home produced food   non-home food

Improved   Increased
nutrition   purchasing power

Additional   Non-food
food   purchases

Improved
nutrition

Selection of nutritional cost-effective commodities requires the definition of both the program mode, (on-site or take-home) and the nutritional objective (energy or specific nutrient increase) (National Research Council, 1982).

The nutritional effectiveness of the indirect pathway would depend on the magnitude of the increased purchasing power accruing to the household from a particular food commodity or package, referred to as the *income-transfer efficiency* (Reutlinger, 1984) and the marginal propensity to spend on nutrition of that particular household and not on the nutritional quality of the food commodity (Reutlinger and Katona-Apte, 1984).

Alpha Value

To assess the income-transfer efficiency the measure of alpha value of commodities has been developed (Reutlinger and Katona-Apte, 1984).

$$\text{alpha} = \frac{\text{Per unit value of commodity to recipient}}{\text{Per unit cost of delivered commodity}}$$

An alpha value of 1 means that a dollar spent by the food aid program is worth a dollar to recipients whereas an alpha value of 0.5 would bring them only 50 cents. The higher the alpha value, the higher the food's cost-effectiveness in terms of income transfer.

The monetary value of a commodity to recipients varies depending on the price paid by them for the one replaced by food aid. This cost represents the commodity's delivery costs borne by the food donors and intermediary agencies. (See Reutlinger, 1984 and Reutlinger and Katona-Apte, 1984).

Thus, some food commodities have a higher alpha value than others. Alpha values for a particular food commodity vary from country to country and by area or region within a country because of different market prices, delivery costs and storage, etc. In rural areas, alpha values tend to be lower because transportation costs are usually high. Studies suggest that a direct income transfer from the monetization of food aid in an urban area would be more effective for obtaining nutritional effect in rural areas (Reutlinger, 1984).

A review of alpha values of commodities used in the Title II programs in Bangladesh, India, Indonesia, Morocco and Pakistan, have indicated that grain and grain-based processed foods delivered between $ 0.30 - $ 1.00 of purchasing power for each dollar spent by the donors, while vegetable oil delivered $1.00 - $1.80, and non fat dry milk (NFDM) from $3.00 up to $9.00. The alpha value for grains was low because of shipping costs and because in many countries for which it was calculated, grain prices were kept low as a matter of policy. Oil, however, was less costly to ship and was scarce in several of these countries. NFDM had a very high alpha value because as a surplus commodity, it was available to food aid programs at a fraction of its market value (National Research Council, 1982).

In contrast, an analysis of the nutritional effectiveness of food commodities used in a WFP in China showed oil to have a lower cost-effective value than wheat (Katona-Apte, 1984) because it was provided in quantities larger than the demand for it. In Peru oil was also cost ineffective because in this country it was abundant and inexpensive (Katona-Apte, 1986).

Marginal Propensity
to Purchase Food

A positive nutritional effect could occur if the increased income is used to buy more food or food of better nutritional quality than otherwise available (Reutlinger and Katona-Apte, 1984). This is the "marginal propensity" of a household to spend on nutrition. A review of surveys on the relationship between household consumption and expenditures in selected developing countries shows that in PL 480 Title II-aided households, a 10 percent difference in household income is associated with a 7 - 10 percent difference in expenditures for food and with differences of 4 - 6 percent in food energy and of 5 - 9 percent in protein intakes (National Research Council, 1982).

Additional purchasing power may also result in increased purchases of more expensive foods. The marginal propensity to spend on food was higher for food than for energy, because increases in income led to purchase of more expensive foods in terms of energy units. (For example, in Indonesia, people replaced tubers, which were locally cultivated, with rice, some of which had to be imported.) Several studies suggest that people also consumed tastier and/or more convenient foods and increased the quantity and quality of protein in the diet. For example, in Brazil, income elasticities for energy in rural areas was about 0.52 and for protein 0.68 - 0.74. In urban areas, the corresponding elasticities were 0.33 and 0.51 (Reutlinger and Katona-Apte, 1984). Similar patterns emerged among urban citizens in Colombia and in rural areas of India and Pakistan. However, this is not a universal finding; in Thailand and Malaysia, for example, increases in income led people to consume more of the same diet rather than to a change in the mix of foods (Kennedy, 1983).

Food As Income-Transfer

The nutritional motivation is a strong element, implicit or explicit, in much food aid thinking and practice (Fitzpatrick and Storey, 1988). Most food supplementation programs still attempt targeting particular individuals by imposing restrictions on how the food is to be used (Pinstrup-Andersen, 1983).

In some food aid circles, however, there is a shift away from focussing mainly on the nutritional benefits of food aid towards considering it as a wider "income transfer" to the poor which in some way may contribute to improve the quality of life of the intended beneficiaries. Those who do so propose that income-transfer efficiency through food aid results in nutrition efficiency as well. Indeed, there is evidence that suggests that the nutritional impact is not a function of the nutritional quality of a food commodity given as aid. For example, in one study where mothers and preschoolers were supplemented with two protein levels no nutritional advantage was found for the higher protein recipients because the foods were used as substitutes for and not as additions to the normal diet (Baertl et al., 1970). In Colombia, Mora et al. (1978) documented that supplemented families had an economic advantage over unsupplemented ones because they utilized a significant portion of the food supplements to substitute for food previously purchased. These findings have been confirmed elsewhere (Anderson, 1977).

However, income from food aid may not necessarily increase food purchases, but be used in other ways, perceived as important by food aid beneficiaries. Purchases of non-food items (i.e., for housing, clothing, education) are not necessarily less important than added food consumption, for the improvement of the recipients' nutritional status. They may free overworked women from low paying occupations allowing them more time for nurturing or for productive activities. Such expenditures could also contribute to improving the general living environment (in terms of improved housing, for example) or allow beneficiaries to acquire inputs to produce food or to generate income (Katona-Apte, 1986). Field evaluations and studies of small samples show non-nutritional benefits that have been reported by women receiving food aid. (See Table 2.)

Table 2
NON-FOOD BENEFITS
DERIVED FROM FOOD AID[1]

Savings used for

Philippines	educational expenses of children
Bangladesh	remarriage (!)
China	purchase of: bicycles/sewing machines blankets/household, farm implements
Peru	purchase of kerosene transportation
Bolivia[2]	income generating activities
Kenya[3]	FFW: increased own farm prod., income, employment

[1]Katona-Apte, 1986
[2]Food aid sold for small fee
[3]Deaton and Siaway 1988

Questions that Arise

Considering food aid as income transfer to households rather than as nutritional supplement raises crucial questions. An important one is how would increased or better quality food in the household affect the most vulnerable members of the family? Would they be better off, the same, or perhaps worse off than before? Does increase in non-food expenditures indirectly benefit vulnerable household members (Katona-Apte, 1983)? While the WF and other food donors (CRS, CARE) now routinely evaluate their programs in terms of income transfer they provide to households, little effort has yet been made to study in detail how this would alter household behaviour. It is recognized, however, that in addition to data on the marginal propensity to consume more food, it is important to understand how household food acquisition and allocation behaviour would be affected with increased income transfers through food aid. Programs targeted to women are of special interest because, unlike other forms of aid, they have the advantage of placing food or income under the control of women, making it more likely that they would be of benefit to them and their households (Katona-Apte, 1986).

The Need to Understand Household Behaviour

Developmental efforts have traditionally stopped at the door of the household (Lorge-Rogers, 1983) but there is an increasing awareness that in order to plan effective programs to help the poor, more information on intrahousehold decision making and resource distribution is required. It has become evident that households cannot be regarded as homogeneous units (Kumar, 1983) and that a multiplicity of factors influences household behaviour. For example, changes in the demand for women's time, income composition, and the degree to which it is transitory or permanent, intrahousehold budget control, range of foods and services competing for the household income allocation (Pinstrup-Andersen, 1983) and age and gender composition of households all have an effect on household behaviour.

Income

Income which enters a household is not totally homogeneous and its use will depend on who earns it and who controls it. Studies have shown that women have greater control over the income that they earn themselves, than that earned by other household members. Therefore, in situations of conflict, women prefer to maximize their income rather than total household income. Household obligations and entitlements are in many countries affected by cultural norms; in some cultures, in Africa in particular, it is traditional for women to make decisions pertaining to their own spheres of activity. Nevertheless, even in strongly patriarchal societies, such as in Bangladesh, women who bring in wage income have a greater say in how the income is spent than those who work only at home (Alamgir, 1977).

Research has shown that income controlled by women is

disproportionately allocated to purchasing food and household necessities in comparison with men's income, for they keep a large portion of it for personal and other uses. Thus, income accruing to women may translate into greater benefits to vulnerable household members than that of men. For example, a Kerala study (Kumar, 1978) found that children's nutritional status was more highly correlated with women's income than with total household or with men's wage income. Other studies show a correlation between infant mortality and patriarchal family control. A socio-econometric analysis of household behaviour in the Philippines showed that the father's wage had a statistically significant negative effect on the child's relative calorie allocation, but the mother's wage had a significant positive effect (Senauer et al., 1988). It has been pointed out, however, that since it is in the poorest income groups that women work for wages, it is not surprising that their incomes should be spent on family necessities (Singh, 1977).

Intrahousehold Food Distribution

To address the issue of who benefits nutritionally from food income transfers to the household, it is necessary to know the patterns of intrahousehold food distribution and how likely they are affected by increased food availability. Intrahousehold food distribution is not an equitable phenomenon (Van Esterik, 1985) and neither member requirements, household income, nor caloric availability are guarantors of the nutritional well being of children (Kennedy, 1983).

The generalization that women and children are always at a disadvantage in terms of food distribution is not supported by the evidence (Haaga and Mason, 1987). However, under severe resource constraints, decisions with respect to the allocation of resources are dictated by survival needs given a context that offers few if any alternatives (Lorge-Rogers, 1983). Food, health care and education are allocated according to systematic patterns which determine who in the household is most likely to be favoured. The economic argument proposes that the allocation of resources to children, who are of potential benefit to the household unit, would depend on the expected benefit to the household from each of them. This, in turn, is determined by employment opportunities and by socio-cultural factors that influence work allocation and the potential returns expected from each individual (Kumar, 1983).

Evidence suggests that within poor households food is allocated according to the "perceived" economic contribution of members. (It is important to note that this perception may be distorted because non-cash generating but essential activities required for survival, generally contributed by women, are not recognized in the household structure of entitlements). Therefore, often preference is given to adults and older male children who are old enough to earn wages or bring home income; preschool children, especially girls, are in these circumstances given lower priority (Rosenzweig and Schultz, 1982; Carloni, 1981; Senauer et al., 1988). For example, in Bangladesh, taking care of girls is "like watering the neighbour's garden." In these societies infant mortality rates and malnutrition are higher for girls than for boys, especially among the poorest families. On the other hand, Rosenzweig and Schultz have shown that in India, female infants received better care and had higher survival rates in areas where employment opportunities and potential for earning wages for adult females were high. In areas of Africa where a bride prize is paid, girls are also better nourished.

Demands on Women's Time

Another important factor to consider with respect to nutritional benefit is women's time. Food and women's time were found to be complementary in producing nutritional well being of the youngest child in households receiving FFW in Panama (Franklin and Harrell, 1985). However, increased household income from the introduction of cash crops resulted in decreased well being of children because the innovation increased time demands on women in Malawi, who found themselves unable to fulfill nurturing activities (Engberg et al., 1988).

Research Needs

It is encouraging to see that econometric analyses of

consumption behaviour of households receiving food aid are beginning to appear in the literature (Senaur et al., 1988). Recently an analysis of the socio-economic impacts of school feeding programs (although not using international food aid) at the village level in Tamil Nadu has been reported (Babu and Hallam, 1989). This analysis comprised a survey of a whole village (450 households) from January to June 1984. Data collected included demographic characteristics, total income and sources of income (crop income, non-farm income and off-farm income), employment particulars (especially number of employed household members), food and non-food expenditures, and number of children participating in the supplementation project. Quantities of food provided to each child were recorded and converted to energy and protein equivalents. Changes in the daily intake of energy and protein at both individual and household levels, and changes in food expenditures and total expenditure for an average household of five members with three children participating in the school feeding program, were also calculated.

Gini coefficients of inequality for nutritional intake, food expenditure and total consumption expenditure were calculated before and after the inclusion of the school food program.

The school food supplement, when included with the already existing intake, resulted in a 50.4% and 21.9% reduction in inequality in energy and protein, respectively. The inequality of food expenditure and total consumption expenditure were reduced by 30.2% and 35.6% respectively.

Households in the study village were stratified into three different groups, cultivator households (high income), silk weavers (middle income) and agricultural labour households (low income). Low and middle income households relied on children's labour participation for their subsistence. Therefore, school enrolment was limited. The analysis showed that in these groups there was a significant increase in school enrolment of children and in continuing education beyond the elementary level associated with the food supplementation program, although a stronger incentive would be needed to support high-school education because of its higher opportunity cost.

The school food supplement also influenced expenditure distribution: it was associated with a reduction in cereal food expenditure and an increase in milk, vegetables, fruit and non-vegetarian food. A substantial increase in expenditure on non-food items in the agricultural labour (low income) and silk weaver households (middle income) was also evident. In both of these groups there was also a decrease in the share of food in total expenditure, indicating a reduction in spending inequality between village households. On the other hand, the school food supplement did not influence cultivator households to increase children's school attendance (they were already in school) since the food supplied at school was inferior to that taken at home. There was little variation in the expenditure pattern of cultivator households, resulting from the nutritional program.

More research along these lines is necessary. Testing of hypotheses pertaining to household behaviour to explain why people living in poverty often sell or barter food instead of consuming it would also seem important. Lustig (1985) has proposed the hypothesis that families below a certain income threshold define floors of consumption for various categories of products. Once the food floor is reached, the family may devote any extra income to reach other floors (such as clothing or housing) even if the consumption floor for food is inadequate from the nutritional point of view, because the inadequacies as perceived by the household are much higher in other commodities. This would mean that the marginal propensity to spend on food will be high until the floor for food is reached. It will then decrease because the extra income will be dedicated to reaching other floors. However, it may rise again after the household reaches the threshold income at which all the floors are reached (this rise may reflect a change in quantity of food/and or quality). If such is the case then programs in which food is subsidized for households that find themselves between a floor for food subsistence and the overall subsistence satisfaction income level will have a relatively small impact on food intake and nutrition. This hypothesis assumes that malnutrition cannot be eradicated in isolation from the fulfillment of other basic needs.

In terms of food aid provided as income transfer to women, research is needed that would indicate the most effective ways in which such transfers could be carried out.

Perhaps the research which is most needed is that which would examine the internal household power structures, family relations and decision-making processes. Research evidence exists suggesting that the household's structural characteristics have a strong influence on food acquisition and allocation practices, as well as on the nutritional status and the well-being of family members in rural households. It would be desirable to determine by whom and how food related decisions are made and what their consequences are, in order to design the most effective and appropriate food aid delivery systems for specific populations.

APPENDIX I

Development of Food Aid

1954-65 – Initial period of food aid to developing countries: most food aid provided by the United States (small contribution from Canada) by virtue of Public Law 480 enacted in 1954. The bulk, under Title I, destined to friendly countries on a concessional or soft loan terms; Title II provided for use of food aid for emergencies on a strictly grant basis (FAO, 1985).

1966-67 – Food aid reached a record of 17 million tons in 1965/66, followed by a sharp decline in the overall volume and a high degree of year to year variability. Initiation of multilateral food aid and creation, in 1962, of the World Food Program (WFP) (Singer, 1987, p.28) intended to channel food surpluses on a grant basis to support projects with developmental objectives as well as emergencies. By the late 1960s donors other than the United States and Canada began making contributions on a voluntary basis.

In 1967 the Food Aid Convention (FAC) was signed with 17 donors undertaking to provide a minimum of 4.2 million tons of food aid in cereals per year. (Canada's obligation is 600,000 metric tons of wheat equivalent (CIDA, 1988)). Total food aid shipments decreased to less than 6 million tons in the food crisis period of 1973/74; concern about the crisis led to the formation of the International Emergency Fund Reserve (IEFR), initially set up at 500,000 tonnes of cereal equivalent (total contributions were of 769,528 in 1985). A yearly target of 10 million tons of food aid was set at the 1974 World Food Conference; this target was not reached in the following years although food aid was increasingly needed. Food aid recovered to about 9 million in 1976/77, but only reached a volume of 10 million tons in 1984. Minimum commitments under FAC were revised to 7.6 million tonnes a year in 1980, 1983 and 1986. Food aid fluctuates above this level depending on availability of surpluses in donor countries. In 1989 food aid volume will be reduced by about 25% from previous years reflecting recent poor harvests (Food Outlook, Feb. 1989).

Food Aid Donors

In the eighties the USA provides about fifty per cent of all food aid (World Bank, 1986). A series of revisions of its food aid policy have been effected. Since 1975 the bulk of food aid through Title I was to be directed to the poorer developing countries and a new amendment (Title III, Food for Development) was added to provide multi-year aid and enable the use by recipient governments of 'counterpart funds' to help small farmers, sharecroppers and landless labourers increase food production and to stimulate rural development in general (World Bank, 1986). High priority is also now placed in using Title II to increase development impact (human capital, agroforestry and natural resources activities) (Pines et al., 1988). Other major donors are the EEC (with 9 members of which Germany, the United Kingdom, France and Italy are the main contributors) which provides about 30% of food aid, and Canada, Australia and Japan contributing collectively about 14% (World Bank, 1986). In 1983 the EEC also adopted new guidelines to integrate food aid with developmental strategies of recipient countries and to reduce disincentive effects. Canadian food aid policy also has developmental objectives.

In spite of the multiplicity of donors (in 1987, 27 developed and 66 developing countries contributed to the WFP — Food and Nutrition 1987, p.12-13) the volume of food aid has declined as a percentage of total development assistance and is more closely related to the needs of donors to dispose of surplus stocks, particularly milk products, and to political and vested interests than to developmental objectives leading to food security (World Bank 1986; FAO, 1985, p. 42; Singer et al., 1987: 35-38). Table 3 provides an overview of the volume and value of food aid presently.

Table 3
Food Aid in Figures[1]

Volume	12.4[2, 3] million tonnes
Value	2.6[4] US billion dollars
As % of development aid	7.9[4] percent
As % of total world cereal trade	5-6 percent
As % of total world cereal production	0.6-0.7 percent
As % of US cereal production	3[5] percent

[1] Data obtained from FAO Outlook, February 1989 unless otherwise specified.

[2] Figure for 1986/87. Estimated at 12.5 mmt in 1987/88; forecasted as 9.4 mmt in 1988/89.

[3] Minimum food aid requirements have been estimated by FAO/WFP at 18-20 MT (Singer et al., 1987: 195)

[4] In 1986. Food Outlook Statistical Supplement, FAO, 1987, Table 35.

[5] In 1985/86 (Deaton, 1988)

Food Aid Recipients

The geographical distribution of food aid has undergone large changes. Up to the early 1970s Asia accounted for most of food aid (70% in 1970/71) but its share has declined (34% in 1983/84); however, food aid to sub-Saharan Africa increased sevenfold during this period. During the crisis period of 1984/85, food aid shipments to this region amounted to about 47% of global shipments (FAO, 1985: 36).

Priority in the allocation of food aid is given to food deficit countries with low per caput income according to criteria agreed by the Committee on Food Aid (CFA) (Singer et al., 1987: 65). Eighty-five percent of cereal food aid was destined to these countries in 1986/87 (FAO, 1989). Other countries may also receive food aid. The largest food recipients are Egypt and Bangladesh which received about 15% and 13% respectively of total cereal aid in 1986. Table 4 lists the largest recipients in 1986 and compares what food aid changes have occurred within this decade.

Food Aid Channels and Conditions

Food aid is provided on a bilateral (country to country) basis or a multilateral basis (mostly through the WFP or regional institutions) and through non-governmental organizations (NGOs). Almost one quarter of food aid is provided multilaterally (23.3% in 1986, Food Outlook Statistical Suppl., 1987). The largest availability of food aid as credits or loans comes from the US Title I program. The IMF recently made available lines of credit for food purchase in certain food deficit developing countries (Singer et al., 1987: 75).

To protect the commercial interests of donors, recipient countries must comply with the Usual Marketing Requirements (UMR) regulations which require them to maintain commercial imports at a specified level even though they are also receiving food aid. Monitoring of compliance is carried out by an international Committee on Surplus Disposal (CSD) which convenes monthly in Washington, D.C. (Singer et al., 1987: 40). While implementation of this legislation has been generally flexible, cases of non compliance have sometimes been harshly penalized (Singer et al., 1987: 50).

Grants of food aid are given bilaterally in emergencies or for some specific "target" purposes; all multilateral food aid is in the form of grants. Multilateral food aid is apolitical and can be provided for more than one year (Singer et al., 1987: 75); conditions for reception consist of mutually agreed purposes of food utilization over a determined period with recipient governments, provision of reporting and periodic evaluations of progress.

Table 4

FOOD AID IN CEREALS –
MAJOR RECIPIENTS FOR 1986/87[1]

Low income food deficit countries

	1979-80	1986-87
	thousand tonnes	
Egypt	1758	1869
Bangladesh	1479	1589
Sudan	212	864
Morocco	119	611
Ethiopia	111	544
Indonesia	831	378
Mozambique	151	309
Sri Lanka	170	284
El Salvador	3	226
India	343	207

Other developing countries

Pakistan	146	56
Tunisia	164	396
Peru	109	235

[1]Data obtained from Food Outlook, Statistical Supplement, Table 37, 1987.

Table 5

CANADIAN FOOD AID BY CHANNEL
AND DESTINATION 1987/88[1]

Total	437 million dollars
Bilateral	54%
WFP	34%
IEFR	5%
Other	7%

Destination of bilateral contributions	
Asia	45%
Africa	40%
Americas	9%

[1]CIDA, 1988

A recent innovation in the food aid area, triangular transactions, in which funds provided by donors are used to make purchases of food commodities from neighbouring developing countries for the benefit of recipient countries, offers great potential but in practice accounts for only about three to four percent of total food aid (FAO 1985, p.17) largely because of lack of funds (only Japan, Finland and Norway contribute cash under FAC) and uncertain availability of food suppliers.

Food Aid Commodities

About 90 percent of food aid commodities consists of cereals of which wheat is the most important (71%) of total cereal volume; coarse grains, mostly maize, but also oats, barley and sorghum constitute about 16%; and rice about 12%. Australia, Canada the EEC and the United States provide most (93%) of wheat used as food aid; 80% of coarse grains are provided by the USA and 13% by the EEC. With respect to rice the main donors are the USA and Japan which collectively provide 85% (FAO, 1985). Title II programs also make use of blended cereal products (corn-soya milk, wheat soy blend, etc.). A whole industry depends almost exclusively on this outlet for such products (National Research Council, 1982). Other important commodities are fats and vegetable oils (564 thousand tonnes in 1986/87) and skim milk (342 thousand tonnes for the same period — Food Outlook Statistical Supplement, 1987). About two-thirds of dairy products are provided by the EEC (FAO, 1985). Table 5 provides details of the distribution and destination of Canadian food aid commodities. Table 6 shows the food commodity composition of Canada's food aid program. At least 25% of the Canadian contribution consists of non-cereal products. Purchases of these commodities are of benefit to the Canadian agriculture, fishing and dairy industries (CIDA, 1988).

Table 6
CANADA'S FOOD AID – COMMODITY COMPOSITION[1]
1987/88

	Million dollars	%
Wheat	200	58
Wheatflour	48	14
Corn	85	13
Skim Milk Powder	11	3
Legumes	8	2
Oils (canola)	33	10
Fish	33	10

[1]CIDA, 1988

REFERENCES

U.S.A.I.D. (Agency for International Development). 1988. *Monetization Field Manual Title II and Section 416(6) Programs.* Washington, D.C.: Bureau for Food for Peace and Private Voluntary Assistance.

Alamgir, Susan F. 1977. *Profile of Bangladeshi Women: Selected Aspects of Women's Roles and Status in Bangladesh.* USAID Mission to Bangladesh. (Cited in: Lorge-Rogers, 1983: 26).

Anderson, M.A. 1977. *CARE Preschool Nutrition Project. Phase II Report.* New York: CARE.

Anderson, M.A., J.E. Austin, J.D. Wray, and M.F. Zeitlin. 1981. *Nutrition Intervention in Developing Countries: Study 1. Supplementary Feeding.* Harvard Institute for International Development. Prepared for: Office of Nutrition, USAID. Cambridge, Mass.: Oelgeschlager, Gunn and Hain Publishers, Inc.

Antrobus, P. 1989. *The Impact of Structural Adjustment Policies on Women: The Experience of Caribbean Countries.* Santo Domingo, Dominican Republic: UNDP/UNPPA Training Programme on Women in Development, Instraw.

Austin, J.E. 1978. "The Perilous Journey of Nutrition Evaluation." *American Journal of Clinical Nutrition.* 31: 2324-

2338. (Cited in Kennedy and Pinstrup-Andersen, 1983: 28).

Babu, S.C. and J.A. Hallam. 1989. "Socioeconomic Impacts of School Feeding Programmes." *Food Policy*. 14: 58-66.

Baertl, J.M., E. Morales, G. Verastegui, and G.G. Graham. 1970. "Diet Supplementation for an Entire Community." *American Journal of Clinical Nutrition*. 23: 707-715.

Beaton, G.H. and H. Ghassemi. 1982. "Supplementary Feeding Programs for Young Children in Developing Countries." *American Journal of Clinical Nutrition*. 35: 864- 916.

Bezuneh, M., B.J. Deaton, and G.W. Norton. 1988. "Food Aid Impacts in Rural Kenya." *American Journal of Agricultural Economics*. 70: 181-191.

Bryson, J., W.S. Cole, M.P. Johnston, and A.O. Kern. 1984. *Assessment/Redesign of the CRS PL 480 Title II Program in Indonesia*. Washington, D.C.: Prepared for Agency for International Development, June, 1984.

Carloni, A.S. 1981. "Sex Disparities in the Distribution of Food within Rural Households." *Food and Nutrition*. 7: 3-12.

Cassen, R. 1986. *Does Aid Work?* Clarendon Press, Oxford: Report to an intergovernmental taskforce.

Chavez, A. and C. Martinez. 1978. *Nutrition and Development of Children from Rural Areas*. Monograph L- 37, Mexico: D.F. Division de Nutricion, INN - Tlaplan.

CIDA. 1986. *Food Aid: Programming Issues*. Ottawa, Ontario: Food Aid Coordination and Evaluation Centre, November.

CIDA 1988. *Nutritional Impact of Food Aid*. 54. Ottawa, Ontario: Mimeo provided by Ginette Saint-Cyr.

Cornia, G.A., R. Jolly, and R. F. Stewart. 1988. *Adjustment with a Human Face*. Vol. II. Oxford: Clarendon Press, UNICEF.

Deaton, B.J. and A.T. Siaway. 1988. *A Food Aid Strategy for Haiti: Maximizing Developmental Effectiveness*. A report of the technical support to mission USAID/Haiti.

Doughty, P., E. Burleigh and M. Painter. 1984. *Peru: an Evaluation of PL 480 Title II Food Assistance*. Washington, D.C.: Agency for International Development.

Engberg, L.E., J.H. Sabry & S.A. Berkerson. 1988. "A Comparison of Rural Women's Time Use and Nutritional Consequences in Two Villages in Malaw." In Poats, S., Schmink, A., and Spring, A. *Gender Issues in Farming Systems Research and Extension.* Boulder & London: Westview Press: 99-110.

FAO. 1985. *Food Aid and Food Security: Past Performance and Future Potential.* Rome, Italy: Food and Agriculture Organization, (FAO Economic and Social Development paper 55.)

Figas-Telemance, I. 1985. *Nutritional Implications of Food Aid: an Annotated Bibliography.* Rome, Italy: Food and Agriculture Organization.

Fitzpatrick, J. and A. Storey. 1988. *Costs of Food Aid.* New York: CARE.

Fleuret, A. 1985. *Consumption Effects of Food Aid. Household Utilization of Title II Foods in Rural Kenya.* Washington, D.C.: U.S.A.I.D. (Prepared for the Bureau of Food for Peace and Voluntary Assistance.)

Franklin, D.L. and M.W. Harrell. 1985. "Resource Allocation Decisions in Low-income and Rural Households." *Food Policy.* 10 (2): 100-108.

Gongora, I. and D.J. Shaw. 1977. "World Food Programme Assistance for Supplementary Feeding Programmes." Rome: Paper prepared for Bangkok Consultation on WFPs Supplementary Feeding Projects. (Cited in Anderson et al., 1981).

Grissa, A. 1973. "Agricultural Policies and Employment: Case Study of Tunisia." *OECD Development Centre Studies, Employment Series No. 9.* Paris: OECD (Cited in Kennedy and Pinstrup-Andersen, 1983: 28).

Gupta, M.C. and K. Hou. 1984. *Evaluation of PL 480 Title II School Feeding Program in India.* Washington, D.C.: U.S. Agency for International Development.

Haaga, J.G. and J.B. Mason. 1987. "Food Distribution Within The Family." *Food Policy.* 12: 146-160.

Hammam, M. and N.H. Youssef. 1986. "The Continuum in Women's Productive and Reproductive Roles: Implication for Food Aid and Children's Well Being." *Food Aid and the Well-*

Being of Children in the Developing World. New York: UNICEF/WFP: 89-103. (Workshop held at UNICEF, N.Y. 25-26 November, 1985.)

Hopkins, R.F. 1983. Food Aid and Development: the Evolution of the Food Aid regime. Rome, Italy: UNICEF/WFP. *Report of the WFP Government of the Netherlands Seminar on Food Aid,* The Hague, 3-5 Oct. 1983.

Jackson, T. and D. Eade. 1982. *Against the Grain: The Dilemma of Project Food Aid.* London: Oxfam.

Jolly, R. and G.A. Cornia 1984. *The Impact of World Recession on Children.* New York: Pergamon Press. (Report prepared for UNICEF.)

Karlin, B. 1976. *APHA Summary on the State of the Art of Delivering Low-Cost Health Services in Less Developed Countries.* Washington, D.C.: American Public Health Association. (Cited in Anderson et al. 1981: 29)

Katona-Apte, J. 1983. "The Significance of Intra-household Food Distribution Patterns in Food Programmes." *Food and Nutrition Bulletin.* 5 (4): 35-41.

Katona-Apte, J. 1984 K-A. *A Brief Description of the Function of WFP Food Aid in China.* Rome, Italy: UNICEF/WFP.

Katona-Apte, J. 1986. "Women and Food Aid. A Developmental Perspective." *Food Policy.* 11: 216-222.

Katona-Apte, J. 1988. *Meeting Household-level Food Security Needs Through Project Food Aid in Sudan.* Washington, D.C.: World Bank Consultancy Report.

Kennedy, E. 1983. "Determinants of Family and Preschooler Food Consumption." *Food and Nutrition Bulletin.* 5 (4):22-29.

Kennedy, E. and P. Pinstrup-Andersen. 1983. "Nutrition Related Policies and Programs." *Past Performance and Research Needs.* Washington, D.C.: International Food Policy Research Institute.

Klein, R., Arenales, P., Arévalo, J. et al., 1975. "Malnutrition and Human Behaviour: a backward glance at an on-going longitudinal study." Paper presented at the Cornell Conference on Malnutrition and Behavior. Ithaca, N.Y. (Cited in Anderson et al., 1981: 26)

Knudsen, Odin. 1981. "Economics of Supplemental Feeding of Malnourished Children: Leakages, Costs and Benefits." New York: World Bank. *Staff Working Paper.* (451).

Kumar, S.K. 1978. "Role of the Household Economy in Child Nutrition at Low Incomes." Cornell University, Ithaca, N.Y.: *Occasional Paper No. 95*, Department of Agriculture Economics.

Kumar, S.K. 1983. "A Framework for Tracing Policy Effects on Intra-household Food Distribution." *Food and Nutrition Bulletin.* 5 (4): 13-15.

Lorge-Rogers, Beatrice. 1983. "The Internal Dynamics of Households: a Critical Factor in Development Policy." Medford, Mass.: Agency for International Development and Tufts University School of Nutrition.

Lustig, N. 1985. "Direct and Indirect Measures to Ensure Access to Food Supplies." In *World Food Security: Selected Themes and Issues. FAO Economic and social development papers..* (53).

Maxwell, S. 1978. "Food Aid for Supplementary Feeding Programmes. An Analysis." *Food Policy.* 3 (4): 289-298.

Maxwell, S. 1986. "Food Aid: Agricultural Disincentives and Commercial Market Displacement." England: University of Sussex, Institute of Development Study. *Discussion paper* 224.

Mora, J.O., J. Clement, and N. Christiansen, et al. 1978. "Nutritional Supplementation and the Outcome of Pregnancy." *Prenatal and Neonatal Mortality. Nutr. Rep. Intern.* 18: 167-175.

National Research Council. 1982. *Nutritional Analysis of Public Law 480 Title II Commodities.* Washington, D.C. : Food and Nutrition Board, National Academy Press.

Nieves, I. 1988 (Cited in Pines et al., 1988: 32-33)

Pines, J., J. King and J. Lowenthal. 1988. "Evaluation of Guatemalan PL-480 Programs." Washington, D.C.: John Snow Inc., unpublished consultancy report (January-March), Prepared for US AID.

Pinstrup-Andersen, P. 1983. "Estimating the Nutritional Impact of Food Policies." A Note on the Analytical Approach. *Food and Nutrition Bulletin.* 5 (4): 16-21.

Reutlinger, S. 1984. "Project Food Aid and Equitable Growth:

Income-Transfer Efficiency First!" *World Development.* 12 (9): 901-911.

Reutlinger, S. and J. Katona-Apte. 1984. "The Nutritional Impact of Food Aid: Criteria for the Selection of Cost Effective Foods." *Food and Nutrition Bulletin.* 6 (4): 3-10.

Reutlinger, S. 1987. A Summary Report of a World Bank/WFP Consultation on Food Aid for Structural and Sectoral Adjustment. Washington, D.C.: World Bank, Dec. 15-17, 1986.

Reutlinger, S. 1988. "Efficient Alleviation of Poverty and Hunger." *Food Policy.* 13 (1): 56-66.

Rosenzweig, M.P. and T.P. Schultz. 1982. "Market Opportunities, Genetic Endowments and Intrafamily Resource Distribution: Child Survival in Rural India." *American Economics Review.* 72: 803-815.

Sahn, D. 1984. "Methods for Evaluating the Nutritional Impact of Food Aid Projects: Lessons from Past Experience." *Food and Nutrition Bulletin.* 6 (5): 1-16.

Senauer, B., M. Garcia and M. Jacinto. 1988. "Determinants of the Intrahousehold Allocation of Food in the Rural Philippines." *American Journal of Agriculture Economics.* 70: 170-180.

Singer, H.W., J. Wood and T. Jennings. 1987. *Food Aid. The Challenge and the Opportunity.* Oxford: Clarendon Press.

Singer, H.W. 1987. "Food Aid: Development Tool or Obstacle to Development?" *Development Policy Review.* 5: 323-339.

Singer, H.W. and R. Longhurst. 1986. "The Role of Food Aid in Promoting the Welfare of Children in Developing Countries." In: UNICEF/WFP *Food Aid and the Well-Being of Children in the Developing World.* New York: (Workshop held at UNICEF, N.Y. 25-26 November, 1985.) UNICEF/WFP: 27-66.

Singh, A.M. 1977. "Women and the Family: Coping with Poverty in the Bastes of Delhi." *Social Action.* 27:3 (Cited in Lorge-Rogers 1983: 22.)

Stewart, Frances. 1986. "Food Aid: Pitfalls and Potential." *Food Policy.* 11 (4): 311-322.

Stewart, Frances. 1988. "Adjustment With a Human Face." *Food Policy.* 13 (6): 18-26.

Tagle, M.A. 1980. "Operational Conflicts of Food Aid at the Recipient Level: Those Who Know Don't Plan and Those Who Plan Don't Know." *Food Nutrition Bulletin.* 2 (3): 5-15.

UNICEF/WFP. 1986. *Food Aid and the Well-Being of Children in the Developing World.* New York: UNICEF/WFP. (Workshop held at UNICEF, N.Y. 25-26 November, 1985.)

United Nations, WFP. 1976. Interim Evaluation Report: Bangladesh 2197Q Relief Works Programme for Land Water Development (WFP/CFA 2/12-A) (Cited in Kennedy and Pinstrup-Andersen, 1983: 28)

Uribe, Mosquera. 1983. "Colombian Food Coupons: What They Used To Be." In: *Report of the World Food Programme.* The Hague : Government of the Netherlands, Seminar on Food Aid, 3-5 October: 137-149.

Van Esterik, P. 1985. *Intra-family Food Distribution: Its Relevance for Maternal and Child Nutrition.* Ithaca, N. Y.: Cornell International Nutrition Monograph Series. (14).

World Bank. 1986. *World Development Report.* New York: Oxford University Press.

"A WOMAN'S BURDEN"
This painting, by the Indonesian artist Rustamadji of Klaten Central Java, indicates the heavy burden imposed on many women in Asia, Africa and Latin America as a result of the daily tasks involved in the provision of basic needs.

Photo courtesy of the Bank Bumi Daya Calendar, 1982.

Chapter 15

ENDING HUNGER:
AN IMPLEMENTABLE PROGRAM
FOR SELF-RELIANT GROWTH

John W. Mellor

PART I:
THE OPPORTUNITY

We are now within hailing distance of the elusive goal of a world free of hunger. The essential knowledge and resources are at hand. This chapter describes the problem and sets out a simple but large-scale incremental action plan on which foreign assistance can focus. In the analysis of a focussed action plan careful note is also made of critical ancillary efforts that must be maintained. The essential intellectual and political foundations for achieving the goal of a world free of hunger are now in place.

Unlike a few decades ago, we now know both who the poor and the hungry are and the varying circumstances in which they live. We understand the close, but complex relationship between hunger and poverty. We not only know that the hunger of vast numbers of the hungry poor can and must be dealt with through growth, but we also know the nature of the growth that will do so. We know far more than a decade ago as to how food aid can be used in the immediate future to concurrently eliminate present hunger and to catalyze self-reliant growth. A wealth of varied, contrasting and conflicting experiences from the past few decades are there to guide us as to which policies and actions are likely to be most effective, and under which circumstances.

In particular it is time to stop separating growth and poverty alleviation efforts, to the immense detriment of each. Food aid,

485

public works projects and feeding programs are not providing the growth and hence self-reliance they are capable of providing. Vast investments in factories, the amenities of megalopolis and even large scale irrigation projects are not providing the poverty alleviation of which those resources are capable.

The massive international and national structural problems of the 1980s and the consequent economic stagnation of so many developing countries have marred the increased capacity for future growth by virtually all developing countries. Economic growth is basically a matter of building human capital. That involves increased education, better nutrition and health, and more effective organization of institutions. The human capital resources and the institutional capacities of developing countries are far greater now than they were a decade ago. This is true even of countries that have seemed to stagnate, or even to have retrogressed, during the immense structural maladjustments of the 1980s.

Now that we are close to coming out of those maladjustments and nascent signs of a return to growth are apparent, it is time to turn our attention to a concerted effort to achieve an end to hunger. In the ultimate analysis, hunger alleviation is linked to long-term self-reliant growth. Yet, there is an equally persuasive case for short-term solutions through foreign assistance, including food aid that will help initiate specific programs that facilitate long-term objectives. It is time for the world to turn its attention to a major increase in the foreign aid package meant specifically for a fresh offence against hunger. Part I delineates the magnitude of the problem and focusses on those characteristics of the poor that provide policy guidelines for the formulation of specific programs. Part II delineates the essential programmatic thrusts.

The innovative elements of this analysis of an implementable program for self-reliant growth are demonstrated through discussion of six propositions. The first proposition is that a large portion of the worst poverty can be eliminated through a high rate of return growth in rural areas responsive to modern agricultural technology. It is assumed that as a consequence there will be high returns in poverty reduction through the use of foreign aid focussed on these areas, particularly in the poorest countries. Secondly, there is a relation between growth and poverty reduction in low growth potential rural areas and a consequent need for foreign assistance to such areas, including foreign assistance to middle income developing countries. Thirdly, there is a relation between foreign assistance, poverty reduction and environmental protection. Food aid can be used in much larger quantities to reduce poverty and environmental assault in the short run and provide sustainable, self-reliant growth in the long run. Conversely, food is currently used as a developmental resource at a grossly sub-optimal level. Fourth, there is a need for integration of food aid and other forms of aid, with food aid constituting a significant but far from dominant proportion of the total. Fifth, there is a potential for feeding programs, particularly for children, to reduce short-run poverty and to add to growth producing human capital. Sixth, there is potential for a large addition to foreign assistance by focussing on two massive programs which are simple enough to catch the imagination of developed country electorates and which provide the leverage for major policy shifts in developing countries.

THE DIMENSIONS OF HUNGER

Are Hungry People Massive in Numbers?

Hunger cannot be separated from the more general problem of poverty, and hunger and poverty together are a massive social problem. In 1980, roughly one fourth of the population of the developing market economies did not have the minimum food intake "below which even maintaining health becomes impossible" (FAO, 1985a). If these proportions do not decline, then, even by this unacceptably narrow definition, by 1990, 700 million people in developing countries will have grossly inadequate diets (Table 1). The definition of hunger used here does not even allow sufficient energy to maintain the level of activity required to make a living by physical activity. A more reasonable definition would include over a billion people.

Is There a Geographic Concentration of the Poor?

Of the 700 million hungry people, about 350 million will be in South Asia, 140 million in Africa, and 75 million in China. The remaining 135 million will be about half in Latin America and the rest in East Asia/Pacific and North Africa and the Middle East. Clearly, there is room neither for complacence nor the expectation that the elimination of hunger is either simple or easily achieved.

It is clear that although the number of hungry people in other regions is not inconsequential, the major effort for the abolition of hunger must focus on South Asia, Africa and China, which include 80 percent of the hungry poor. As we will see later, the hungry in the other regions of the world — typically middle income countries — represent a less tractable problem that will require more resources per capita in solution than is the case for the poorest countries of South Asia and Africa. Even the effort to abolish hunger in China is a major problem, but it may be more easily managed than the abolition of hunger in middle-income countries where the resources per capita required for a solution are even greater.

Is the World Making Progress in Reducing Hunger?

The number of people in the developing countries who are so poor as to be grossly undernourished increased by 14 percent from 1970 to 1980 (Table 2). The same percentage increase from 1990 to 2000 would add nearly 100 million people to the group of unacceptably poor. If the extrapolation is done separately for the low-income and middle-income countries, the increase would come to over 200 million due to the increased relative weight of the poor countries. That is indeed depressing news.

But, there is both a challenge and a basis for effective action within those numbers. From 1970 to 1980, the middle-income developing countries reduced the numbers of hungry poor by 44 percent (The World Bank, 1986). It is in the poor countries (per capita income under $400 in 1983) that the numbers of hungry people grew, by 54 percent, from 1970 to 1980. And, since the poor countries are much larger in population size than the middle-income countries, their very poor performance "over-balanced" the good performance in the middle-income countries. If we extrapolate those numbers to the 1990-2000 period, the number of poor in the middle-income countries would decline from 169 million to 95 million, a decline of 74 million, while they would rise by 289 million in the poor countries. At that point, 90 percent of the poorest people would be in the poorest countries.

Three observations are pertinent. First, growth is capable of major reductions in poverty. Second, it is in the poorest countries that poverty seems to be out of hand, suggesting a resource scarcity as a major cause of poverty and that intense poverty is increasingly a problem of the poorest countries. Third, it is largely in Africa and South Asia that poverty and hunger are increasing.

Given that normal growth seems capable of bringing about a major reduction in poverty, three questions arise for the 1990s:

(1) Can the low-income countries be moved onto a growth path similar to that of the middle-income countries in the 1970s?
(2) Can growth be achieved in such a way that the numbers of poor and hungry in the low-income countries would drop more rapidly than in the middle-income countries?
(3) Are there policies which could reduce the numbers of poor at a faster pace in the middle-income countries?

To deal with those questions, we need to know more in detail about who the poor are and under what conditions they reside in from the point of view of production. Thus we ask whether the poor are rural based and the extent to which high-yield agricultural technology can reduce poverty.

Are the Poor Rural Based?

The vast majority of the poor in developing countries are in rural areas. The less developed the country, the greater the proportion of the population that is poor and the greater the proportion of the impoverished that live in rural areas. In part this reflects the limited urbanization of the poorer countries but even in Latin America where the magnitude of urbanization and urban poverty is the highest, the incidence of poverty is higher in the rural areas. Available country studies suggest that in Africa, about 90 percent of the poor live in rural areas; in South Asia, about 80 percent; and in Latin America about 60 percent. In all, over three quarters of the world's poor live in rural areas (Table 3).

The lesson that emerges is that abolition of hunger must be a rural process since this is where the majority of poor, hungry people are living and where the problem is most acute. The solution, too, must come from within that system. Even for the roughly 125 million of the poor in 1990 who will be urban based, vigorous rural development will reduce the competition for jobs in the major metropolitan areas, reduce rural-urban migratory flows, and thus help to reduce urban poverty as well.

To What Extent Can High-Yield Agricultural Technology Reduce Poverty?

The Green Revolution has markedly reduced poverty in Asia. Its effects have been direct, through increased agricultural employment, as well as indirect, through low food prices and increased nonagricultural employment stimulated by increased farmer incomes. In the North Arcot region of India, for example, the introduction of high-yielding rice varieties, expansion of irrigated area, and increased fertilizer use increased cropping seasons from one per year to three. While farmers' margins were reduced as costs increased, multiple cropping seasons increased average farm incomes by 169 percent between 1973/74 to 1983/84 and smallholders farm incomes by 28 percent. The indirect linkage effects of that growth on poverty are illustrated by an increase in family income, which includes both agricultural and nonagricultural wages, by 77 percent for smallholder families and by 138 percent for landless workers (Hazell and Ramasamy, forthcoming). Similarly in Bangladesh, in villages with well-developed irrigation and with high rates of adoption of modern rice varieties, household income was 29 percent higher and per capita income was 22 percent higher than in villages without such technology. Most important, the proportion of the population below the poverty line in those technologically-developed villages was lower, 32 percent, as opposed to 47 percent, in the underdeveloped areas. That record is analogous to the decline in poverty in the middle-income countries.

The extent to which the Green Revolution can have a major effect in reducing poverty in the future depends in large part on whether the poor are located in those rural areas where the Green Revolution is likely to have a significant future impact. The Green Revolution has tended to have its greatest impact under ecological conditions already favourable to agriculture. That is because the increased genetic potential is based on the strategy of taking advantage of ecologically favourable conditions. Thus we can usefully rephrase the question in terms of the yield potential of the various agricultural conditions. Moreover, since the density of rural population already supported is a good proxy for the initial productivity of resources and the responsiveness to high-yield varieties, we can rephrase the question further, vis: To what extent are the poor concentrated in areas of high rural population density?

The data available for answering this question are spare, but they do suggest two inportant conclusions. First, a very large number of the poor and hungry are in high rural population density areas — perhaps 250 million of them. In India, about half the rural poor live on the eastern Gangetic Plain — traversing Uttar Pradesh, Bihar, Orissa, and West Bengal — on barely 22 percent of the total land area of India as a whole. (Centre for Monitoring the Indian Economy, 1982). Add to these the poor population of Bangladesh, on its fertile deltaic area, and we have a very high concentration of the poor in one geographical area which is also very fertile and potentially highly responsive to new technology if adequate infrastructure is provided. Within these high population density areas, the poor are found in disproportionate numbers in the still better areas with greater density. Similarly, in the low-population density areas, the poor are concentrated in the relatively higher population density sub-areas.

In Kenya, three provinces — Nyanza, Western and Central — account for between 64 percent to 77 percent of the rural poor. Population density reflects ecological potential (World Bank, 1983) and it is clear that a large proportion of the poor live in areas of high agricultural potential.

Second, such a concentration of poverty in the high population density areas seems to be the case for the low-income countries, but not so for the middle-income countries, which in turn suggests that as development progresses, poverty is rapidly and largely eliminated from the high-potential areas. Thus a major portion of the poverty problem in the low-income countries seems reducible by rural growth of a type we understand well. But, conversely, the remaining rural poverty problem in the middle-income countries is much more intractable. We will draw important programmatic conclusions from this in Part II below.

There is a sound logic for these relations. Highly productive soils in a static technological situation favour expansion of the population to a high density and can support far more people than are needed to till the land. As a result, a landless labourer class gradually develops. The final result is that, compared to low productivity situations, there is a higher average income, but also a large group of intensely poor. The percentage of very poor in the total population tends to be lower in the high potential area; but, because of the high population density, the total population of poor will be very large. With development, these numbers drop rapidly leaving the poor concentrated in the low-potential areas.

The case of the middle- and higher-income countries differs from that of the low-income countries. Known development processes in these areas have lifted the whole population to a much higher level of living and largely eliminated poverty and hunger. Where rural poverty remains it is found in areas that are environmentally fragile, have soils or climates not typically suited for traditional agriculture or are otherwise constrained by their institutional structures.

In Thailand and Brazil, almost half of the poor are concentrated in the Northeast region of each country, which are areas of relatively low population density (Meesook 1979). Poor soil quality is identified to be the major cause of the low productivity and resultant poverty in this sub-region of Thailand (Meesook, 1979). The reasons for the relative backwardness of the Northeast of Brazil also lie embedded in poor soils, vulnerability to droughts, grossly inequitable distribution of land (FAO, 1984b) and piecemeal efforts on the part of the government to develop the region. The Northeast in Brazil "exemplifies the extreme case of a large and persistent pocket of poverty in an otherwise dynamic, rapidly developing country" (Kutcher and Scandizzo, 1981). In Peru, rural poverty is almost completely concentrated in the Sierra region which is a region of tough mountainous terrain.

Poverty alleviation initiatives in these "difficult" areas of middle-income countries will necessarily be somewhat different from those in the low-income countries. These areas will yield lower rates of return to investment than the high potential, high density areas in poorer countries. Policies in these "difficult" areas must be tailored around the specific features that have caused them to lag behind the rest of the economy.

What about Women and Children?

The situation with respect to women and poverty is highly variable. However, in general, households headed by women do not figure disproportionately among the poor. It seems that single headed households are more prone to poverty but the sex of the single head is not as important a determinant of poverty as are other independent variables.

There is, however, evidence that at least in Asia within poor households, women and children receive a disproportionately small share of their caloric needs. Recent studies in Bangladesh and Papua New Guinea as well as earlier ones for Ghana, Guatemala, and Nigeria confirm that mothers and young children in general receive a smaller share of the family's food in relation to their requirements (FAO, 1985). Moreover, the lot of the mothers and children is interlinked. In Kerala, the participation of women in economic activities had a significant effect on nutritional status of the child (Kumar, 1988). At the same time, the nutritional status of the woman herself seems to be linked to her productive status.

Broad inter-regional contrasts indicate that a lower relative involvement of the females in productive or gainful activities may be an influence in gender bias. The ranking of the regions by activity ratios for women to men reflects the sex ratio and life expectancy rankings (Table 4). Northern Africa is an outlier, possibly because of the additional sociological constraints on women working in Muslim countries.

Additional evidence also confirms that the lot of women and children is worse in South Asia, where the activity ratios of women are lower than in Africa, even though the aggregate levels of undernourishment are the same in both regions (Table 5).

It is possible that the burden of infectious disease is higher in Africa or that the reference standards are too high. The differences may also be overstated due to the high incidence of non-traded crops in the diet in Africa which may not be captured in many estimates.

All this, however, argues for explicit, though not exclusive, attention to programs that address the special nutritional problems of women and children and this may be especially true for South Asia.

In summary, the poor and hungry are concentrated in the poorest or low-income countries, although their numbers are still large in middle-income countries. They are rural, and, in low-income countries, are disproportionately located in high-agricultural potential and high population density areas. Children are disproportionately represented among the poor. Thus, poverty alleviation programs must be rural-based, concentrated on the low-income countries and emphasize particularly the children. There is considerable scope for rapid progress in raising more than 250 million of the poor out of hunger in high-potential rural areas of low-income countries.

PART II:
A PROGRAM TO REMOVE HUNGER

What are the Basic Principles
Driving An End to Hunger?

There are four basic principles that will be necessary to keep in mind if we wish to remove hunger from the world.

First, growth can and does bring about rapid reduction in hunger. Of course, the more growth occurs where the poor are located (rural areas), the more it increases food production (the critical consumption item of the poor) and the more employment it creates (the basic source of income of the poor) the better. Thus, all the various complex policies needed for an agriculture driven, employment-oriented growth process need to be

494

pursued vigorously. Those processes of technology generation and input supply are well underway even in Africa. The efforts to expand them and to fine tune them must not slacken. Fine tuning includes increasing sophistication with respect to the interaction and the appropriate balance of private and public sector activities in these complex, decentralized processes of rural, employment-oriented growth.

Second, agriculture grows and has large employment linkages only when it is fully integrated into the total economy by the same system of roads, communications, and electric power that are so essential to urban growth. In the low-income countries in particular infrastructure is so inadequate as to leave half or more of the rural areas outside the processes of growth. It is in those unserved areas where poverty is the greatest.

Third, the concentration of the hungry poor in high-potential areas of poor countries — while the formerly hungry poor have been raised out of poverty in such areas in the middle- and high-income developing countries — tells us that there is a major resource constraint to reducing hunger in the poor countries. From the second point above, we know that this resource constraint is reflected particularly in deficient rural infrastructure.

Fourth, because economic growth in the middle-income countries has been and continues to be so effective in reducing poverty, it is important that this growth be maintained. However, the resources needed to reduce poverty in these countries are greater per person because poverty is now concentrated in the still rural but low-potential areas where returns to investment are lower and risks are higher. Continued rapid growth elsewhere in the economy will reduce those numbers in poverty, largely by out migration. Resource transfers from the wealthier countries can greatly accelerate the reduction of poverty by allowing large investments in these areas to be undertaken even as investment in accelerated growth continues for the rest of the economy.

Thus, substantial incremental increases in allocation and utilization of resources could greatly accelerate the process of removing hunger both in the low-income and in the middle-income countries.

What Form Should
a Major Incremental Aid Program Take?

Now is the time for a major action program to end hunger. For it to be effective, it must be:

(1) Large enough to have an impact. Increased foreign aid to eliminate hunger must be mobilized in programmatic and impact terms.

(2) Focussed enough to have visibility, clarity, and credibility. Increased foreign aid must have a *measurable* impact: first on the instruments of poverty reduction, and then on the end objective.

Because so much progress has been made on broad processes of development, such a formal program is now feasible, while it would not have been so 20 years ago. The focus is a response to the need for clarity and credibility in a current world in which much else is being done. It is not a reflection that development can be defined as involving only one or two efforts. It recognizes that a massive foreign assistance effort that is tightly focussed operates in a context in which many other efforts are proceeding and improving. In particular, technological progress must continue in agriculture, particularly in the poor countries; and the growth of the nonagricultural sector must move ahead, a process facilitated by growth in agricultural incomes.

There are two areas of investment which fulfil our major criteria: (1) To be programmatically delineable; (2) To have a major monitorable impact on growth that will make removal of hunger self-reliant; (3) To sharply and measurably reduce hunger in the short run while self-reliant growth gets underway; (4) To be designed to counter the malnutrition bias against children and women (especially important from the point of view of social integration, the quality of human capital, and the increasing educational skills the economy will demand); and, (5) To have substantial political appeal in major donor countries.

The two areas are rural public works and large-scale feeding programs, of which school lunches are central. In the past, foreign aid has supported programs of this kind, but typically they have been episodic, geographically confined, and only incidental to the general economic growth policies. We see them as integral parts of an onward-looking growth-based strategy that recognizes the crucial interlinkages in the economy.

The scale required to largely end hunger in five years (which would provide sufficient time to build up the requisite institutional structure) and make it self-reliant in 15 to 20 years (which would provide the added time for the investment in roads, institutions, health, and education to pay off) would be on the order of an incremental $20 billion per year — $15 billion for rural infrastructure and $5 billion for feeding programs. About one-quarter or $5 billion would be in the form of food aid.

What are the Major Sources of Lack of Credibility of Such a Program?

Do rural public works provide large, long-term employment multipliers? For the high-potential rural areas of poor countries, the answer is clearly documented through comparison of poor and middle-income countries (the latter have largely eliminated poverty in high-potential areas); and by comparisons of good and poor infrastructure areas in poor countries. Poor countries underinvest in these areas because of the large resource requirements and some continuing doubt about the size of the economic payoff.

Can a massive program of rural infrastructure investment be developed in a short period of time? In answering this question, the problems should not be underestimated. There are five problems and each is more uncertain than the first question of the returns to infrastructure for which the answer is now clear.

First, a massive infrastructure program requires decentralized administration not only to invest but to maintain as well. Ideally, that would be through local governmental bodies. However, true decentralization recognizes that instruments will vary greatly from place to place. The low-income Asian countries have now demonstrated a fully adequate level of capability to build and maintain such capacity and a build-up over a few years would be appropriate. The middle-income countries clearly have such institutional capacity. What about Africa, and to a lesser extent politically backward areas of Asia, such as Bihar state in India? Building such capacity and bringing the political commitment, would be a major element of the effort. A large-scale effort such as this could demand a focus on efficient management that would push the process forward in this area. The benefits to overall development of marshalling such commitment to decentralized development would be immense.

Where national capacities for massive infrastructure investment are limited, it would be useful to consider use of private voluntary organizations, both national and foreign. They could certainly play an important role in Africa as they have done already in Asia. Use of these agencies would allow one to get started on a large scale even as efforts were initiated to build up the national capacities. It should be reiterated that development of a national capacity at the local rural level to provide rural public works is a highly desirable element of both economic and political development.

The second major problem involved in a massive increase in rural public works programs is a donor problem. It is the problem of co-ordinating food aid and financial aid. Historically, these two areas have been kept relatively rigidly separated. Food aid has been seen not so much as a developmental input, but as a relief mechanism simply to provide food for poor people (or for dumping surpluses). In the thrust discussed here, we are talking about food aid as a developmental device. Rural infrastructure is something which is desirable in its own right. There is underinvestment in rural infrastructure in the developmental process which means that there is an underinvestment in employment of rural labour and hence an underutilization of food as a factor of production.

Now this process must be turned around. One must start with the assumption that if hunger is to be removed, at least in high-potential areas, there must be a massive investment in rural infrastructure. This means that the institutions with financing and project planning capacity, such as the World Bank and the financing part of bilateral foreign assistance agencies, must plan major rural infrastructure projects on a massive scale. They must delineate the various resources needed: the investment in cement culverts, the investment in the hard surface on the road, and investment in gravel, and of course the investment in labour. The investment in labour then must be converted into the food requirements. If labour will represent 50 percent of the input into a project and the labourers will spend 70 percent of their incremental income on food, then the food component is 35 percent. There must then be co-ordination with the food aid agencies to see that the additional food aid will be provided either in the form of Food-For-Work project food aid if that is appropriate, or perhaps, as program food aid which is just simply putting food into the market and using the proceeds for financing labour costs. On this, as elsewhere, considerable flexibility will be required. The magnitude and the complexity of the task is suggested by the likelihood that major developmental agencies would have to reorganize and restaff to suit such a thrust. The suggestion is major; it is not a bit more of what is already being done.

Why do we translate this thrust into food aid and not simply, as with other resources, provide the financing to purchase the incremental food which is necessary? That is because food aid tends to be substantially, 80 percent according to World Food Programme surveys, incremental foreign assistance which is based on a major additional constituency. Thus when we talk of a $20 billion incremental foreign assistance program to abolish hunger, we can think of it in terms of $5 billion or so of that as not being as politically costly as the remaining $15 billion. Thus, we want to keep the two elements co-ordinated but separate.

If food aid and financial aid are to be co-ordinated, then the efforts now going on between the World Food Programme and the World Bank must be increased in order to make the financing of infrastructure a central element. IFAD could perhaps play a role in this process. Bilateral agencies, such as USAID, also need to co-ordinate their food aid with their financial aid programs. To repeat, one needs to start with the development process of building infrastructure and then trace that back to the food requirements.

The third barrier to the program delineated, is the acceptability to developing countries of large additions of food aid. Food aid has a bad name. It is seen as part of the worst kind of dependency on developed countries. This attitude is particularly noticeable in India, which was sharply burned in 1968 by food aid upon which it had become very dependent, being put on a month-by-month shipping basis. Thus the problem is very real.

There are a variety of ways to make increased food aid for

the purposes indicated here acceptable to developing countries. First, it needs to be set forth as a step towards self-reliant growth. It should be seen as a bridge loan — food being received now in order to build the capacity to produce more food in the future. There is a significant possibility for acceptability of this approach by developing country officials. It must be clear that massive rural infrastructure and human capital will be built, requiring large increases in food consumption above present levels in low-income countries for developmental purposes.

However, something more needs to be done than simply to indicate food aid as a step towards self-reliant growth. The real problems of reliability and variability must be dealt with. Food aid tends to be highly unreliable. Indeed, it tends to be in shorter supply when there are world shortages of food, and in longer supply when there are surpluses. This is the opposite of what developing countries need. There seems little hope that the developed countries will themselves become reliable funders of food aid. Thus there must be other mechanisms for dealing with this problem. The most obvious one is to broaden the scope of the International Monetary Fund Cereal Facility so that it provides guaranteed low-cost loans to deal with the needs arising from sudden increases in commercial cereal imports. Thus, if a country was suddenly cut off from the food aid component of the package which was put forward here, it would have immediate recourse to the International Monetary Fund. The IMF must also be brought into discussions of how to reduce hunger — not in a negative way to show necessary structural adjustment, but in a positive way, to innovate institutional support, within its mandate, of important, growth-oriented, hunger reducing efforts. Further, there needs to be an explicit statement by the developed countries (particularly the U.S. and the EEC) that they will manage their acreage reserves and their food stocks in such a way as to increase the reliability of their commercial supplies as well as food aid. If being a reliable supplier of food aid in the short run could be seen as building commercial markets in the long run, this would elicit a favourable response.

This brings us to the fourth problem with respect to the program, and that is the willingness of the food aid donors to increase their food aid substantially. The program delineated here would call for a tripling of food aid. That is adding 20 million tons to the current approximate 10 million tons of food aid. The lobby in developed countries for food aid is basically present — farmers, who are interested in larger markets, and the public generally who would like to help alleviate the worst form of poverty. What is lacking is the conviction by farmers that food aid represents truly incremental markets; and by those concerned with poverty reduction that it generally brings about a reduction in poverty. We have laid out the basis for carrying these points. They need to be driven home.

The fifth problem that arises is with respect to the low-potential agricultural areas. We can demonstrate clearly that a full one-third of the hungry poor in developing countries are in high-potential areas. What about those in urban areas and those in the low-potential areas? In the low-potential areas it needs to be recognized that the impact of a particular expenditure on self-sustaining growth will average out to be lower than in the high-potential areas and will be much riskier. Despite the lower returns there is a three-fold argument for such an effort for the low-potential areas. First, there is always a chance that some of these areas will turn out to have high-potential, development proceeds, as demand structures diversify, and infrastructure is provided. Second, if these are truly areas of poor and perhaps even nonexistent potential for local growth, then their populations need to be integrated into the larger society. Many of these people will have to migrate, as they may already be doing on a large scale. They will not be able to do so productively without education. Education requires the institutional development of schools which in turn require infrastructure if good teachers and administrators are to be brought to such areas. Infrastructure provides the means to gradually integrate those areas into the larger economy. Third, with large numbers of poor in such areas, how else can we improve their human capital, give them relief in the short run, and prepare them to move out other than through rural public works programs. There is a large history of such efforts, which have worked successfully of which perhaps the most striking is the Employment Guarantee Scheme (EGS) in the state of Maharashtra — a state that has large areas of relatively low-potential resources.

Perhaps special justification is needed for large-scale

infrastructure investment in the low-potential areas of the middle-income developing countries. These are countries which in some respect should be able to finance those efforts themselves. As pointed out above, however, it is very important that high overall growth rates be maintained in the middle income countries, as that is the long-term solution for a high proportion of the poor in the low-potential areas who will migrate to the rapidly growing high potential areas, particularly the urban areas.

Finally, it would be reasonable to recognize that the low-potential areas are areas of particularly severe environmental degradation either because of low rainfall or steep topography, or because of the assault of poverty as growing populations claim fragile resources in a context where technology cannot raise the productivity of existing resources. It therefore would be useful to give heavy emphasis to environmental programs. Such emphasis would be in part productive, providing the basis for increased incomes from forestry and related activities. They might also involve substantial water conservation efforts through small tanks as well as through bunding and terracing. As a result of the widespread worldwide concern with environmental problems, such efforts might be highly favoured by developed countries even though the discounted rate of return on such investment would be lower than in the high-potential areas.

The environmental thrust would be major and two-fold. First, accelerated growth of the high potential areas, which generally are areas that can manage high input levels and are not environmentally fragile, would help reduce the pressure in the environmentally fragile areas. Second, in those latter areas major programs of environmental support would be required and aided in large part by food aid.

Feeding Programs

It needs to be recognized that, as the employment multipliers and growth linkages work from agricultural growth, it will be possible to increase employment sufficiently rapidly so that the human capital with respect to the health, nutritional status, and education of the poorest members of the society will gradually become limiting to increases in employment. It behooves us to begin immediately to improve that human capital so we can see those employment opportunities growing rapidly in the next five, ten, fifteen, or twenty years.

It is clear that the nutritional status of infants and children is particularly poor in low-income families. Low-income families must allocate a disproportionate share of the limited food supply to the principal wage earner, who tends to be the male household head. Women and children suffer. Further, in very poor households, the value of children's labour in tending cattle, scavenging, and other low rate of return activities tends to be greater than the discounted present value of the schooling they might have obtained. It is common in developing countries that offer universal primary education to have practically all children start school in rural areas, but a very high percentage drop out as the value of their labour begins to increase as they approach age 10 or thereabouts.

School-feeding programs or noon-day meals as they are called in some countries are doubly desirable. They improve the nutritional status of children of school age, and they provide a return to those children that can be fully competitive with the alternatives which they can earn outside of school. The effect on school attendance is dramatic. Thus one is building human capital directly by feeding these children, and indirectly by keeping them in school.

With respect to feeding programs, a number of criticisms must be dealt with promptly. First, it is argued that the gross addition to consumption by school children through a school-feeding program is greater than the net additions, that is, they get somewhat less food at home. This should be seen as an advantage not a disadvantage. It means that the nutritional benefits are being spread more broadly in the family. If this increases the ability to work of the male members, so much the better. Obviously, if the female members are improving their already low-standard of food intake that is highly desirable as well.

Second, there is the argument that for poverty reduction there are higher rates of return programs than school feeding. For example, feeding of preschool children is generally shown to have a bigger impact per dollar spent than feeding of school-age children. The response to that is simple. The returns to school-feeding programs are very high. However, if the returns are higher in other activities, they should be done. We can here make the point that with these two simple thrusts of feeding programs and rural public works, with each receiving massive resources, there will be more resources available for countries to make fine tuning decisions about other programs which are complementary. Preschool-age feeding programs would undoubtedly be a very important one of these.

The third problem with feeding programs that must be faced up front is that there are substantial administrative costs. For example, in Tamil Nadu, where resources were quite short for running a school-feeding program, the school teachers have operated the program. This has reduced the amount of teaching done. The response to such a situation is simple: Recognize the administrative costs, add them into the total program, and have them reflected in the budget numbers. In the Tamil Nadu case there would be a further advantage in that while the teachers are teaching, lower paid very poor women could be provided employment.

In India, the state of Tamil Nadu runs a very effective school-feeding program and the state of Maharashtra runs a very effective rural public works employment program. It is notable that there is no way that either state could afford both of these programs. How better to make the point of the need for substantial additional resource flows if we are serious about removing hunger in the near future.

Cost

At this stage only a notional cost calculation can be provided. If we take the FAO *Fifth World Food Survey* measure of the dietary gap, in 1979-81 and inflate it to 1990 (estimated 700 million people in hunger), 20 million tons of cereals would be needed to fill the gap. The monetary cost of the food would be about $4 billion. Assuming an income elasticity of demand for food to be 0.6, an incremental income of $6.6 billion would be needed (which implies, therefore, that other consumption goods, including higher value food of a value of $2.6 billion would be required). Assuming that the labour requirement in public works programs was 33 percent, about $20 billion in total would be needed. That leaves the food component at 20 percent of total costs — not an unreasonable proportion if the object is growth. The food component in rural public works is estimated at between 15 and 40 percent. School feeding would have a higher food proportion but other infrastructure efforts might be less. If one takes the Maharashtra Employment Guarantee Scheme and the Tamil Nadu school feeding programs and run each on a scale to cover all the poorest people in the world, the cost would be $15-$20 billion.

The proportional breakdown of the sum by geographic area would be:

	Billion US$
Africa	4.0
South Asia	10.0
East and Southeast Asia	0.8
Latin America	2.0
Near East/North Africa	0.8
China	2.0

The tonnage breakdown would be the same for the 20 million tons of cereals.

The major problem area in absorbing that quantity would be Africa, where a major administrative effort would be needed.

The division among donors would be complex. A large number of variations are possible. One suggestion would be to split the additional aid required among the donors in the proportion they have been operating at in the 1980s. For example, the U.S. would be expected to provide an increment of 20 percent or $4 billion, half of which would logically come from increased food aid. If Japan also provided $3 billion, in financial aid only, the average share of food aid in the aid package of the 2 countries would be 25 percent. The $2.0 billion of financial assistance from the U.S. would require reallocation of 10 percent of foreign aid away from security supporting assistance towards developmental assistance — a shift fully consistent with the current shifts in geo-politics.

Implementation

A massive program of $15 billion a year for rural public works and $5 billion for feeding programs will require major donor co-ordination. It would seem logical that the World Bank and the World Food Programme should join together to become the lead agencies for such an effort. They would then demonstrate how project-oriented development projects of rural public works, school attendance, or school-feeding programs, could be developed as development projects and financed in part from food aid and in part from direct development resources. The major multilateral agencies are currently not structured to accommodate a major innovative program of this type and there would need to be a high-level meeting to discuss the full range of problems. At a very early stage, the President of the World Bank and the Director of the World Food Programme would have to come together. Their principal operating personnel would need to be brought on board.

The effort laid out is massive. Each country would have to give a primary concern to rural public works and to human capital involved in feeding programs. They would have to have a program for completely covering their country with rural roads and related infrastructure, for employment in the low-potential areas on environmental and infrastructural projects, and for the massive feeding programs which are indicated. Many countries already have the structures in place but they would have to be enlarged. Some countries would have to institute them de novo.

Monitoring

A monitoring process for the foreign assistance donors and the countries receiving the assistance would be required given the scale of the effort to be undertaken. This process would require a monitoring of the inputs — measurement of the roads built, the numbers of people fed, school attendance — as well as monitoring of the output — numbers of people who are lifted out of poverty in the short run by the direct effect of these projects, and the growth of employment in the longer run. The standards of monitoring would have to be reasonable, recognizing administrative cost and inefficiencies.

Conclusion

We have attempted to make the case that such a massive effort at ending hunger and eradicating poverty, as outlined here, makes sense only if both development of human capital and rural infrastructure are seen as absolutely central elements in the development process. The program as set forth here is fully incremental to existing efforts. It is a simple impact-oriented program which can appeal to donors and recipients alike and provide a focus for both raising resources and for using them effectively. But, the program faces the reality that many other efforts must proceed concurrently if hunger is to be eliminated. Furthermore, the politics of foreign aid and national allocations have determined much of the present allocational pattern and it seems unreasonable to expect major changes to occur in the future.

However, if the current quantity and allocation of foreign aid is in equilibrium, why is it possible to make a major increment at this time. Two changes are underway. First, changes in the cold war status may call for reallocation of at least that part of the foreign aid expenditure that is effectively military-security oriented currently, to a redefined sense of security interests. Second, a clearly delineated hunger eradication objective can mobilize and strengthen new constituencies for foreign assistance. The Ending Hunger program is an effort to do just that.

Could there be at least some reallocation of resources in the hunger eradication direction? One should hope so. After all, the Ending Hunger program is a growth program and one which relies less on investment in highly capital-intensive industry and inefficient megalopolis. Some efficiencies and reallocations are quite possible but it is certainly difficult to see more than one third of the share from reallocation. It is particularly important to recognize that in such a program with a clear simple focus on large scale initiatives much else remains to be done and must be expanded — especially agricultural technology on the direct production side, and targeted programs to infant health and health generally on the direct human welfare side. Indeed, returns to those programs will be greatly enhanced by the two prongs set forth here.

NOTES

1. This paper draws substantially on an earlier internal publication on Ending Hunger and Poverty by John W. Mellor and Jyoti Shukla. I am grateful to Rajul Pandya-Lorch as well as to other colleagues at IFPRI for major contributions to this and earlier drafts.

2. The criterion used for undernourishment is 1.4 times the Basal Metabolic Rate. This is one of the criteria the Fifth World Food Survey uses for energy requirements "below which even maintaining health becomes impossible" and is the activity associated with eating, washing, dressing, etc., as well as minimum movement and other forms of activity needed for communication.

3. Ten percent of the landowners representing only one percent of the labour force hold 70 percent of the land. Such a distribution of land has its inherent inefficiencies of unused land, while labour is underemployed.

4. When mothers are not in the labour force increases in wage income showed no incremental effect on child nutrition. For those mothers that are in the labour force it is their own income that primarily accounts for the positive effect of increased income on improved child nutrition.

Table 1
Projected incidence of undernutrition, 1990[a]

	Total Countries	Low-Income Countries	Middle-Income
		(numbers in millions) [percentages in brackets]	
Africa	137 [20]	99	38
South Asia	350 [50]	350	-
East Asia/Pacific	31 [4]	-	31
Latin America	72 [10]	2	70
Near East	34 [5]	4	30
China	76 [11]	76	-
Total	700 [100]	531	169

[a] The estimated incidence of hunger in 1990 is calculated using the proportions undernourished in 1979-81 as reported by the Fifth World Food Survey and the projected population for 1990 as reported in the World Development Report, 1988. The breakdown of the Far East into South Asia and East Asia/Pacific is on the basis of the distribution of poor in the two areas as given in *Poverty and Hunger*, World Bank, 1986. Division on the basis of low income and middle income is by the distribution of population in the two groups in each region. Incidence of poverty among low-income countries is assumed to be double that in the middle-income countries and this proportion is applied to each "region-specific" number. Low-income countries are those with per capita income of $400 or less in 1983. Given the various assumptions in the calculations both in the original estimates and the projections, the numbers should be seen as indicative not definitive.

Table 2
Changes in the prevalence of energy deficient diets, 1970 to 1980[a]

	Percentage Change in Share of Population	Percentage Change in No. of People
Developing Countries[b]	-2	+14
Low-Income	+3	+54
Middle-Income	-9	-44
Sub-Saharan Africa	+4	+49
East Asia and Pacific	-14	-57
South Asia	+2	+47
Middle East and North Africa	-14	-68
Latin America, Caribbean	-4	-21

[a] World Bank, *Poverty and Hunger* 1986. The norm used is a calorie level which the World Bank defines as the benchmark below which there is `not enough intake to prevent stunted growth and serious health risks.' The FAO in the Fifth World Food Survey shows somewhat different trends in that the proportions of hungry people declined in all regions, though for the least developed countries as a group the proportions increased. It should be noted that not only is the FAO methodology different but their definitions of the regions are also not identical to the World Bank, e.g., the FAO does not separate out the poorer regions of South Asia from South East Asia aggregating them together as the Far East so that the disparate trends within the region are obscured. Nor do they separate out Sub Saharan Africa from North Africa. Since we are interested in separating out the economically different regions, we use the World Bank trends. FAO reports over the decade of the seventies, the number of people getting insufficient diets declined by 18 percent while it increased by 19 percent in the low-income countries. From the policy point of view, these are extremely important trends. However, the authors are aware that typically the reduction in the numbers of poor people are derived by extrapolating uniformly an aggregate increase in income over the whole income distribution. Further, disaggregated research is needed to explore the link between income growth and poverty reduction.

[b] Does not include China.

510

Table 3
Rural-urban distribution of poverty and the estimated number of people living in areas of high potential, 1990[a]

				Agricultural Potential	
	Total	Urban	Rural	High	Low
Africa	137	14	123	61(50)	62
South Asia	350	70	280	140(50)	140
East Asia	31	5	26	6(25)	20
Latin America	72	29	43	11(25)	32
Near East	34	10	24	11(33)	23
China	76	-	76	26(33)	50
Total	700	118	548	255	327

[a] The distribution by rural and urban classification is based on a survey of country poverty studies. All poverty in China is grouped under rural poverty. There are indications that there is little malnutrition in urban areas but this should not be seen as a statement on the absence of poverty in urban China, rather a reflection on the paucity of definite data. All numbers are tentative and should be seen as merely indicative.

Table 4
Gender bias in survival and female earning activities[a]

Region	Sex Ratios 1980 f:m		Life Expec. Ratios 1980-5 f:m		Activity Ratios 1980 f:m	
	Values	Ranks	Values	Ranks	Values	Ranks
Northern Africa	1.024	1	1.071	1	0.645	1
Eastern and SE Asia	1.008	2	1.066	2	0.610	2
Western Asia	0.940	4	1.052	3	0.373	3
Southern Asia	0.935	5	0.989	5	0.336	4
Northern Asia	0.986	3	1.050	4	0.158	5

[a] Sen, Amartya. *Africa and India: What Do We Have to Learn from Each Other?* WIDER Working Paper No. 19, 1987.

Table 5
Indicators of malnutrition[a]

Children Under 5 Year

	Low Wt/Age		Low Wt/Ht		Low Birth Wt	Anemia in Women
	m	%	m	%	(%)	(%)
Africa	22	26	4	7	14	40
Asia	115	54	33	16	19	58
Latin America	9	18	2	4	10	17

[a] *Fifth World Food Survey*, FAO, 1985.

REFERENCES

Agarwal, Bina. 1985. *Women, poverty, and agricultural growth in India*. New Delhi: Institute of Economic Growth.

Agency for International Development. 1987. *Women in development: AID's experience, 1973-1985*. AID Program Evaluation Report, Vol. 1 (No. 18, Synthesis Paper). Washington, DC.

Ahmed, Raisuddin and Mahabub Hossain. 1988. *Infrastructure and development of the rural economy in Bangladesh*. Washington, D.C.: International Food Policy Research Institute.

Alderman, Harold. 1986. *The effect of food price and income changes on the acquisition of food by low-income households*. Washington, D.C.: International Food Policy Research Institute.

Altimir, Oscar. 1982. *The extent of poverty in Latin America*. World Bank Staff Working Paper No. 552. Washington, D.C.: The World Bank.

Altimir, Oscar and Jean Sourourille. 1980. *Measuring levels of living in Latin America: An overview of the main problems*. World Bank Living Standards Measurement Study. Working Paper No. 3. Washington, DC: The World Bank.

Anand, Sudhir. 1983. *Inequality and poverty in Malaysia: Measurement and decomposition.* Washington, D.C.: The World Bank.

Anderson, M.A.; Austin, J.E.; Zeitlin, M.F.; and Wray, J.D. 1981. *Nutrition intervention in developing countries: Study 1, supplementary feeding.* Harvard Institute for International Development. Cambridge, MA: Oelgeschlager, Gunn, and Hain.

Bagchee, Sandeep. 1984. "Employment guarantee scheme in Maharashtra," *Economic and Political Weekly,* Vol. 19 (No. 7, September).

Bangladesh Institute of Development Studies and International Food Policy Research Institute. 1985. *Development impact of the food for work programme in Bangladesh: Final report.* Washington, D.C.: International Food Policy Research Institute.

Bautista, Romeo. 1988. *Agricultural growth and food imports in developing countries: A re-examination.* Washington, D.C.: International Food Policy Research Institute, mimeo.

Beaton, George and Hossein Ghassemi. 1982. "Supplementary feeding programs for young children in developing countries." *American Journal of Clinical Nutrition,* Vol. 34 (No. 4, April), Supplement.

Bell, Clive; Peter Hazell; and Roger Slade. 1982. *Project evaluation in regional perspective: A study of an irrigation project in Northwest Malaysia.* Baltimore, MD: The Johns Hopkins University Press.

Berg, Alan. 1987. *Malnutrition: What can be done? — Lessons from World Bank experience.* Baltimore, MD: The Johns Hopkins University Press.

Bezuneh, M.; Brady Deaton; and George Norton. 1985. *Farm level impacts of food for work in rural Kenya.* Blacksburg: Department of Agricultural Economics, Virginia Polytechnic Institute and State University.

_____. 1988. "Food aid impacts in rural Kenya." *American Journal of Agricultural Economics,* Vol. 70 (No. 1, February).

Bhalla, Surjit B. and Paul Glewwe. 1986. "Growth and equity in developing countries: A reinterpretation of the Sri Lankan experience." *World Bank Economic Review (International),* Vol. 1 (September): 35-63.

Blyn, George. 1983. "The green revolution revisited." *Economic Development and Cultural Change,* Vol. 31 (July).

Burki, S. J. 1976. *Public works programs in developing countries: A comparative analysis.* World Bank Staff Working Paper No. 224. Washington, DC: World Bank.

Carloni, Alice. 1981. "Sex disparities in the distribution of food within rural households." *Food and Nutrition,* Vol. 7 (No. 1).

Centre for Monitoring the Indian Economy. 1982. *Basic Statistics, State Level.* Bombay: Centre for Monitoring the Indian Economy.

_____. 1982. *District-level data for key economic indicators.* Bombay: Centre for Monitoring the Indian Economy.

Chernichovsky, Dov and Oey Astra Meesook. 1984. *Poverty in Indonesia: A profile.* World Bank Staff Working Paper No. 671. Washington, D.C.: The World Bank.

Chowdhury, O.H. (ed.). 1983. *Special issue on rural public works programme in Bangladesh.* Bangladesh Development Studies, Vol. 11 (Nos. 1 and 2).

Costa, Emile. 1978. *An assessment of the flows of benefits generated by public investment in the employment guarantee scheme of Maharashtra.* World Employment Programme Research Working Papers No. 12. Geneva: International Labour Office.

Deaton, Brady and Mesfin Bezuneh. 1985. *Food for work and income distribution in a semi-arid region of Kenya: An empirical assessment.* Blacksburg: Department of Agricultural Economics, Virginia Polytechnic Institute.

Faruqee, Rashid and Ethna Johnson. 1982. *Health, nutrition, and family planning: A survey of experiments and special projects in India.* World Bank Staff Working Paper No. 507. Washington, DC: The World Bank.

Food and Agriculture Organization of the United Nations (FAO). 1985a. *The Fifth World Food Survey.* Rome: FAO.

_____. 1984a. *Rural poverty in Latin America and the Caribbean.* Rome: FAO.

_____. 1985b. *Nutritional implications of food aid.* Food and Nutrition Paper No. 33. Rome: FAO.

_____. 1984b. *World food day: Rural poverty in Latin America and the Caribbean.* Rome: Regional Office for Latin America and the Caribbean, FAO.

Gaude, J.; N. Phan Thuy; and C. Van Kempen. 1984. "Evaluation of special public works programmes: Some policy conclusions." *International Labor Review.* 123 (2).

Glewwe, Paul. 1988. *The distribution of welfare in Peru in 1985-86.* World Bank Living Standards Measurement Study. Washington, DC: The World Bank.

Glewwe, Paul and Jacques van der Gaag. 1988. *Confronting poverty in developing countries: Definitions, information, and policies.* World Bank Living Standards Measurement Study. Washington, DC: The World Bank.

Government of India. 1980. *Evaluation of food for work programme: Final report.* New Delhi: Program Evaluation Organization, Planning Commission.

Grigg, David. 1985. *The world food problem: 1950-1980.* New York: Basil Blackwell.

Guyer, Jane. 1980. *Household budgets and women's incomes.* Boston University African Studies Paper. Brookline, MA.

Haggblade, Steven; P.B.R. Hazell; and James Brown. 1988. *Farm — Nonfarm linkages in rural Sub-Saharan Africa.* Agriculture and Rural Development Department WPS 6. Washington, DC: The World Bank.

Hazell, Peter and C. Ramasamy. Forthcoming. *Green revolution reconsidered: The impact of high-yielding rice varieties in South India.* Washington, D.C.: International Food Policy Research Institute.

International Labour Office (ILO). 1977. *Poverty and landlessness in rural Asia.* Geneva: ILO.

Islam, Rizwanul (ed.). 1987. *Rural industrialization and employment in Asia.* New Delhi: ILO/ARTEP.

Kennedy, Eileen and Harold Alderman. 1987. *Comparative analyses of nutritional effectiveness of food subsidies and other food- related interventions.* Washington, D.C.: International Food Policy Research Institute.

515

Khan, Mahmood Hasan. 1987. "Rural poverty in Bangladesh, India, and Pakistan: Profiles and policies." *The Pakistan Development Review*, Vol. 26 (No. 3, Autumn).

Krishna, Raj. 1976. *Rural unemployment — A survey of concepts and estimates of India*. World Bank Staff Working Paper No. 234. Washington, DC: The World Bank.

Kumar, Shubh. 1988. *Role of household economy in child nutrition at low incomes*. Cornell University Occasional Paper No. 95, Ithaca, NY: Cornell University Press.

Kutcher, Gary and P. L. Scandizzo. 1981. *The agricultural economy of Northeast Brazil*. Baltimore: World Bank Research Publication.

Levinger, B. 1986. *School feeding programs in developing countries: An analysis of actual and potential impact*. AID Evaluation Special Study No. 30. Washington, D.C.: U.S. Agency for International Development.

Levinson, F.G. 1982. "Toward success in combating malnutrition: An assessment of what works." *Food and Nutrition Bulletin*, Vol. 4 (No. 3, July).

Lipton, Michael and Richard Longhurst. 1985. *Modern varieties, international research, and the poor*. CGIAR Study No. 2. Washington, DC: The World Bank.

Lucas, R.E.B. and Gustav Papanek. 1987. *The Indian economy: Recent developments and future prospects*. Boulder, Colorado: Westview Press.

Maxwell, Simon. 1978. *Food aid, food for work, and public works*. Institute of Development Studies (Sussex) Discussion Paper No. 127. Brighton, England: IDS.

Meesook, Oey Astra. 1979. *Income, consumption, and poverty in Thailand, 1962/63 to 1975/76*. World Bank Staff Working Paper No. 364. Washington, DC: The World Bank.

Mellor, John W. 1976. *The new economics of growth*. Ithaca, NY: Cornell University Press.

———. 1988. *Global food balances and food security*. Washington, D.C.: International Food Policy Research Institute.

Mellor, John W. and Gunvant Desai. 1985. *Agricultural change and rural poverty*. Baltimore, MD: The Johns Hopkins University Press.

Mellor, John W.; Christopher Delgado; and Malcolm Blackie. 1987. *Accelerating food production in Sub-Saharan Africa.* Baltimore, MD: The Johns Hopkins University Press.

Moses, Brindavan C. 1983. "Noon meals scheme." *Economic and Political Weekly,* Vol. 18 (No. 4, January).

Murty, K.N. 1983. *Consumption and nutritional patterns of ICRISAT mandate crops in India.* Andhra Pradesh, India: ICRISAT.

Osmani, S.R. 1987. *Controversies in nutrition and their implications for the economics of food.* WIDER Working Paper No. 16. UN University, July.

Paul, Satya. 1988. "Unemployment and underemployment in rural India." *Economic and Political Weekly,* Vol. 23 (July).

Piazza, Alan. 1983. *Trends in food and nutrient availability in China, 1950-81.* World Bank Staff Working Paper No. 607. Washington, DC: The World Bank.

Pinstrup-Andersen, Per. 1982. *Agricultural research and technology in economic development: The impact of modern agricultural research and technology on food production, economic growth, and income distribution in developing countries.* London: Longman, Inc.

Prahladachar, M. 1985. "Income distribution effects of the green revolution in India: A review of empirical evidence." *World Development,* Vol. 11 (November).

Ranis, G. and J. Fey. 1987. "Rural linkages in the Philippines and Taiwan." in *Macro-Policies for Appropriate Technology in Developing Countries,* edited by Francis Stewart. Boulder, CO: Westview Press.

Reardon, T. and Peter Matlon. Forthcoming. "Seasonal food insecurity and vulnerability in drought-affected areas of Burkina Faso." In *Causes and Implications of Seasonal Variability in Household Food Security,* edited by David Sahn. Baltimore: The John Hopkins University Press.

Republic of Kenya, Central Bureau of Statistics, and UNICEF. 1984. *Situation analysis of children and women in Kenya, Section 1.* Kenya: Ministry of Planning and Finance.

Reutlinger, Shlomo. 1984. *Policy implications of research on energy intake and activity levels with reference to the debate on the energy adequacy of existing diets in developing countries.* World Bank Agriculture and Rural Development Department Research Unit Discussion Paper (ARU) No. 7. Washington, DC: The World Bank.

Reutlinger, Shlomo and Marcelo Selowsky. 1976. *Malnutrition and poverty: Magnitude and policy options.* World Bank Staff Occasional Papers No. 23. Baltimore: The World Bank.

Riskin, Carl. 1987. *Feeding China: The experience since 1949.* UN University, WIDER Working Paper No. 27 (November).

Sen, Amartya. 1987. *Africa and India: What do we have to learn from each other?* UN University, WIDER Working Paper No. 19.

Thomas, John. 1986. *An analysis of current experiences and recommendations for future performance.* Development Discussion Paper No. 21. Cambridge, MA: Harvard Institute of International Development.

Thomas Vinod. 1982. *Differences in income, nutrition, and poverty within Brazil.* World Bank Staff Working Paper No. 505. Washington, DC: The World Bank.

U.S. Department of Commerce, Bureau of the Census. 1979. *Country demographic profiles: Malaysia.* Washington, DC: The Census Bureau.

Visaria, Pravin. 1981. *Incidence of poverty and the characteristics of the poor in peninsular Malaysia.* World Bank Staff Working Paper No. 460. Washington, DC: The World Bank.

_____. 1981. *Poverty and unemployment in India: An analysis of recent evidence.* World Bank Staff Working Paper No. 417. Washington, DC: The World Bank.

The World Bank. 1980. *Kenya: Population and development.* A World Bank Country Study. Washington, DC: The World Bank.

_____. 1981. *Accelerated development in Sub-Saharan Africa: An agenda for action.* A World Bank Country Study. Washington, DC: The World Bank.

_____. 1983. *China — Socialist economic development.* A World Bank Country Study. Washington, DC: The World Bank.

_____. 1986. *Poverty and hunger.* A World Bank Policy Study. Washington, DC: The World Bank.

CONTRIBUTORS

Johannes ("Hans") Iemke Bakker received his Ph.D. from the University of Toronto in 1979 on the basis of a dissertation on the "cultivation system" on Java (circa 1830-1870) and has been teaching sociology at the University of Guelph since 1980. He has done archival and field research in Indonesia and India on patrimonial-prebendalism, integrated rural development, resettlement and land tenure. His major interests include "comparative, historical sociological theory and research" (CHS), especially the "German Historical School" (e.g., Max Weber). He is also interested in integrated rural development and "development anthropology" especially the Gandhian approach to *swadeshi* ("local self-reliance"). He has published more than thirty articles. Bakker has served as a consultant on human resource development and community development to CIDA and WUSC. He is currently working on a theory textbook and a monograph on the local resettlement of a hamlet of Bajo "sea-nomads" in Southeast Sulawesi, Indonesia. During 1990-93 he will be editor of *Rural Development Notes,* a newsletter and annual review of the Integrated Rural Development Network (IRDN).

Franz von Benda-Beckmann received his Ph.D. in Law from the University of Kiel in 1970 on the basis of a dissertation on Legal Pluralism in Malawi. In 1979 he obtained his Habilitation in Anthropology at the University of Zurich, Switzerland, based upon his book on *Property in Social Continuity in West Sumatra.* Since 1981 he is a Professor of Agrarian Law and the Law of Developing Countries at the Agricultural University in Wageningen, the Netherlands. He has done fieldwork in Malawi, West Sumatra and the Central Moluccas and published extensively on legal pluralism and rural development, rural social security and theoretical and methodological issues in legal anthropology. His research interests currently centre on customary law and adaptation to social change in Ambon in Indonesia. He has established an international reputation as a fine scholar whose attention to empirical detail contributes greatly to the construction of careful and innovative anthropological theory.

John Cairns was one of the organizers of the International Conference on the World Food Crisis that was held at the University of Guelph October 23-26, 1986. He was the Director of the Centre for International Programs at the University of Guelph (1974-85) and instrumental in giving international development activities on campus greater visibility. He has had experience as an international human resources development planner in Africa, Asia and Latin America. Previous to his work at Guelph he was Director of the Experimental World Literacy Program and the Division of Adult Education at UNESCO, Paris (1968-1974) and Head of Adult Education for the Northwest Territories in the Department of Indian Affairs and Northern Development, Ottawa (1966-1968). He obtained his MA from the University of Western Ontario in 1958 and his Ontario Secondary School Certificate in 1959. He has published books on TESL. He was a District Officer and District Commissioner in Tanganyika, East Africa (1951-1958) and served with the RCAF during World War II in India and Burma. His book *Bush and Boma: The Life of a District Officer* was published in London by Murray (1958). He has published articles and consultancy reports and has represented UNESCO at many international conferences. In 1986 he received the Lewis Perinbam Award for International Development. He is currently working as a freelance consultant and recently completed an assignment in Pakistan, along with Professor Geoffrey Hainsworth (U.B.C.) and Professor James Shute (Guelph).

E.A. Cebotarev is a Professor at the University of Guelph and has recently been active as the Director of Graduate Studies in the Department of Sociology and Anthropology. Her research interests in Latin America have involved close collaboration with several Latin American and Caribbean universities on integrated rural development, "women in development" and "gender-sensitive development." She has received significant funding for her research and applied development work from CIDA. (the Canadian International Development Agency) which she has used to greatly improve the opportunities for further graduate training for a number of highly capable Latin American and Caribbean students. She has been an active participant and officer in the Rural Sociological Society and the International Rural Sociological Society. She is one of the founders of the Canadian Rural Studies Association. She has published a number of articles in sociological journals, both in English and in Spanish. Multilingual, she also speaks a number of other languages, including German and Russian. Her current interest is in Paolo Freire's "conscientization" approach to participatory planning and development and the "empowerment" of disadvantaged groups, particularly poor rural women.

Lila E. Engberg, Ph.D. (Cornell) is a retired faculty member from the Department of Family Studies, University of Guelph. She served as Home Economics Officer for the Food and Agriculture Organization of the United Nations (FAO) in Malawi (1963-68); member of the University of Ghana/Guelph Project in the Home Science Department, Faculty of Agriculture, University of Ghana (1970-75); and with the Home Economic Project of Mount Saint Vincent University in Malawi (1982-85). Currently she is involved in a short-term FAO assignment related to development of a training manual with a focus on rural households and resource allocation. Professor Engberg has been involved for several years in program planning, teaching and research related to "home economics" in Africa. Her work in Malawi, Kenya and Ghana has contributed significantly to University of Guelph applied development and research efforts in Africa.

Patricia Garrett received her Ph.D. from the University of Wisconsin-Madison in 1978 on the basis of a dissertation concerning the impact of agrarian reform on men and women in the Central Valley of Chile. She has directed farming systems research and technology projects in Guatemala and Peru. Her publications include analyses of peasant economy, social stratification, women and development, and the methodology of farming systems research. Her current work centres around transformations in women's work and their impact upon families and child care. She has taught at Cornell University in Ithaca, New York. Her contribution to this volume, along with Professor Schulman, is part of a large empirical research effort on "smallholders" which has been funded by the U.S. Agency for International Development and the North Carolina Agricultural Research Service.

Edward J. Hedican received a Ph.D. from McGill University in 1978 and is presently an Associate Professor in the Department of Sociology and Anthropology at the University of Guelph. His research has focussed on the Native People who live in the boreal forest region of Northern Ontario. Research interests include the role of local leadership in implementing community development projects, the use of subsistence resources in maintaining local economic viability, as well as the study of different perceptions that people hold regarding what constitutes "development." He is the author of a book on these subjects entitled *The Ogoki River Guides* (Waterloo, Ontario: Wilfrid Laurier University Press, 1988), as well as a number of articles in various sociological and anthropological journals.

Robert D'Arcy Henderson received his Ph.D. from the University of Manchester, England in 1979. His research interests include foreign policy analysis, arms control and disarmament, Third World development and foreign assistance, and southern African regional relations. His publications include articles in: *International Affairs Bulletin; International Perspectives; Journal of Modern African Studies; ORBIS; The World Today*, etc. In addition he has made several contributions to collections of readings on the global arms race, Third World development issues, and Southern African affairs. He is the editor (along with Peter Desbarats) of *Encounter '87: Media, Democracy and Development* (London, Ontario: Graduate School of Journalism, University of Western Ontario, 1988). He is currently working as a Research Analyst and Co-ordinator for the Solicitor-General of Canada, Ottawa. Dr. Henderson presented the first draft of the paper published in this volume at the Workshop/Symposium held at the University of Guelph on February 11, 1988, funded by the "Inter-College Activities Fund" of the University of Guelph. He has a continuing interest in the study of African development issues.

Thomas Hoban is an Assistant Professor at North Carolina State University. He is also state Sociology specialist with the North Carolina Agricultural Extension Service. Dr. Hoban's major responsibilities involve working with other departments at North Carolina State University to improve the assessment and transfer of new technologies. His research interests include understanding how new technologies affect agriculture, natural resources, and communities. His recent work also involves assessment of public opinion about water quality and biotechnology.

Dr. Hoban received his Ph.D. in Rural Sociology from Iowa State University where he worked with the USDA Soil Conservation Service on a number of projects related to soil conservation education. He has two Master's degrees from the University of Wisconsin in Agricultural Journalism and Water Resource Management. He received a Bachelor of Science degree from the University of Illinois in Biology.

Janet Marie Huddle received her M.A. degree in Political Studies at the University of Guelph in 1988, in part on the basis of her thesis concerning the Blue Revolution, a portion of which is presented here. The thesis was awarded a "distinction" by the Political Studies departmental graduate committee. (Her advisor was Professor Jorge Nef.) She worked as a researcher with the Centre for Food Security. Her insightful analysis of the "blue revolution" and the "green revolution" as similar approaches to the problem of food production has been noted by Professor William Tossell, director of the Food Security Program at the Centre for International Programs of the University of Guelph as an "excellent contribution." Ms Huddle continues to be interested in research on the strengths and weaknesses of the "blue revolution" approach.

Hamid Jorjani is a doctoral candidate under a joint academic program between the University of Guelph and the Agricultural University of Wageningen in the Netherlands. He is an agricultural analyst with several years of consulting and academic experience. His interest in agriculture dates back to 1965 when he joined the Center for Agricultural Training in Sari, Mazandaran, Iran. Subsequently, he was sent to India to pursue further training in agriculture on a scholarship program. He joined the University of Guelph in January 1980 and received a Master's degree from the Department of Agricultural Economics. For the last eight years he has worked on economic aspects of agricultural drainage in Ontario, Canada, and in the Ijsselmeer (Ijssel Lake) polders, the Netherlands. He has authored and co-authored a number of research papers, journal articles and project reports. In 1986 he was invited to participate in a think tank workshop sponsored by a government agency in Ottawa, to discuss management of renewable resources in Canada. In 1987 he was one of the seven doctoral candidates from Holland who were invited to join the Young Scientists Summer Program at the International Institute for Applied Systems Analysis (IIASA) in Laxenburg, Austria, to work with a group of international scientists on land use aspects of a global project concerning the biosphere. He has recently worked on a project entitled "A Framework to Assess the Economic Value of Agricultural Drainage in Ontario."

Franz ("Mishaquod") Koennecke was born in Germany in 1941. He attended Wilfrid Laurier University, Waterloo, Ontario where he received his Bachelor of Arts in Anthropology in 1975. At that time he started to work with Canadian Native people in Ontario as a researcher. Continuing his graduate studies at the University of Waterloo, Waterloo, Ontario he received his Master of Arts in History (Ethnohistory) in 1984. His thesis is entitled "Wasoksing: the History of Parry Island, an Anishnabwe Community in the Georgian Bay 1850-1920." Since that time he has been employed by the Anishinabek of Georgian Bay and Lake Nipissing as a researcher for their Rights and Treaty Research unit. He presently resides with the Anishnabwe community on Parry Island. He has led workshops on "native ways of knowing" on Manitoulin Island, Ontario, Canada. He has a deep interest in the human rights of Native People.

Olga Martinez taught with the Department of Nutrition at the University of Guelph after receiving her Ph.D. She is presently employed as a consultant in Toronto. Her interests include nutrition and international development. She has published a number of scientific articles on nutrition and food. She is currently continuing her exploration of the impact of projects funded by international donors on food security, especially in

Latin America. Dr. Martinez has been active with many local organizations in Guelph and is well respected for the contribution she has made to improving undergraduate teaching in nutrition.

John W. Mellor is Director of the International Food Policy Research Institute (IFPRI). He has served previously as Chief Economist of the U.S. Agency for International Development (USAID) and at Cornell University where he was Professor of Economics with a joint appointment in the Department of Agricultural Economics, Department of Asian Studies, and Department of Economics. Born in France, he is now an American citizen. He received a B.Sc., M.Sc., and Ph.D. from Cornell University and a Diploma (with distinction) in Agricultural Economics from Oxford University as a Fulbright Scholar. Mellor has served as a consultant to various agencies including the International Bank for Reconstruction and Development (IBRD), the Food and Agriculture Organization (FAO) of the United Nations; the Rockefeller Foundation and the United States Agency for International Development. He was a resident and visiting researcher and scholar in India for a total of nearly five years.

Dr. Mellor is author of *The New Economics of Growth - A Strategy for India and the Developing World*, Cornell University Press, Ithaca, N.Y., 1976; *The Economics of Agricultural Development*, Cornell University Press, Ithaca, N.Y., 1966, (winner of award in 1978 by the American Agricultural Economics Association for "his publication of enduring quality") and co-author of *Developing Rural India: Plan and Practice*, (with Thomas F. Weaver, Uma J. Lele and Sheldon R. Simon), Cornell University Press, Ithaca, N.Y. 1968; and was editor of *India: A Rising Middle Power*, Westview Press, Boulder, Colorado, 1979; *Agricultural Change and Rural Poverty: Variations on a Theme by Dharm Narain*, The Johns Hopkins University Press, Baltimore, Maryland, 1985. He also serves on the editorial board of several journals. In addition, he has written and published some 75 shorter scholarly papers. Among these are: "Towards a Theory of Agricultural Development," in Herman M. Southworth and Bruce F. Johnston (eds.), *Agricultural Development and Economic Growth*, Cornell University Press, Ithaca, N.Y., 1967 pp. 21-61 (Winner of Award in 1967 for Best Published Research given by the American Agricultural Economics Association); "The Role of Agriculture in Economic Development," (with Bruce F. Johnston), the *American Economic Review*, Vol. LI, No. 4, Sept. 1961, pp. 556-593; and "Food Price Policy and Income Distribution in Low-Income Countries," *Economic Development and Cultural Change*, Vol. 27, No. 1, October 1978.

Dr. Mellor is the 1985 recipient of the Wihuri International Prize — the first social scientist to be so designated "in recognition of (your) constructive work which has remarkably promoted and developed the securing of nutrient supply for mankind." He is a Fellow of the American Academy of Arts and Sciences and the American Agricultural Economics Association.

Jorge Nef is a Professor of Political Studies and International Development at the University of Guelph. He has taught at the University of Chile, the University of California at Santa Barbara and McGill University and has been a Visiting Professor at various Canadian and foreign universities and institutes. His research is concentrated on development issues, food security, terrorism, comparative public administration, authoritarian regimes and international politics, with special emphasis on the Latin American region. Between 1981 and 1983 he was President of the Canadian Association of Latin American and Caribbean Studies. His articles have appeared in *Latin American Perspectives, Interamerican Review, North/South, The Canadian Journal of Development Studies, Latin American Research Review, New Scholar, Laurentian University Review, The Nation, The Indian Journal of Public Administration, Public Administration and Development, Etudes Internationales, Relaciones Internacionales, Revista Centroamericana de Administracion Publica, The Indian Journal of Political Science, International Perspectives, Prajna, Konflicternes Verden, New Internationalist, The Canadian Journal of Latin American and Caribbean Studies,* and in over twenty edited collections. He is the author, co-author and/or editor of *Canada and the Latin American Challenge* (1978), *Repression and Liberation in Latin America* (1982), and *Administracion Publica: Perspectivas Criticas* (1984). He has recently co-edited *Ethics and Technology: Ethical Choices in the Age of Pervasive Technology,* along with Jokelee Vanderkop and Henry Wiseman (Toronto: Wall & Thompson, 1989). His research interests include the study of power elites in less developed countries. His work is characterized by comparative analysis and careful attention to empirical materials. Dr. Nef has worked as a consultant and/or co-operant with the Pan American Health Organization, the Canadian International Development Agency (CIDA) and the International Development Research Centre (IDRC). In addition to his large scholarly output, Professor Nef has also published a novel and many poems.

Wayne C. Pfeiffer received his Ph.D. in 1970 and has a joint appointment as a Professor of Agricultural Economics and Rural Extension Studies at the University of Guelph. He has taught in China and been involved in research work in Northern China with a CIDA funded project. During 1987 he worked on a major curriculum development project with Heilongjiang "August 1st Land Reclamation" University and Liu He Cadre Training College, both located in Heilongjiang Province. He has done field research on the development of agriculture in Northern China and has supervised the graduate degree program of several Chinese students. He has published many articles in scholarly journals.

Truman P. Phillips obtained his first degree in Mechanical Engineering at Stanford University and a Ph.D. in Agricultural Economics at Newcastle University in England. Dr. Phillips is currently a Professor of Agricultural Economics and Assistant Director of the Centre for Food Security at the University of Guelph. With over sixteen years of experience in international development, his research activities have included several studies in the identification and estimation of potential world markets for cassava and other tropic root crops; farming systems research; and studies of food security and insecurity. He has been a consultant to the FAO, IDRC, IFPRI, IITA, CIAT, CGIAR, CIDA and the World Bank. He is the author of many articles in refereed journals.

Michael D. Schulman received his Ph.D. from the University of Wisconsin-Madison in 1975. His research interests include Southern textile workers, smallholder survival, and the consequences of the North American farm crisis. At North Carolina State University, he is Co-Director of the North Carolina

Farm and Rural Life Study. He has worked on farming systems research projects in Ecuador and Peru. His theoretical work involves the Lenin/Chayanov debate and capitalism in agriculture. The paper published in this volume is one of several papers that have been written in collaboration with Professor Patricia Garrett and others under the North Carolina State Univesity Title XII Strengthening Grant (AID/DSAN-XII-G-103) funded jointly by the U.S. Agency for International Development, the North Carolina Agricultural Extension Service, and the North Carolina A&T State University at Greensboro, N.C.

Mr. Changqing Song, M.Sc., teaches at Heilongjiang "August 1st Land Reclamation" University in Mishan, Heilongjiang, People's Republic of China. He was one of a select group of scholars who came to Canada for post-graduate study under the auspices of the Black Dragon River Consortium, which was sponsored by CIDA and the PRC. He received his M.Sc. degree in agricultural economics in 1988 from the University of Guelph, under Professor Wayne Pfeiffer. His area of interest is agricultural production economics and he has been studying the impact of policy changes on the farming system in Heilongjiang Province.

Sarah Southwold-Llewellyn is a Lecturer in the Department of Sociology of Rural Development at Wageningen Agricultural University, The Netherlands, where she teaches courses on applied research methods and economic anthropology. She received her D. Phil. from the University of Sussex, United Kingdom, in 1987. Her dissertation was based on a study of a rural community in the Kurunegala District of Sri Lanka. The central role of credit in the management of households and businesses was examined, with particular consideration of the implications of these relations for increasing coconut productivity and altering the patterns of coconut marketing. The D. Phil. thesis also explored variants of the cultural constructs of "the trader" and "the cultivator" that are used by policy-makers, traders, and cultivators, in order to legitimize contradictions in their behaviour and policies.

Her current research interests are: (a) the use of rural credit in both the formal and informal sectors in promoting economic development, particularly with regard to joint liability group credit schemes; (b) public participation in project identification and management; household economic strategies; management of business enterprises, particularly with regard to credit and investment strategies; (c) agricultural marketing; and (c) how the cultural constructs of researchers (including "methodology as a cultural construct") affect policy making.

Daphne S. Taylor obtained her first degree in Economics at Carleton University, Ottawa, Ontario, Canada, and an M.Sc. in Agricultural Economics at the University of Guelph. For the past two and one half years she has been very actively involved with research at the Centre for Food Security at the University of Guelph. Her research activities have included an examination of agricultural price distortions in fifty-five countries, development of a conceptual framework for food security assessment, and analysis of household food security in selected communities in Indonesia, Malaysia, the Philippines and Thailand. (Some of that research has been carried out in conjunction with Professor Truman Phillips.) She played a key role in the organization of the "Ethics and Technology" conference, the third major international conference of its kind held at Guelph. In November 1989 she took up a position as a Visiting Scientist with the Economics Program at the International Maize and Wheat Improvement Center in Mexico.

Sergio Trindade is an Assistant Secretary-General at the United Nations and has been the Executive Director of the United Nations Centre for Science and Technology for Development (UNCSTD) since January, 1986. He is a chemical engineer and obtained his Ph.D. from M.I.T. in 1973. Previous to holding his current position with the United Nations, Dr. Trindade was an international consultant on energy and technology planning (1982-86). He was also a corporate director in architectural engineering and techology planning (Promon, Brazil, 1975-82), managing director and senior consultant (Arthur D. Little, 1970-75), process engineer (Stone and Webster, Boston, 1969), independent consultant (1968) and chemical process engineering manager (Getec, Brazil, 1964-67). Dr. Trindade presented a draft of his paper when he came to Guelph to participate in the Workshop/Symposium on "Science and Technology in the World Food Crisis" that was held February 11, 1988, and funded by the "Inter-College Activities Fund" at the University of Guelph.

Gayle Valeriote received her B.A. in History (with a focus on Africa) from the University of Guelph in 1985. She has worked with the Centre for International Programs at the University of Guelph. She has also worked with the Ontario Africa Working Group, the Southern Africa Interest Group, the Ontario Public Interest Research Group, and the Guelph Food Co-operative. In 1988 she was the co-ordinator of the International Women's Day program in Guelph. The theme for 1988 was "Women: All One Nation"; the program concentrated on the struggles of women in developing countries. In 1978-1981 she worked with the CPPS Mission Projects (affiliated with the Fathers and Brothers of the Precious Blood) in Tanzania and Canada. She is the mother of "an energetic baby boy" and "extremely interested in all political issues." She is the editor (along with John C. Cairns) of the *Conference Summary* for the Conference on Science and Technology in the World Food Crisis held at Guelph October 23-26, 1986.

Jokelee Vanderkop received her M.A. degree from the Department of Political Studies at the University of Guelph in 1986 in part on the basis of a thesis entitled: "The State of Canadian Foreign Aid." She worked on the organization of the international conference on Ethics and Technology held at the University of Guelph and edited the pre-conference publication entitled *Ethics and Technology: Ethical Choices in the Age of Pervasive Technology* (Toronto: Wall & Thompson, 1989), along with Jorge Nef and Henry Wiseman. She has published articles in *Konflicternes Verden*, the *Canadian Journal of Development Studies* and *North/South*, as well as in several edited volumes. She has worked as an editor and translator. In 1975-1977 she was an Administrative Assistant to the Director of Conferences and General Services, United Nations' Office, Geneva. She is currently an instructor at Norval Secondary School in Palmerston, Wellington County, Ontario.